March 2004

To Stephen with best

William Carr.

A Pitman's Anthology

William Maurice in the drawing room at 'The Elms', Hucknall near Nottingham, 1908.

A Pitman's Anthology

Compiled by
William Maurice 1872–1951

With a biographical essay by
William Jackson

William Maurice © William Jackson 2004
Compilation © The Wolf Safety Lamp Company Ltd 2004

First published 2004
ISBN 0 907 383 971

Book jacket design by Ian Pape, FONDA
Photography of art works by Andy Gallacher Photography Limited
Designed and typeset in 11/13pt Monotype Centaur by John Rice
Printed and bound by Butler & Tanner Ltd

Published by James & James (Publishers) Ltd
Gordon House Business Centre
6 Lissenden Gardens, London NW5 1LY

Half-title illustration:
reproduction of a bronze by Constantin Meunier

George Bissill

Foreword

Renovations to the offices at The Wolf Safety Lamp Company of Sheffield in the early 1990s brought to light a valuable amount of historical material. Amongst it was William Maurice's final draft manuscript for *A Pitman's Anthology*. This extensive collection of poems and prose was compiled from books and articles on mining subjects that he collected throughout the 1920s and 30s; but it was never published.

Many avenues were explored at the time, and even the general appeal of such an anthology was questioned, but the looming prospects of a major European conflict, and then the War itself, put the project out of mind. With the gradual recovery of the industry in the 1950s, and the death of William Maurice in 1951, there were more important matters to be addressed by the Company, then in the hands of his daughter Monica. There is, though, a suggestion in the last draft introduction that a further attempt to publish was made in the immediate post war era.

The important archive was left in good order by Monica Maurice though, with the exception of the pictures, no list or inventory existed. Perhaps the decision to publish this anthology was deliberately left to her successors. Ironically, whilst the original typescripts, with the alternative title, *The Coal Miner's Anthology*, were being scrutinised and re-arranged, another anthology of mining, edited by Professor Tony Curtis, entitled *Coal* had just been published. Nevertheless, the first line of Maurice's foreword is still valid in stating, 'It is believed that this is the first attempt to compile a Miner's Anthology'.

Superficially this rival might have rendered the Maurice compilation redundant. However, Curtis' *Coal*, a seminal publication, spans a greater period, up to more contemporary times, and is illustrated with wash drawings of Welsh miners and their families by the late Joseph Herman. On closer study, it was realised that only seven of the fifty-seven authors selected by William Maurice were duplicated in the Curtis anthology. Furthermore, the latter is an academic's overview while the other reflects the intimate perspectives and experiences of a pitman, working during the great period of the industry's modernisation and the introduction of the radical Coal Mines Act of 1911.

With the encouraging support of Professor Curtis and others, it was decided to explore various publishing options on the basis that Wolf Safety Lamp Company might sponsor such a venture. At the same time, the anthology was considered to be too long, well over four hundred pages, so a substantial reduction was required. It was felt that the spirit and originality of the anthology would not be diminished, indeed it might even be improved, if some of the very long prose passages were abridged.

The original draft introduction, probably written by Monica in the 1940s, is a masterpiece of its kind. In it are references not just to the source materials, the majority of which were produced between 1910 to 1940, but to the artists and playwrights inspired by the pride of miners and the dignity of their communities. The piece provides an

William Maurice at a conference in the Royal Agricultural Hall, London — mid 1930s. The lamp is a benzene flame safety-lamp, type 100 — American pattern, manufactured by the Wolf Safety Lamp Company of America Inc. between 1910 and 1930.

invaluable insight into the cultural achievements of miners through the words of both miners themselves and those observers from outside the industry who have been touched by these fine people. The vigour of her text says much about the enthusiasm and commitment of the compiler to the subject. Thus it deserves its place in the book as a succinct and passionate plea to preserve the prose and poetry of this important era in the history of the industry.

As an appropriate embellishment to the anthology, as originally envisaged, it was decided to illustrate the book with images by Meunier, Kätelhön, Steinlen, Bissill and others, from Wolf Safety's art collection, acquired during this same period by William Maurice.

No apology is given for the inclusion of the only non-English speaking author. Emile Zola's novel *Germinal* is one of the great works of literature which embraces all the emotions of drama, compassion, hardship and deceit in a fictional mining community in France towards the end of the 19th century, where working conditions for miners were close to intolerable.

It was then a question of engaging a sympathetic publishing partner as a purely private publication would reduce the possibility of exposure to a wider audience. By coincidence, a book on the history of a family business came to light, published by James & James. A number of telephone conversations and meetings later, this enthusiastic publisher was appointed.

If this anthology had been published in the 1930s, it is clear that not only would there have been no illustrations, but it would probably have contained, if at all, only a very modest biography of William Maurice, doing little justice to the scale of his achievements. The biographical essay in this publication relates much of this remarkable man's lifetime contribution to electrical engineering in mining, as well as providing some insight into his personality and family life.

William Jackson
December 2003

Acknowledgements

I would like to thank my brother John for giving me the opportunity to be involved in such an exciting project, and the Directors and Shareholders of The Wolf Safety Lamp Company Limited of Sheffield for sponsoring the publication of this unique Anthology. My special thanks go to my two aunts, Cynthia Thompson and Pauline Forster and to my sister Willa, for their wholehearted support. My thanks also go to the National Coal Mining Museum of England and, in particular, to Alison Hennessy, Librarian, and also to the Curatorial Director, Rosemary Preece, for her technical advice and for bringing this anthology to our attention. Finally, my thanks go to Professor Tony Curtis for his support, Judy Jackson for the thankless task of transcribing the original typescript onto disk, Robin Garton for artists' information and Christina Niederberger for translation of German text, Jill George and Clare Slemeck for their assistance in the final proof reading, Michael Farrenkopf, senior archivist at the Deutches Bergbau-Museum, Bochum, and Hamish MacGibbon and Anna Waddell of James & James for their professional guidance in editing the prose sections.

George Bissill

Publisher's Note

There are obvious difficulties with maintaining consistency of grammar in an anthology of works from different styles, regions and periods. On the whole, the text is based on the typed manuscript originally provided by William Maurice. Where there were inconsistencies, we have given priority to the original text.

Where we were unable to find the source cited by William Maurice, we have sought an alternative reference. Both Maurice's source and the other source are cited where possible.

The sources for all additional notes and for biographical information are listed below. These include library visits, correspondence and extensive internet searching. Due to the fact that searches unearthed both biographical information on the authors and information on the original sources from which the poems and extracts are taken, we have not divided the references into different search-oriented sections.

Sources

LIBRARIES

The British Library general resources, Biography and Genealogy Master Index, World Biographical Index, British Biographical Index, American Biographical Index, National Union Catalogue, Cambridge University Library

The London Library

National Coalmining Museum

The Poetry Library, London

Sussex University Library

Wigan Library

WEB SEARCHES

General searches

Google, Ask Jeeves, Amazon

Specific sites

Libraries

Library of Toronto, www.library.utoronto.ca

National Library of Wales Archives, www.llgc.org.uk/lc/lcs0074.htm

Mc Master University, www.library.mcmaster.ca/archives/findaids.htm

Newcastle Library, www.newcastle.gov.uk/libraries

Cornell University Library, www.cdl.library.cornell.edu/moa

Columbia University Library, www.columbia.edu/cu/lweb/

Others

Working Press Research Pamphlets (working-class artists self-publishing), http://ourworld.com
    puserve.com/homepages/working_press/FREE.

Local Northern Website, www.Rotherham.co.uk

Folk Archives, www.folkarchive.de/mines.html#top

National Record of Archives, Historic Manuscripts Commission, www.hmc.gov.uk/nra

Local Presentation in Historical Society, www.fynesg.freeserve.co.uk/Genealogy/RICHARD
    FYNES.htm

Antiquarian books searches, e.g., antiqbook.com, alibris.com

Houses of Commons Debates website, http://www.parliament.the-stationary
    office.co.uk/pa/cm/cmpubns.htm

Ruskin College, Oxford, http://www.ruskin.ac.uk/home.htm

New General Catalogue of Old Books and Authors, www.kingkong.demon.co.uk/ngcoba

Canadian Journal of History XXXII, 1997, http://www.usask.ca/history/cjh/mcd_897.htm

H. V. Morton web page by John Baker, http://www.nzcal.com/hp/hvmorton/

Genealogy Messaging Boards, e.g., www.genealogyregister.com

J. B. Priestley Official Website, www.jbpriestley.co.uk

Walt Whitman Archive (with Ernest Rhys information),
    www.whitmanarchive.org/archiveI/works/leaves/english/britishleaves/1886/index.html

Literary and Philosophy Society of Newcastle Upon Tyne, www.litandphil.org.uk

Scottish Enthusiast's Website (with David Wingate information), http://www.geocities.com/scot
    landsmahame/davidwingatecollierpoet.html

Francis Brett Young Society, www.fbysociety.co.uk

Book Directory, www.knowledgerush.com

Myers Literary Guide to North East England,
    http://online.unn.ac.uk/faculties/art/humanities/cns/m-index.html

British Mining Database, www.ap.pwp.blueyonder.co.uk/bmd/bmd.htm

Information on Thomas Wilson, www.geocities.com/athens/atlantis/6280/page8.htm

BOOKS

Boase, F. 1922, *Modern English Biography 1892–1921*. Truro Netherton & Worth.

Browning, D. C. 1960, *Everyman's Dictionary of Literary Biography, English and American*.
    J. M. Dent.

Burke, W. J. & Howes, W. D. (eds) 1963, *American Authors and Books*. Nicholas Vane Ltd.

Carpenter, E. (ed) 1888, *Chants of Labour. A Song Book of the People*. Swan & Sonnenschein
    & Co.

Cousin, J. W. 1958, *Everyman's Dictionary of Literary Biography, English and American*.
    E. P. Dutton & Co.

Davies, R. 1969, *Print of a Hare's Foot: An Autobiographical Beginning*. Heinemann.

Drabble, M. (ed) 2000, *The Oxford Companion to English Literature*. Oxford University Press.

Farbman, M. (ed) 1929, *Political Britain.* Europa.

The Herald Book of Labour Members, 1923. Labour Publishing.

Kirk, J. 1891, *A Supplement to Allibone's Critical Dictionary of English Literature.*
J. B. Lippincott Co.

Lloyd, A. L. 1952, *Come All Ye Bold Miners. Ballads and Songs of the Coalfields.*
Lawrence & Wishart.

Lowe, L. (ed) 1986, *Directory of Popular Music 1900–1980.* Peterson Publishing Co Ltd.

Peacock, J. c.1800, *A Favourite Collection of Tunes.* W. Wright.

Unsworth, W. 1968, *Because It Is There.* Gollancz.

Who Was Who 1929–1940 V.3, 1947. Adam & Charles Black.

Who's Who in Wales 1921. Hutchinson & Co.

The publishers are grateful for permission to include the following poems and extracts from the copyright owners listed below.

Despite diligent searching we have been unable to trace copyright owners of some of the pieces and for any of these who may have been omitted we apologise and beg their indulgence.

Thanks are due to the following copyright owners for their kind permission to reproduce the following works or extracts.

Joe Corrie, poems from *The Image O' God and Other Poems* (1937), and *Poems by Joe Corrie* (1955) – **Copyright © Morag Corrie.**

Rhys Davies, excerpts from *A Pig in a Poke* (1931) – **Copyright © Estate of Rhys Davies.**

John Gould Fletcher, 'Coal' – **Copyright © Fletcher Literary Estate.**

Wilfred Gibson, poems from *Collected Poems* (1926) and *Fuel* (1934) – **Pan Macmillan Ltd.**

Jack Lawson, excerpts from *Under the Wheels* (1934) – **reproduced by permission of Hodder & Stoughton Ltd.**

H. V. Morton, excerpts from *In Search of Wales* (1932) – **Methuen Publishing Ltd. on behalf of, Copyright © Marion Wasdell and Brian de Villiers.**

Herbert E Palmer, poem from *Summit and Chasm, A Book of Poems and Rimes* (1934) – **Copyright © Alan Denson.**

J.B. Priestley, *English Journey* (1934) – **(Copyright © Estate of J.B. Priestley 1934) by permission of PFD on behalf of the Estate of J. B. Priestley.**

Ernest Rhys, excerpts from *The Black Horse Pit* (1925) – **Copyright © Stephen Rhys.**

Siegfried Sassoon, poem from *Satirical Poems* (1926) – **Copyright © Siegfied Sassoon by kind permission of George Sassoon.**

Contents

CONTENTS

This Anthology is dedicated to William Maurice's three daughters, Monica, Pauline and Cynthia.

William Maurice 1872–1951
The life and times of a mining engineer

William Maurice devoted his entire working life to safety in the field of electrical mining engineering, to which he had a passionate commitment. Throughout its history, the industry has paid more heavily in human lives than any other, causing terrible misery and hardship to miners and their families. And yet, work in the coal mines was traditionally passed down from father to son for generations. The pay was latterly better than for others in hard manual labour, but the prospects of serious injury or death were far greater. For most, there was little choice and was a risk worth taking. It was coal that fuelled the Industrial Revolution. It drove the steam engines in the factories and on the railways; it fired the giant furnaces that made iron and steel and, latterly, the generators of the new age of electrical power. During this period, many colliery owners cared little for the lot of the miner, though there were exceptions. The introduction of the Coal Mines Act of

Staff outside the Saxon Road Works, spring 1938. William and Monica Maurice are centre front and Pauline Maurice's future husband, Raymond Forster, is at the extreme left front.

1911, the most important piece of employment and safety legislation to date, ensured miners' basic rights for the first time and changed working practices and labour relations in mines for ever.

During the great cultural age of the Scottish Enlightenment, one such humanitarian coal mine owner was John Clerk of Eldin, the seventh son of Sir John Clerk of Penicuik, a man of many parts who was also known in art circles as the 'Father of Scottish Etching'. Having prospered as a clothier in Edinburgh, he bought Pendrick Coal Fields near Lasswade in the mid 1750s, and some adjoining land on which he built the small mansion house of Eldin, and became a coal merchant. When on occasions he ran into financial difficulties, as the seams of his mines were worked out, he continued to pay his miners, 'So as to retain their services and their good will'.

In Clerk's day and earlier, the only method of mine lighting and gas detection was by candles or open oil lamps. These crude methods of illumination were totally reliant upon good air ventilation for the prevention of firedamp explosion. It was between 1730 and 1750 that the 'flint and steel mill' was invented by Carlisle Spedding and were first used in collieries in Tyne and Wear. It worked on the principle that the sparks from the hand rotated wheel were too cool to ignite mine gas, but with the increased level of firedamp the colour of the light would change from blue to blood red. The use of this device is described in a poem by John Dalton DD., published in 1755:

> "Nor strikes the flints, nor whirls the steel
> Of that strange spark-emitting wheel,
> Which, formed by Prospero's magic care,
> Plays harmless in the sulphurous air,
> Without a flame diffuses light
> And makes the grisly cavern light".

The reference of Prospero is of course to Spedding himself. As more was discovered about the characteristics of firedamp in the latter part of the 18th century, it was realised that the steel mill was by no means foolproof and indeed, in at least one incident, was directly responsible for an explosion at Wallsend mine in June 1785. Much research into the understanding of firedamp was also carried out at this time in Germany, where Baron Friedrich Alexander von Humboldt published his important book on mine gases in 1799.

It could be said that the history of safety-lamps began in 1813 with the formation of The Society in Sunderland for Preventing Accidents in Coal Mines, which lead directly to Sir Humphry Davy's experiments and the invention of the Davy safety-lamp. The Society was formed as a result of a catastrophic explosion at Felling Colliery on 25 May 1812, in which ninety-two men and boys died.

It was also in 1813 that Dr William Reid Clanny invented his first safety-lamp, but his was for safe general illumination rather than for the detection of explosive gasses. It was

Vignette depicting Friemann & Wolf's Zwickau Plant 1927.

not until 1815 that the first successful experiments were carried out on flame safety-lamps and by then, George Stephenson, better known as a railway engineer, had entered into the controversial 'safety-lamp debate' about who was the first to invent a practical gas detection device. Both used the principle of wire-gauze shielding, as did the later Clanny lamps, but, according to Hardwick and O'Shea, it was the Davy lamp that was progressively developed and modified throughout the 19th and well into the 20th century. Clanny though was the first to incorporate a glass chimney to the flame enclosure, thus providing a brighter light with increased protection from draughts. European advances in the field should not be ignored, as was pointed out by the influential South Shields Committee in their report of 1843 on Belgian lamps, when they stated, 'Genius and humanity are exclusively of no country'.

As more safety regulations were imposed, locking and re-lighting modifications were adopted, as well the use of lighter fuels and better wicks for greater illumination. But, after eighty years of British, Belgian and French lamp manufacturing supremacy, the end of the 19th century was to become the great era of German safety-lamp production and domination.

William Maurice's career was always associated with coal mining, initially as a trainee electrical engineer with John Davis & Son of Derby, a colliery electrical engineer, and then as a Colliery Manager in the north Nottinghamshire coal fields. But, had it not been for a certain encounter between complete strangers in Zwickau in Saxony in 1882, he might never have become a lamp manufacturer. Carl Wolf, the son of a miner, had just invented the first benzene light-fuelled re-lightable flame safety lamp and was attempting to register its patent. His chance meeting at the patent's office with Heinrich Friemann, a man of financial means and commercial experience, resulted in the formation, two years later, of Friemann & Wolf GmbH. This company flourished to become the giant of mining lamp production, dominating the field of mine lighting worldwide for the first four decades of the twentieth century.

By 1907, Friemann & Wolf were producing eleven different open oil and acetylene lamps, nine acetylene safety-lamps and over one hundred different models of the patented Wolf flame safety-lamp, with future proposals for nine electric mine lamps. With the death of Carl Wolf in 1915, his son, Paul, assumed the role of Managing Director until his death sixteen years later, when control of the firm passed to long-time employees, Paul Stoppel and Wilhelm Blumberg. The year 1915 also marked the production of one million of each of their flame safety and acetylene lamps, growing to two million of each by 1947, a staggering quantity despite the intervention of two world wars. By the late 1920s, they had developed a nickel cadmium accumulator safety-lamp together with a powerful compressed air driven turbine lamp, designed for coal face lighting. This hugely powerful lamp is still in production at Wolf Safety in Sheffield, though substantially modified and lightened and is now supplied to the oil and gas industry throughout the world.

In Germany alone, Friemann & Wolf employed over two thousand workers in seven cities and had fabrication plants in Poland, Czechoslovakia, China, Japan, USA, India and South Africa, with agents throughout the rest of the world. The exception was Great Britain, where The Wolf Safety Lamp Company of Sheffield was in sole ownership of the Maurice family. It was Monica Maurice, William's eldest daughter, who on her many extensive visits to Germany throughout the 1930s, supervised the production in Zwickau of Wolf lamps for the British market and oversaw modifications and re-labelling to her father's own patented designs.

Indeed, a specific area of the factory was dedicated to Wolf Safety Lamp Company of Sheffield, for production and research and development, as can be clearly seen on contemporary plans. After the Second World War, Friemann & Wolf rebuilt their Duisburg factory to concentrate the company's surviving assets and expertise in one location. By the early 1980s, all lamp production had ceased, and they now specialise solely in battery technology.

William Maurice was born in Macclesfield in 1872 where his parents were hoteliers, his father, Frederick William Maurice, later became Mayor of the town. Frederick died relatively young, his widow, Emma Jane Maurice, moving to the picturesque village of Ashford in the Water in the Peak District of Derbyshire where, years later, Monica and her husband, Arthur Jackson, a medical practitioner, spent their retirement.

William studied chemistry and metallurgy at Manchester Polytechnic, but in 1890 he joined John Davis & Son of Derby as an articled electrical engineering student. He played an active roll in the installation of some of the earliest mining electrical plants in the country and acquired his first practical knowledge of lamp making. In 1892–93 he installed lamp rooms and electrical equipment for the 'Big Hole' at Kimberley in South Africa on behalf of Davis of Derby. In 1894 he was appointed electrical engineer at Swanwick Collieries, Alfreton and subsequently became assistant to the manager, J W

William Maurice demonstrating The Wolf Safety Lamp range to lamp-room managers, c 1930.

Eardley, under whom he qualified as a colliery manager. By 1899, he had obtained his Colliery Manager's certificate and was appointed manager of the Babbington Coal Company's Tibshelf New Colliery, where he remained until 1903 before moving to Hucknall.

During his career as a colliery manager, he introduced many safety innovations in mines in the Nottinghamshire coal fields. In 1905, when he was General Mine Manager at Hucknall Collieries, he installed the first exhaust steam turbo-alternator to be used in a British mine, and in 1908, added a booster motor generator and equalising battery. This combination of an equalising battery with an exhaust steam turbine is unique in the history of engineering developments and was, at the time, the only example of its kind in the world. He was also the first to develop the thin coal seams of the Leen Valley Colliery, and the first to make use of electric coal-cutters in the area. He passionately believed that electricity, both for lighting and machinery, was the only way forward for the future development of the safety and efficiency of coal mining production. In 1911 he moved to Sheffield to embark upon a long and distinguished career as a mining safety-lamp manufacturer.

The relationship between Friemann & Wolf and William Maurice began in 1911, spanning nearly 30 years, though the licence agreement for the insolvent Wolf Safety Lamp Company of Leeds was not signed until the 13th February 1913. In the meantime, Maurice had established his own Federation Lamp Company in Sheffield two years earlier.

This agreement did not allow Maurice to sell Wolf products outside Britain, and equally, Friemann & Wolf would not sell lamps to British customers, other than through Maurice. For his services, William Maurice would receive a monthly remuneration of

£50, plus 15% net profit commission. Furthermore, only two extra administrative staff were allowed with an extra £70 per month to cover their wages. A first year turnover of £4,000 was required, with annual increases of £1,500 per year, up to a maximum of £15,000. The business started well, but within three years, as a result of the 'Trading with the Enemy Act of 1916', Maurice was able to purchase the entire British business of The Wolf Safety Lamp Company, at a 'Fair Market Value'.

The Company, which also embraced Maurice's Federation Lamp Co. Ltd., grew from a one man business with a few technicians, run initially from Boston Street in 1911; then from a workshop in the outbuildings of the family home at 358 Mushroom Lane; to the Star Works in Young Street in 1920; finally moving to South Street behind the Midland Station in 1923.

Throughout the 1920s, the Company had a manufacturing agreement with another major German lamp manufacturer, Concordia (CEAG) of Dortmund, with a jointly managed office at 16a John Street, London. During this period, William Maurice registered 10 patented improvements to acetylene, flame and airturbo safety mining lamps. This era was the heyday of William Maurice and his company. He was an extraordinary visionary and a man of many parts, a natural orator and a gifted writer. Many of his technical papers were published in the *Institute of Mining Engineer's Journal* over a forty year period and over sixty are recorded.

The earliest of these papers, dating from 1897, deals with 'Electric Blasting'. Sixty-five pages and diagrams describe the various designs, applications and the follies of poor management.

> As with coal-cutters so with exploders: no one type can be considered 'the best', each has advantages and disadvantages, which makes it suitable or unsuitable, as the case may be, for any given range of work.

This is very much a plea for caution. In the last few pages he describes graphically the injuries sustained from the misuse of equipment as a result of lack of care and inadequate training. The majority of these papers continued to advocate the greater use of electricity for general lighting and the use of more modern electric safety and gas detection lamps. In his paper, 'More About Better Mine Lighting', published in the 'Colliery Guardian' in 1928, he describes poor lighting as one of the contributing factors to injury and therefore higher insurance costs.

> There are approximately 1,000 fatal and 200,000 non-fatal accidents in mines every year. Light, being one of the three basic factors in the prevention of accidents, must therefore inevitably help in the reduction of this heavy drain on humanity. It is directly contributory to accident reduction because, as a general proposition, there is always less danger where there is more light. It is indirectly helpful,

because the knowledge that risks have been lessened gives men greater confidence, and in various psychological ways tends to increase their capacity for work.

But as a younger man, perhaps William Maurice's proudest achievement was as a founding member and first President of the 'Association of Mining Electrical Engineers', formed on the 24 of April 1909 when he was 37 years old. This event and those present were recorded on a linen napkin.

In his first Presidential Address on the 17 December 1909, he stated:

This is a new Association. It is not an offshoot, nor is it a rival of any existing corporate body. On the other hand, it will seek to work in harmony with all whose objects are in any way related to its own. It is new in a wider and deeper sense than in merely forming the latest addition to the already almost uncountable number of technical societies, for although it is intended that it shall seek to obtain professional authority and distinction, it stands initially as the inspiration of a small body of hitherto unrecognised electrical craftsmen. It is new in its conception, for its Memorandum of Association comprises features which I believe have never previously been embodied in the design of any technical society. It is new in its title, for the mining electrical engineer – that is to say, the electrical engineer possessed of special experience in the use of electricity in mines – is only just coming into existence. Thus the Association of Mining Electrical Engineers stands as a symbol of the rise of a new and, let us hope, exceptionally vigorous class.

In the articles of association signed on the 14 September 1910, the objectives for which the Association is established are:

To consider means for minimising the risk attending the application of electricity to the industry of mining, and to promote the adoption of approved methods and devices to increase safety.

It is worth dwelling on more extracts from William Maurice's significant Presidential Address, as he contrasts the advanced and antiquated conditions in mines and the progressive as well as the dogmatic attitudes that prevailed in the Coal Mining Industry at the time. It is a powerful message, critical of the failings of management structures and the need for better labour relations between managers and miners. How much of a bearing the publication of this address and the formation of the Association had on the passing of the Coal Mines Act of 1911 one can only speculate, but it is certain that this highly regarded and influential group of mining electrical engineers were taken very seriously in many quarters.

At a meeting of Mining Electrical
Engineers held at the Grand Hotel Manchester
on April 24th 1909 at which the following
gentlemen were present
W Maurice
J H C Brooking
J Kirkby
H Cusworth
H J F Stewart
J a Bashes
J Glyn Williams
and at which meeting Mr Maurice Presided
it was discussed as to the formation
of a New Institution of Mining Elec. Engineers
    The above gentlemen agreeing that such
Institution would be useful & beneficial
it was then proposed by Wm Maurice and
seconded by E Ivor Davies that an Institution
be formed under the Title of
    Institution of Mining Electrical
        Engineers
This proposition was carried unanimously.

Proposed by J C Williams that W Maurice be
elected President seconded by J H C Brooking.

Minutes of the first meeting of the Association of Mining Electrical Engineers.

On Electric Lighting and Power he further states:

In a few years the use of electric light and power in mines has wrought the most astonishing change that ever came over an industry. So recently as 1889 – only twenty years ago – there were only some three or four electric power installations in mines in this country. There were at the same date only forty-two mines sufficiently advanced to have adopted electric light. Of these forty-two, twenty were in South Wales, seven in Staffordshire, four in Derbyshire, five in Lancashire and six in Durham and Northumberland. To-day, practically every colliery in the country has its own electric generating station, and many of these rival in the extent and perfection of their equipment the central power stations of large municipalities. The hand worker may appear to have been displaced by the machine, however the use of machinery makes it possible to work otherwise wholly unprofitable seams. Dreamers may assert that the introduction of machinery cripples the faculties of hand and eye and judgement, and up to a point there is no doubt that they are right. But when machinery provides employment where previously there is none, and when it, in addition, makes that employment less physically exhausting than it would be unaided by ingenious applications of Nature's forces, what legislator, what preacher, what artist, what poet, what social worker of any kind will venture to say that he is doing more towards the regeneration of man-kind?

The coming of the engineer, who, 'after the Architect of the Universe (as Mr W D Ennis has neatly said), gives form to that which was without form and void,' has, it need scarcely be said, not stopped short in its effects at the miner; it has penetrated and permeated the entire administration of mines. No individual is now rightly competent to undertake the direction of any single department of a mining enterprise unless he is - on the larger definition - an engineer. The relative importance of the various departmental officers of a mine has changed so radically since the passing of the MinesAct of 1887, that the Royal Commission which is now engaged in the revision of mining regulations might with advantage have recommended some changes in the disposition of legal responsibility for the more effective recognition of the important part which engineering now plays in the management of a colliery.

In passing, it may be worth while to observe that the course of training and qualifications required of a mine manager in South Africa are many years in advance of official home requirements.

On the value of efficiency he stated:

It is worth while to make yourself a good engineer, for when you seek this title you are preparing to attach yourself to one of the highest, most universally beneficent callings in which man can be engaged. It is the engineering profession, Mr Harrington Emerson has said - and I heartily endorse his dictum - that, "we must look for salvation from our distinctly human ills, it is to engineering knowledge and practice one must look for redemption from existing evils".

There is a pronounced tendency at the present day for an undue proportion of the community to evade responsibility, and wish for things to be done with the least possible trouble to themselves. We hear a great deal of nonsense talked at the present time about unemployment being caused by the few having appropriated that which belongs to all. The question has entered the arena of current politics, and I shall not, therefore, allude to it further, except to point out that the problem would be solved itself if it were possible to put to an end the enormous wastes which occur in every phase of human life.

"It is distinctly the business of the engineer to lessen waste - wastes of materials, wastes by friction, wastes of design, wastes of effort, wastes due to crude organi-sation and administration – in a word, wastes due to inefficiency", from Emerson's *Efficiency as a Basis for Operation and Wages.*

The final extract from the Presidential Address is on Improving the Status of the Engineer in the form of advice for the younger inexperienced engineering member;

Remember that the Association cannot do other than reflect the collective character and ability of its members. If they are careless, or apathetic, so will the work of the Association be carelessly, or half-heartedly done.

If its members are unable to rise above the purely personal views of semi-civilised man the Association will infallibly exhibit the motives by which they are actuated.

If members are incapable of sustained effort the work recorded in our "Proceedings" will provide unfailing indications of the fact.

If, on the other hand, its members have knowledge and judgement, if they are careful and thorough, if they are persistent and wisely progressive, so will those qualities be discernible in the work of the Association.

Endeavour, each one of you to make this a truly great Society, great in numbers, great in authority, great in service to the industry which is itself the greatest and most important in our land.

It should be noted that the Association did grow and prosper but was eventually to become the Association of Mechanical & Electrical Mining Engineers. The 'Thornton Lecture', established and sponsored by William Maurice, in memory of one of the great research engineers of the time, Dr W. M. Thornton, also survived well into the 1980s. His Address, also touched on the Royal Commission that was to advise Parliament in the preparation of the Coal Mines Act of 1911. The Act did indeed do much to enforce better working conditions and safety procedures in establishing, for the first time, pit-head baths and changing rooms, lamp rooms and regulated hours of work underground. But, most importantly, Inspectors of Mines, which included all the ancillary areas and equipment relating to the essential management of mines, would in future be directly responsible to the Secretary of State. 'Provisions as to Safety' read:

> such general regulations for the conduct and guidance of the persons acting in the management of mines or employed in or about mines as may appear best calculated to prevent dangerous accidents and to provide for the safety, health and convenience and proper discipline of the persons employed in or about mines, and for the care and treatment of horses and other animals used therein.

One would like to have believed that these more humanitarian attitudes would have been applied to other areas of British Industry at the time, but they were not. No such industry had been so thoroughly and scientifically researched in preparation for an Act, and although reform of the Coal Mining Industry was long overdue, it was introduced on purely economic grounds. British coal mines had become the most efficient and productive in the world and coal a major export earner. Even so, when the Bill was introduced into the House of Commons, the then Home Secretary, Winston Churchill said:

> A large modern colliery, with its extensive and carefully elaborated equipment, including the various appliances for getting the coal and bringing it to the surface of the ground, or transmitting power through long distances underground, or causing great volumes of air to flow through confined passages many miles in length, or draining wide areas underground and raising water to the surface, or sorting the coal into various sizes, separating it from the intermingled dirt: that spectacle, as has been said, is one of the most remarkable specimens of human activity in its struggle with, and triumph over matter.

In 1906, while William Maurice was still at Hucknall, he married Helen Laura Wheeler, whose family were in the wine importing trade and were of considerable means. Monica, the first of three daughters, was born at The Elms, Hucknall in 1908. Cynthia was born a year later and Pauline in 1914, by which time the family was established in Sheffield. They lived firstly at Ridgeway, then Mushroom Lane, and later Endcliffe Vale and Chapeltown Farm. But in 1920, William Maurice purchased a twenty year lease on Park Grange, a house on part of the Norfolk estates on the hillside above Farm Lane and Granville Road, long since demolished and built over with high-rise flats. PG, as it was known in the family, was a large Victorian mansion house, designed and built by Joshua Hawksley and set in acres of fields and parkland with spectacular views of the city. It was a happy household for the three young girls with caring and affectionate parents, hosting many parties, gatherings and musical evenings throughout the 1920s and 1930s.

A further example of Maurice's liberal attitudes, rare in engineering circles at the time, was that his three daughters were educated at Bedales, a progressive co-education-al boarding school in Hampshire, where Monica became head girl. In the late 1920s, she studied languages in Paris and Hamburg Universities and in February 1930 she joined the Company.

She became a director of the newly formed Hiring Company in 1932, formerly William Maurice's own Federation Lamp Company, and a director of Wolf Safety Lamp Company in 1934. This was the beginning of a career in the Company and in safety engi-neering that spanned over 60 years.

In 1933, the Company purchased a large industrial freehold property and site in Saxon Road, Heeley on the south side of Sheffield, overlooking the station and river Sheaf, which it still occupies today. Under the supervision of the head of architecture at Sheffield University, Professor Stephen Welsh, and the experienced works manager Paul Roedel, formally of Friemann & Wolf, the buildings were completely reconstructed and installed with new independent electrically operated machinery, the first in Sheffield, creating a 'Model Factory'. The first floor offices were also reconstructed and fitted with Pilkington tiled fireplaces, new modern office furniture and filing systems, constructed in oak and ebony, and steel framed leather upholstered chairs, all to Monica Maurice's own designs.

The entire building was equipped with an internal telephone system and central heating through hot water pipes. Daylight was maximised in the offices and on the fac-tory floor by way of glazed roof sections. It would be fair to assume that the moving power behind this ambitious and innovative expansion was Monica, as by this time William Maurice was in his early 60s and semi-retired, devoting much of his time to the anthology and his beloved library at Park Grange.

A year later, with an increased work force, the new factory was in full production, manufacturing a range of safety lamps as broad and diverse as any in Britain. In 1936, Monica Maurice organised a conference for the Women's Engineering Society at Sheffield University, which included a tour of the Wolf Safety Lamp Company's Model Factory of the New Electric Age. The President of the Society that year was Mrs J A Mollison, better known as Amy Johnson the world famous aviator, who was no stranger to Sheffield as she had studied at the University a few years earlier. Monica and Amy Johnson knew each other well through the Society and had much in common, sharing a passion for flying and fast sports cars.

Monica was not only a talented organiser but a gifted and natural linguist, fluent in French and German. She had studied office management before embarking on her train-ing with the Company and the associated parent company in Saxony. Throughout the 1930s she made many extensive visits to Germany, but in 1939, she only just managed to return home with great difficulty a few weeks before war was declared. On a number of

The Women's Engineering Society at Wolf Safety, Sheffield, 1936. Second right Joy Davison. Next to her William Maurice,
then Mrs J. A. Mollison (Amy Johnson) and Monica Maurice. Far left, Miss Caroline Haslett (Hon. Sec.).

occasions, she presented papers on William's behalf, in French to the Congress International des Mines in Liege, and at a later date in German at similar conferences held in Berlin and Karlsruhe. She was also an active member of the Institute of Mining Engineers and attended conferences on Scientific Management. During the war years, the Company continued making lamps, but as part of the war effort they produced aircraft parts and fuel pumps. During this period, Monica served on a British Standards Committee for standardising screw threads. She married Dr Arthur Jackson in 1937, and their daughter was born in 1941 and twin sons in 1943, the younger, John, now manages the company.

When in pre-war Germany, she had developed a very special friendship with the Wolf family and in particular Paul's daughter Erika. She often stayed with them at their country estate at Schonsee, near Weiden on the Czech border. In 1947 she was invited to participate in a British Intelligence Objectives Sub-committee Survey Team, to assess the war damage and reclamation of the German battery industry. She leaped at the opportunity and the prospect of seeing Erika Wolf again. With the rank of Colonel, a team of five engineers, two drivers and two cars, she covered dozens of sites in all four occupied zones in six weeks. During this visit she did meet up with her close friend, but in much changed and distressing circumstances. This was the last occasion on which they met and marked the end of a forty year friendship between the Maurice and Wolf families.

In his personal life, William Maurice was essentially a very private and often reclusive man with a love of literature. He was immensely well read and built up an impressive library of first editions by contemporary authors, some of whom he knew. Over the

A family outing with friends at Alton Towers, May 1935. Far left Cynthia, centre William, far right Monica .

years he collected and commissioned sculptures, paintings, prints and drawings on mining subjects, some by major German Expressionist artists. The artist George Bissill, originally a miner, designed one of his bookplates and they were in regular correspondence
over many years. There were also communications with other artists including Henry
Moore, though unfortunately on that particular occasion, it did not result in the purchase of any of his work.

Over the years he formed a number of very close lifetime friendships with people
who had nothing to do with his professional life. One was Noel Getliff, whom he first
met in South Africa in 1892 and another, Burt Smale, was an importer of furs and pearls
and lived in London. His two other close friends resided more locally. Dr Robson, with
whom William would 'get up to no good' as the family put it, lived at Somercote near
Belpher. It is said that on one occasion in the kitchen of his house, they carried out a
minor corrective surgical operation on a willing farmer who had a distrust of hospitals.
Will Handbury was probably his greatest friend and was a constant guest at PG. He was
an archaeologist by profession and an attentive godfather to Monica who would return
from visits to his house in Derby with quantities of artefacts.

William was devoted to his three daughters, and would spend as much time with
them as he could. Family holidays were also very important, be it Klingberg in Germany,
Nice in France or Portmeirion in Wales.

But it was Monica whom he saw most often as they worked together for over twenty years. They had similar ambitions and objectives, particularly for the Company. In any
event, by the late 1930s, Cynthia was abroad much of the time as an army officer's wife

and Pauline was studying at the Central School of Art & Design in London and then embarked upon her own career as a jeweller and silversmith of great talent.

It would appear that at this time and throughout the 1940s, William was content to step back to allow Monica and the new team of managers to run the Company. He was by then well beyond retiring age.

The household at PG had always been efficiently run by Helen with much support latterly from Miss Ethel Jones, the family house keeper and Mrs Chapman, who did the ironing and sewing for five shillings a day. In the early days there were two live-in maids and a butler, Lucien, who was, according to the daughters, 'foreign' and was appointed by William. There was much excitement from the three young girls when one day Lucien was asked to leave, as it transpired that he had been taking advantage of the proximity of his room to that of the maids. This was the first and last time that William was involved in the management of the household. During this period his daughters had a German governess, Elly Kulicke, who remained a close friend and would meet up with the family on their regular visits to Germany throughout the following decade.

William thrived in the competitive and intellectual atmosphere of his family in which he was thoroughly spoilt. Even so, when all three of his daughters were still at PG, the four national newspapers, covering the diverse political views at the time, were delivered early in the morning. There was therefore a mad scramble to the hall to secure a paper to read over breakfast. The last down would have to suffer the most outrageously invented fictitious headlines from the other four, but on occasions, these so called 'bluffs' were true.

Latterly, William's daily routine would be that Nelson, who looked after the various cars and the grounds, would drive him into the 'Works', as it was known in the family. By midday he would be collected by one or more of his daughters for lunch at PG. On one hot summer day, Cyn and Paul had spent the morning sunbathing and rushed to the car to collect him, only to run out of petrol on the London Road. As they walked to the Works in their swim suits, a group of women on a door step were heard to say, 'Oh, its just those mad Maurice girls again'. The afternoons and early evenings would be occupied with correspondence with authors, colleagues and friends, writing technical papers and reports, and reading in the sanctuary of his library, a large impressive room to the left of the main hall, lined from floor to ceiling with books. It would have been in this room that most of the reading, selection and compilation for the 'Anthology' would have been made.

When his wife died in 1949, William never quite recovered from his loss; they were devoted in many ways, though at times their lives appeared to have been quite separate. One of his greatest pleasures in the last two years of his life were the regular visits of his daughters and his grandchildren. He would spend the previous day secreting small packets of sweets around the garden, if it was fine, or in the house, if it was wet. The following day was then full of the excited onslaught and shrieks of small children running wild in search of hidden treasure. Then, after tea served in the dining room, came the formal presentation of the latest copies of the *Eagle* and the *Girl*, well thumbed by him the previous day.

The post-war period and the beginning of the decline of British coal mining in the 1970s were times of great concern and anxiety for all in the industry. For the Wolf Safety Lamp Company, safety-lamps for coal mines were the life-blood of the business. The diversification into the oil industry with the 'Airturbo' lamps regenerated the Company. Then, with the development of Industrial Safety Handlamps, its fortunes were transformed.

Perhaps William Maurice should have been better recognised and more publicly acclaimed for his great and unrelenting contribution to safety engineering, but it was the nature of the man to be modest about his achievements. He was a progressive man who had no time for mediocrity and idleness. He was courteous and punctilious in his professional and private life and his daughters inherited these great qualities as well as his gift for friendship.

He would be proud of the modern company, changed beyond recognition, as a world leader in the field of portable safety lighting equipment. His grandson, John Jackson, is securely at the helm of one of the most successful family owned specialist engineering companies in the country and his great grandson, Alex Jackson, has recently designed a new range of advanced certification safety torches which have been launched in the market place with great acclaim. It is hoped that the publication of William Maurice's Anthology, a personal vision of miners and the coal mining industry through his choice of art and literature, will be a lasting and fitting tribute to this truly remarkable and talented Pitman and the Company he founded ninety years ago.

Monica Maurice in the new model factory at Saxon Road, Sheffield, 1934.

Introduction

by William Maurice and Monica Maurice

It was the late James Agate, writing in the *Daily Express* of March 30th 1944, who reminded us of these almost forgotten notes by quoting Joseph Skipsey's 'The Miners' (better known as 'Get Up') and remarking that he had never seen this little jewel in any anthology. This 'little jewel' had been in our basic collection since January 1929, when we used it as a gap filling paper for the entertainment of a Mining Society. A year and a half later the original material was extended to include some Continental imaginative mining literature and read by one of us at a meeting of the *Congres International des Mines, de la Metallurgie et de la Geologie Appliquée* at Liege, Belgium. The question whether anyone today wants to read poems and stories by coal miners and about coal miners, their homes, their work, their play time occupations, is one to which there is none but a speculative answer. Many young miners are known to be great readers but as a rule they do not read so much about their own occupation as to find ways of taking themselves out of it. Before the year 1910 there were not very many 'pit' verses or stories, but such as there were, although often simple in diction and colloquial in style were, and are still by the elderly, regarded as little 'pit' classics. (Every colliery is 'the pit' and all those who have been trained to coal mining are 'pitmen'.)

From around 1910 until 1940 there was an almost continuous succession of verse, short stories and novels about this or that aspect of mining life; from which it is perhaps permissible to draw the conclusion that there must be interested readers.

Arnold Bennett, it would appear from his essay on 'The Mysterious People' in Paris Nights, thought there were (before 1911) only two writers – Emile Zola in *Germinal* and W. E. Tirebuck in *Miss Grace of all Souls* – and one artist – Constantine Meunier – who had dealt with colliers and collieries. Actually much of the work best known to mining folk was done considerably earlier. Edward Chicken wrote *The Colliers Wedding* (curiously reminiscent of Suckling's *Ballad upon the Wedding*) about 1740. Thomas Wilson, of Newcastle Upon Tyne, wrote *The Pitman's Pay* in 1826. William Mitford, known as the Newcastle poet, wrote before 1851 and Joseph Skipsey's first volume of poems appeared in 1871. There were writers of 'pit' stories too who were contemporary with Arnold Bennett. H. W. Nevinson has a characteristic tale in the volume *In the Valley of Tophet*, the date of which is 1896. Mrs Humphrey Ward's once much-read novel *Sir George Tressady* (1897) is a story with a mining background. Joseph Keating's Welsh mining romances (1905–1909) were once popular. And Jules Verne wrote a highly improbable but entertaining tale (never translated so far as we know) which is, unexpectedly, about a Scottish colliery, wherein a family – and eventually a large mining community – dwell for years on the shores of an underground lake. As to the artists, it may be observed in parenthesis, that while Meunier was the outstanding plastic interpreter of mining life there were many other notable contibutors to the same topic. Steinlen, for example, was a wonderfully human draughtsman. There must still be people who remember the tragic explosion at Courrieres Collieries, Pas de Calais, in 1906, wherein eleven hundred men and boys lost their lives and four pits were devastated. Steinlen's striking image *The Widows of Courrieres* is a profoundly moving expression of the great distress which followed that historic disaster.

Considerations of cost unfortunately make it impracticable to reproduce such work. But, illustrations apart, it is from the range of material thus broadly indicated that we have made our selections. Very much has been omitted. And no mining plays have been included, although there are some which are well known and quite a number of others which have, or had, a local reputation. *The Widowing of Mrs. Holroyd*, D. H. Lawrence's first drama, has not, we think, been staged. Harold Brighouse's one act play *The Price of Coal* was first produced by the Scottish Repertory Theatre in 1909. *The Shadows of Strife*, a play dealing with the conditions in a Yorkshire miner's cottage during the General Strike of 1926, was written by John Davison, a young working engineer, and presented at the Arts Theatre Club by Sir Barry Jackson on 8th December 1929. An unemployed colliery deputy, George Fullard, wrote a play entitled *Clogs* which was produced by Mrs. Nora Ratcliff on the stage of the Sheffield Left Theatre Club in December 1938. The well known ex-pitman author who writes under the pseudonym of Roger Dataller, wrote *Three Industrial Plays*, one of which is 'Mr. Stephenson's Lamp'. It speaks of the difficulties George Stephenson met with in introducing his safety lamp, subsequently and until fairly recently known to all the miners of Durham and Northumberland as the 'Geordy'. D. H. Lawrence wrote other (unacted) plays, but it was not until four years after he died that his play *A Collier's Friday Night* was published. According to Edward Garnett's introduction thereto this play was written almost before he had published anything and when he was only nineteen or twenty. Noting that in the year of his death, 1930, he wrote, 'I haven't got any important unprinted works and I don't think that any exist,' it is probable that he did not regard *A Collier's Friday Night* as worthy of publication. As a play he was doubtless right, but it is characteristic colliery cottage conversation of the homely kind. This is not a compilation for the critical eyes of the literary stylist, nor will it comfort the social moralist.

Our intention is to portray every aspect of 'pit' life as it was, and as it, to some extent, remains. The crudenesses, the vulgarities, the indecencies, the swearings, the drunkenness; (not so many years ago when a miner was brought before one of the compilers to be reprimanded for being drunk he protested that it was quite impossible, he had 'only had a couple of gallons') all these truly represent some, and no inconsiderable group of miners. It goes without saying that there are others, very many others, whose lives are gracious and entirely admirable. One of us lived for many years in their homes and the other was born in a colliery village and knows them very well. Both are agreed that there are no men of finer quality in the British Isles, and no kinder women.

We have some little doubt as to the one liberty we have taken. We have gone outside what might properly have been regarded as a sufficiently extensive home range to include some extracts from Emile Zola's *Germinal*, which is generally taken to be the greatest coal mining novel. We have done this because it is powerfully expressive, it provides a change of flavour without altering the essentials, and it is not so far removed from the conditions which exist in home colliers before the days when Elizabeth Barrett Browning wrote *The Cry of the Children*.

May 1944

'The Widows of Courrieres' by Theophile Alexandre Steinlen.

Proem[*]

Living thy life, O thou heart, in these desolate colliery places
Soon shall a change come upon thee and make thee most whole,
Soon shalt thou leave the drab streets and the woebegone faces,
The smoke, the dust and the dirt, the hewing and cutting of coal.

Soon shalt thou bathe and be clean, and a new wisdom wed thee
And standing alone by thyself with the love that is thine,
Thou shalt turn and look back from the place where thy striving hath led thee,
And behold the tall chimneys, the headstocks and screens of a mine.

Then thou shalt remember, O heart, long days and nights in such mines,
The daily descent into peril, the darkness, the pain,
And remembrance shall urge thee on softly with whispers and sighs,
And bid thee leave learning a moment and live in the old days again.

Not learning shall help thee at that time, not love of the modern wiseacres,
Not logic account for the error – the unsettled debt,
Their voices shall drown in the din of colliery – screens and coal-shakers,
And remembrance shall take thee and fret thee till thou shalt remember and fret.

Days thou thought'st deal shall be at thee – old pit-days and drear figures scrambling,
Fetid, low galleries – the rumble of down-sliding shale;
Darkness and silence; then voices – thick pain-stricken voices rambling:
"What hast thou done for us, comrade? Hast spoken? Hast told thou our tale?"

Frederick C. Boden, *Miner* (1932)

---

*'**Proem**: preface, preamble to book or speech' (O.E.D.).

Mining Places

Hermann Kätelhön

George Bissill

Beauty Never Visits Mining Places

Beauty never visits mining places,
For the yellow smoke taints the summer air.
Despair graves lines on the dwellers' faces,
My fellows' faces, for my fellows live there.

There by the wayside dusty weed drowses,
The darnel and dock and starwort run rife;
Gaunt folk stare from the doors of the houses,
Folk with no share in the beauty of life.

There on slag-heaps, where no bird poises,
My fellows' wan children tumble and climb,
Playing in the dust, making shrill noises,
Sweet human flowers that will fade ere their time.

Playing in the slag with thin white faces,
Where headstocks loom by the railway lines —
Round-eyed children cheated of life's graces —
My fellows' children born for the mines.

Frederick C. Boden, *Out of the Coalfields* (1929)

Herbert Samson

Hagger in Rain

It was a typical November night; typical, that is, of the north-east coast, with grimy bosom bared to the North Sea squalls. Rain had fallen in Hagger for weeks on end – hard, icy, pitiless rain – like bars of white hot iron. Here and there a spluttering street lamp fought to serve some purpose, like a glow-worm in a blizzard. But the fence of falling rain imprisoned the light in its crazy glass chamber and rays failed to penetrate even to the foot of the post. November night in Hagger! Mr. Dante kept a chip shop there. He boasted of his descent from a lovelorn namesake. But he did not think much of his forbear's description of Hell; not after Hagger – no fear!

Hagger had one main street. It began at the pithead and ended at the graveyard. Tonight it resembled a moorland torrent, deserted, desolate, terrifying, black. Not that it ran with water, of course, not much; but with miscellaneous things such as mud, clarts, whinstone, slag, ashes, vegetables, eggshells, tins, dead dogs and liquid from overflowing sewers. On the whole it resembled black grease.

Now and again an object staggered along it; something slithering at an angle nearly horizontal, for everything, no matter what it was, had to stick its head right into the belly of the bitter wind. The object moved scarcely at all. Perhaps feet kept slipping on the smooth black grease. It drew nearer the lamp-post – a battered old tree trunk, banging and groaning. Two thin rods shot out in a grab of desperation. They clutched the post, and slowly the feet drew in from the oily mess. The knees grasped the post viciously. The whole body clung to it, like some slimy reptile's. The wind shut up for a second to get rid of its phlegm. Somebody started playing a concertina – the first, gasping, weak-winded notes, out and in, there and back, no music at all; like a lunatic playing an accompaniment to the yelling blast. No, the sound seemed to be the lamp-post's, or the pest's that clung to it. As a matter of fact it came from a red, fleshy concertina-lungs that were struggling for breath, although all the air of heaven and earth and the spaces under the earth seemed to be packed in the street at that moment.

What seemed curious was that nobody peered at this weird apparition from the over-looking windows. Well, that was because it was merely a pitman on his way from the pit. The others on the shift would follow him pretty much alike – lamp-post to lamp-post. It was quite an everyday occurrence. And on pay weekends, when the pit was more or less idle, it was just the same; they staggered home, post to post; but then they were drunk. That was the only difference. Thank God for lamp-posts!

The shift went home through the drenching rainstorm. The rain felt pleasant to them after the pit. It cooled and cleaned and freshened, even though it stung. The mud of the road mattered little. They were themselves covered with mud – fine, black, dry. Dirt was their element – dirt unto dirt unto dirt. Tonight their monstrous peaks failed to keep the rain from their faces. It ploughed white vertical lines from brow to chin. Savages from the most outlandish tribes never designed such hideous masks – black and white stripes, cavernous cheeks, great jagged bumps of bone and eyes propped open with coag-ulated filth. Nice masks to wear in a civilised country! But nobody seemed afraid of these hideous creatures. Even the sewer rats deigned to consider them equals. They clustered round the lamp-post now, licking offal-laden shoes and climbing up benumbed limbs into pockets stale with crumbs and baccy.

Rain, rain, rain, infernal darkness, wind and dirt – well mixed in they make the Devil's black porridge. He supped every night behind the slag-heaps. One could see the steam ring there. During the day he went down below, but everyone knew where he sat and gorged at night – behind the pit and heaps where there lay a tract of country far more terrifying than any tropical swamp. It spread for miles, as far as the eye could see, which was not very far as a matter of fact, because of the mists that always surrounded the village. There had always been a swamp there. Once a meek and mild rustic affair with water lilies; but for generations now the pit had pittled its filthy water into it. The pale green flesh of the country had disappeared: it was now a cluster of scabs, vivid in pus-yellows, blue-blacks and blood-reds. Deep green blotches showed up here and there; huge, flat, floating pancakes of swamp weeds and fungoid excrescences. And the myste-rious waters from the bladder of the earth often turned the swamp into diluted blood, and the unknown, underground properties, combining with those of their stagnant kin-dred, formed a poisonous solution of incredible repugnance.

J. C. Grant, *The Back to Backs* (1930)

Shotton

If there is a queerer village in all England than this, I have never seen it, and I do not know that I want to see it.

Even in East Durham this village of Shotton is notorious…

If I had been completely alone when I saw it I think that now I should be accusing myself of creating a weird Shotton fantasy, as a symbol of greedy, careless, cynical, barbaric industrialism…

Imagine then a village consisting of a few shops, a public house, and a clutter of dirty little houses, all at the base of what looked at first like an active volcano. This volcano was the notorious Shotton 'tip', literally a man-made smoking hill… The 'tip' itself tow-ered to the sky and its vast dark bulk, steaming and smoking at various levels, blotted out all the landscape at the back of the village. Its lowest slope was only a few yards from the miserable cluster of houses. One seemed to be looking at a Gibraltar made of coal dust and slag. But it was not merely a matter of sight. That monster was not smoking there for nothing. The atmosphere was thickened with ashes and sulphuric fumes; like that of Pompeii, as we are told, on the eve of its destruction. I do not mean that by standing in one particular place you could find traces of ash in the air and could detect a whiff of sulphur. I mean that the whole village and everybody in it was buried in this thick reek, was smothered in ashes and sulphuric fumes. Wherever I stood they made me gasp and cough. Out of one of the hovels there a queer toothless mumbling old fellow came pointing and peering and leering, first at the 'tip' and then at us, but neither of us could understand what he was saying. Perhaps he was the high priest or prophet of the belching black God up there. We retreated a few yards, into the roadway, where we found the landlord of the inn standing at his door. He did not know the height of the giant 'tip' but said that the atmosphere was always as bad as it was then and that sometimes it was a lot worse. And it had always been like that in his time. So it must have been, for a pile of smoking reuse as big as a hill cannot have grown in a year or two. There must have been a lot of labour put into the ground and a lot of wealth taken out of it before that 'tip' began to darken the sky and poison the air. I stared at the monster, my head tilted back, and thought of all the fine things that had been conjured out of it in time, the country houses and town houses, the drawing-rooms and dining-rooms, the carriages and pairs, the trips to Paris, the silks and the jewels, the peaches and iced puddings, the cigars and old brandies; I thought I saw them all tumbling and streaming out, hurrying away from Shotton – oh, a long way from Shotton – as fast as they could go. But I did not stay long, staring, with my head tilted back. The giant 'tip' saw to that. I began coughing again, not being eruption-proof. 'Let's get out of this horror', I said hastily, and out we got.

J. B. Priestley, *English Journey* (1934)

Worsboro'

'Worsbro'! By God!' He spat upon the 'face' deliberately.
'That's a bloody 'ot shop if ther wor one'.
'Wer yer can't knock at a wrong door i' Worsboro'. Ow's owd Nanny Binks goin' on?'
Lambert smiled composedly. 'Wer what is ther i' Tollgate? A bloody open-air market, an' pubs?'
'Yer 'aven't a club worth a tupenny damn – na 'ave yer? Ave yer?'
'Does tha' call that shanty a club at Worsboro'?' rejoined the collier.
'Aye, ah do, an' ah do that!'
'A club? Ho' – derisively – 'a bloody Noah's Ark!'

Roger Dataller, *A Pitman's Note Book* (1925)

Seaham Harbour

Seaham Harbour itself is like no other town I have ever seen. It is a colliery town on the coast. It looks as weird as a cart-horse with scales and fins. Its position on the edge of the sea did not relieve it of any of the usual dreariness of colliery towns. In fact, to my eyes it seemed drearier than the ordinary inland mining towns, perhaps because the coast itself there has a dirty and depressing look. The sea was dingy and had somehow lost its usual adventurous escaping quality. You could not believe that by setting sail on that kind of sea you could get anywhere in particular. It was not the kind of sea you wanted to bathe in. Perhaps in summer it looks different, altogether more inviting; but I do not find it easy to imagine that district in sunshine and under a soft June sky. When I saw it winter had set in and apparently taken possession for ever. The town is almost entirely composed of miners' cottages, laid in dreary monotonous rows. They were all so small that they made the whole town look diminutive, as if it were only playing in a miserable fashion at being a town.

J. B. Priestley, *English Journey* (1934)

Norman Church: New Coalfield

Beneath the hill a littered landscape spread
All newly varnished by the garish sun;
New corn shone harsh and green, but new brick's harsher red
Showed that down there more coal than corn was won.
Tall chimneys flew their smoke as masts fly flags;
Great wheels on headstocks spun, and stopt, and spun again;
Pubs, cinemas, fried fish and chips, and fags –
Such were suggested by that cluttered plain –
Hot asphalt, council schools, packed cottages in rows,
Spoil banks and cinder paths and broken hedges,
Barbed wire, corrugated iron, all that goes
With smirched farms and building land in wedges
And all this litter was so raw, so new,
Even when derelicted each thing glowed,
Shattered but modern; glittered to the view
Like a smashed bottle on a tarmac road.
The very sky, so hot, so smooth, so bright,
Seemed that day newly turned, dust-proof and water-tight.

And then I started; for my glance lit on
A grim grey tower, screened by foliage –
Incongruous, startling, grey pallor shone –
A strayed spectator from another age.
I do not think I should have been
Much more surprised if I had seen
One of those men who many a year before
Had left this vale to fight at Agincourt.
If I had seen him with my eyes,
Tricked out in his forgotten guise,
Himself bewildered, but uncowed,
Pushing his way, come striding through
The gaping, staring, cloth capped crown,
To this old church; to this one place he knew.

Kenneth H. Ashley, *Up Hill and Down Dale* (1924)

Tevershall

The car ploughed uphill through the long squalid straggle of Tevershall, the blackened brick dwellings, the black slate roofs glistening their sharp edges, the mud black with coal dust, the pavements wet and black. It was as if dismalness had soaked through and through everything. The utter negation of natural beauty, the utter negation of the gladness of life, the utter absence of the instinct for shapely beauty which every bird and beast has, the utter death of the human intuitive faculty was appalling. The stacks of soap in the grocer's shops, the rhubarb and lemons in the greengrocers! The awful hats in the milliners! All went by ugly, ugly, ugly, followed by the plaster-and-gilt horror of the cinema with its wet picture announcements. 'A Woman's Love!' and the new big Primitive chapel, primitive enough in its stark brick and big panes of greenish and raspberry glass in the windows. The Wesleyan chapel, higher up, was of blackened brick and stood behind iron railings and blackened shrubs. The Congregational chapel, which thought itself superior, was built of rusticated sandstone and had a steeple, but not a very high one.

Just beyond were the new school buildings, expensive pink brick, and gravelled playground inside iron railings, all very imposing, and mixing the suggestion of a chapel and a prison. Standard Five girls were having a singing lesson, just finishing the la – me – doh – la exercises and beginning a 'sweet children's song'. Anything more unlike song, spontaneous song, would be impossible to imagine: a strange bawling yell that followed the outlines of a tune. It was not like savages; savages have subtle rhythms.

It was not like animals: animals mean something when they yell. It was like nothing on earth, and it was called singing. Connie sat and listened with her heart in her boots, as Field was filling petrol. What could possibly become of such people, a people in whom the living intuitive faculty was dead as nails, and only queer mechanical yells and uncanny will-power remained?

A coal-cart was coming downhill, clanking in the rain. Field started upwards, past the big but weary-looking drapers and clothing shops, the post office, into the little market place of forlorn space, where Sam Black was peering out of the door of the 'Sun', that called itself an inn, not a pub, where the commercial travellers stayed, and was bowing to Lady Chatterley's car.

The church was away to the left among black trees. The car slid on downhill, past the Miners Arms. It had already passed the Wellington, the Nelson, The Three Tuns and the Sun, now it passed the Miners Arms, then the Mechanics' Hall, then the new and almost gaudy Miners' Welfare and so, past a few new 'villas' out into the blackened road between dark hedges and dark green fields, towards Stacks Gate.

Tevershall! That was Tevershall! Merrie England, Shakespeare's England!

D. H. Lawrence, *Lady Chatterley's Lover* (1929) Paris Edition

Nottinghamshire and Derbyshire

'The Bottoms' succeeded to 'Hell Row'. Hell Row was a block of thatched, bulging cottages that stood by the brook-side on Greenhill Lane. There lived the colliers who worked in the little gin-pits two fields away. The brook ran under the alder trees, scarcely soiled by these small mines, whose coal was drawn to the surface by donkeys that plodded wearily in a circle round a gin.

And all over the countryside were these same pits, some which had been worked in the time of Charles II, the few colliers and the donkeys burrowing down like ants into the earth, making queer mounds and little black places among the cornfields and the meadows.

And the cottages of these coal miners, in blocks and pairs here and there, together with odd farms and homes of the stockingers, straying over the parish, formed the village of Bestwood.

Then, some sixty years ago, a sudden change took place. The gin-pits were elbowed aside by the large mines of the financiers. The coal and iron field of Nottinghamshire and Derbyshire was discovered. Carston, Waite and Co. appeared.

Amid tremendous excitement, Lord Palmerston formally opened the Company's first mine at Spinnery Park, on the edge of Sherwood Forest.

About this time the notorious Hell Row, which through growing old had acquired an evil reputation, was burned down, and much dirt was cleansed away.

Carston, Waite & Co. found they had struck on a good thing, so, down the valleys of the brooks from Selby and Nuttall, new mines were sunk, until soon there were six pits working. From Nuttall, high up on the sandstone among the woods, the railway ran, past the ruined priory of the Carthusians and past Robin Hood's Well, down to Spinney Park, then on to Minton, a large mine among cornfields. From Minton across the farm lands of the valleyside to Bunker's Hill, branching off there and running north to Beggarlee and Selby, that looks over at Crich and the hills of Derbyshire – six mines like black studs on the countryside, linked by a loop of fine chain, the railway.

To accommodate the regiments of miners, Carston, Waite & Co. built the Squares, great quadrangles of dwellings on the hillside of Bestwood, and then, in the brook valley, on the site of Hell Row, they erected the Bottoms.

The Bottoms consisted of six blocks of miners' dwellings, two rows of three, like the dots on a blank-six domino, and twelve houses in a block. This double row of dwellings sat at the foot of the rather sharp slope from Bestwood, and looked out, from the attic windows at least, on the slow climb of the valley towards Selby.

The houses themselves were substantial and very decent. One could walk all round, seeing little front gardens with auriculas and saxifrage in the shadow of the bottom block, sweet-williams and pinks in the sunny top block; seeing neat front windows, little porches, little privet hedges, and dormer windows for the attics. But that was outside; that was the view on to the uninhabited parlours of all the collier's wives. The dwelling-room, the kitchen, was at the back of the house, facing inward between the blocks, looking at a scrubby back garden, and then at the ash-pits. And between the rows, between the long lines of ash-pits, went the alley, where the children played, and the women gossiped and the men smoked. So, the actual conditions of living in the Bottoms, that was so well built, and that looked so nice, were quite unsavoury because people must live in the kitchen, and the kitchens opened on to that nasty alley of ash-pits.

D. H. Lawrence, *Sons and Lovers* (1913)

Ling's Pit Yard

When I went up thro' Ling's pit-yard
I walked in silence, staring hard,
Agape with effort to take in
The meaning of the roar and din.
I had not seen pit-yard or pit
Nor heard the proper truth of it.
I went boot-deep in mud and grime
Awed into quiet for a time.
And if I wished to say a word
I had to shout to make it heard.
The hammers of the gas-coal breakers,
The heavy rattle of the shakers,
The iron grinding of the screens,
The whirring belts and belt machines,
The roar of exhausts, and, much worse,
The cut-off screaming at reverse –
All these things do the best they can
To split the eardrums of a man,
And wanting to be heard at all
I had to take deep breaths and bawl.
Thick clouds of coal-dust hung in air,
Clouds of coal-dust everywhere,
It fell so thick it choked the light
And made sweet day as dark as night;
It filled my throat and made me dumb –
I thought I was a fool to come,
I wondered why I'd left my bed
To look around Ling's screening shed,
And never resting, never quiet,
About my ears the exhausts' riot,
The thin hiss of escaping steam
Ascending to a savage scream,
And grimily thro' steam and smoke
The coal-dust hanging like a cloak;
The dust that filled my ears and eyes
And darkened light and hid the skies.
Gladly I left the place behind,
It had no beauty to my mind –

Beauty's all gossamer and grace:
There was no beauty in that place.
So standing at the gantry-top
That spanned a sixty-foot-odd drop
And sloped in one long, clean incline,
From Ling's across the railway-line,
I peered across the cinder-tip
And saw a track did lift and dip
And lift again and writhe about
Till distance blotted it quite out.
And where this track did rise and drop
A good mile from Ling's wagon-shop,
Huddled on the wet, waste ground,
Among the smoke blowing around,
Tall chimneys standing stark behind,
I saw long rows of houses lined;
Huddled in that dreary place
Houses standing face to face;
Bricks and mortar black with weather,
Houses row on row together;
Houses where miners and their wives
Slept and ate and bred new lives.
I stared across the gantry-fence,
Delighted to find this pretence
To leave the handiwork of men
And tread the quiet fields again,
And see the houses side by side
Where miners lived and bred and died.
So down the narrow gantry-slope
Rung by rung I began to grope,
Hardset at times to see at all
Just where each falling foot would fall,
Until at last with eyes astrain,
I reached the muddy ground again,
Skirted the pumps and pit-yard pond
And found, the track stretched out beyond.
Along this track, I had heard say,
Flowers once danced along the way,
Birds once sang and lovers strolled
– so I heard say – in times of old;
But there's no truth in hearsay words,

There was no beauty there, nor birds,
Only a few poor, withered trees
And rusty railings nailed on these,
And ruts filled up with broken bricks
And ditches blocked with stones and sticks,
And lines of tall telegraph poles
And empty tins and puddleholes.
These things, I knew, despite men's clack,
Had always been along this track.
I scrambled on from rut to rut
Splashing myself from head to foot,
And Ling's grew fainter with each stride
Tho' dust hung dark on each hedgeside,
Tho' fields were full of faded things
Stamped with the sign and seal of Ling's.
Oh, sad at heart I clambered on
Watching Lings's smoke blow high and wan,
Heavy at heart I stepped uphill
And reached the top and stood stock-still,
Stared down into the hole below
Crammed full of houses, row on row,
Filled full of roofs and chimney-stacks,
Middens and dark, bricked-in backs.
I walked the widest throroughfare,
Turned down a slimy alley there,
And with the middens, cheek by jowl,
I found a house, begrimed and foul.
A hutch it was, a stinking sty,
Where even dogs would pine and die,
And in that place, in that vile spot,
Three human lives did waste and rot,
Husband and wife and their one lad,
A little, white faced thing, born mad.
The man lay on a bed of rags
Wrapt in old overcoats and bags,
He could not raise himself to sit,
His back was broken in Ling's pit.
The boy was a seven-month's child,
Born when the woman lay half wild
With anguish at the word brought round
Of her man dying underground;

A feeble, helpless thing, half dead,
That lay and rolled its heavy head,
That stared about and made low cries,
Bulging eyes like dead men's eyes.
The woman did all she could do:
She washed and charred to keep the two,
But, scrubbing on the kitchen-stone,
She whimpered to herself alone,
Daft with the double grief she bore
The night her man lay at death's door.
And he, the man, he smiled at whiles,
When she was by he was all smiles,
But when her back was turned again
His eyes hardened with rage and pain,
And watching the boy's big head roll
There was a madness in his soul,
And hopeless in his bagging curled,
Crushed by the weight of all the world,
He stared unseeing into space,
His face a death-like, livid face;
Living again the wretched past,
A ruined life, breathing its last.
What thoughts were his I did not know,
That crippled man who suffered so;
But thro' his vacant, grey eyes peered
A soul dismayed, a spirit seared,
A starved thing held in jail anon,
But straining, yearning to be gone,
Sick of the agony and strife,
The cruel misery of life.
And I myself could no more bear,
I went out in the sooty air;
I strode across the dreary land
Striving to know, to understand
What none have known or understood —
What none can know try tho' they would —
Save one who rules all humankind
And is both merciless and blind.

Frederick C. Boden, *Out of the Coalfields* (1929)

The Black Country

The valley down which they came from the Ruggenham Road widened out towards the south, and Hendiford Town lay across its mouth, with extensions climbing the hills to east and west, at each end of the main street. A line of red and brown roofs, broken into lakes of green where tree-tops thrust up beyond the chimneys, lay dreaming on the further side of a large pool that filled the valley between. Sunlight lay like cream upon the world, but into the virgin sky many black stacks were pouring foul pyres of smoke that drifted solidly away to the north above their heads, seeming to salute them with outstretched, menacing arms. The woman glanced up at them with a little inaudible whimper of apprehension. Must be nice kind of curtains in this air, she was thinking; everywhere pit-stacks, the air full of foul contact, even the placid pool reflecting the streamers of turgid smoke that crossed the sky. She sniffed; surely it must smell?

And then she saw, suddenly peering over the bracke-covered hill on the left side of the road, two great stacks, much nearer and much bigger than she had imagined. There was a pit here, then? Lord, how high they were, and there were larks singing up there above the stacks. The smoke was of all colours, brown and black and like charred pine-twigs and feathery blue and pale ochre. Fancy living all you life under the shadow of such things as them!... And then the hill was turned and the full murmurous activity of the pit met her ears, the grinding of pulleys, the hissing of steam, the whirring of wheels, the clanking of trucks, and the slow grunting of engines. She alone, the stranger, stared, the men pulling on doggedly, natives of the town, indifferent to its sights. She saw microscopic men, black from head to foot, moving about the huge mounds of waste, that were like the grey backs of nightmare elephants, and coal-carts crawling up the road to the pit. She saw a white feather of steam shoot out from a tangle of roofs, and end on the air as abruptly as it had appeared, hanging for a moment like a spirit, and then drifting away, changing form, growing tenuous, vanishing: she saw a great amphitheatre of common beyond the pit, and then a house intervened, closing the view. She sighed, despondent. Her glance crept up to scan the town, and her lids narrowed timidly. It was the biggest collection of houses her country eyes had seen, bigger than Ruggenham or Utchetor or Lichfield, and its reflection in the pool enhanced its size. She sighed, and then raised her head, squared her man-like shoulders with a half-swagger and gave the town stare for stare. If it wasn't for the stacks and the pit-mounds it would look nice in the water.

Bruce Beddow, *A Man of the Midlands* (1928)

Rhondda

Revolutionary and riotous; religious and musical; sporting and artistic, coal-bearing Rhondda.

The starting-point of hunger marches, religious revivals, and Communist miners' delegations to Russia. Place of origin of champion boxers, noted preachers, talented musicians and composers, famous choir conductors, operatic stars and novelists. It has been honoured by the presence of Royalty, and cowed by the military; inspired or otherwise by the speeches of Prime Ministers and ex-Prime Ministers, and fanned into a fury of resentment by world famous (or notorious) revolutionary leaders. Many huge fortunes have been made out of its many pits by mining magnates, and several plans for 'workers' control' such as 'The Miners' Next Step' have been worked out and strenuously advocated by the Rhondda miners' leaders. Strikes, lockouts and explosions have robbed its women of wages and wage-earners; and a woman who ably edits an independent Review is now the proud bearer of the name of this once turbulent and prosperous area.

Jack Jones, *Rhondda Roundabout* (1934)

Leonard Sandrock

A Coal Miner's Disgust

Twenty weary colliers were walking out to dine,
Bandy-legged and black-faced, up from the mine.
Said the wisest to the dullest, 'Now, I'll tell you what
I fears,
We've been mucking up the country for a hundred
bleeding years, –

'Us 'as trimmed the hillside and made the barley grow,
Reared the bonny maypole where the pit-fires glow,
Us 'as wore the green cloth at Crécy and Poitiers,
We've been mucking up the country for a hundred
bleeding years.

'See them dirty cottages, sprawling in a heap,
Fit to make the coping stones of Hellgate weep!
Industry's of Heaven; but where's Heaven's town
That summat in your deep soul wouldn't bang down!
'And all to make a million oiled wheels go round!
I can hear 'em in my head when I'm hewing underground,
Hear 'em in my head till the coal-roof reels,
Listen to the whirring and the winding of the wheels!

'Christ! The blind faces in the street gone blind!
Blind alley places, and blind leading blind!
Look at them and weep, till your brain-roof reels
Listen to the whirring and the winding of the wheels!

'Scarce a single parson heaved the shadow of a sigh;
God was with the prosperous, and Christ was in the sky.
Mates! The flaming dawn behind us is fogged with
filth and tears;
We've been mucking up the country for a hundred
bleeding years.'

Herbert E. Palmer, *Summit and Chasm, A Book of Poems and Rimes* (1934)

First printed as 'The Coal Miner's Dinner March' in *The Empire Review*, September 1926.

George Bissill

Miners' Homes

Hermann Kätelhön

George Bissill

Portrait of a Pitman

He always made his own breakfast. Being a man who rose early and had plenty of time he did not, as some miners do, drag his wife out of bed at six o'clock. At five, sometimes earlier, he woke, got straight out of bed and went downstairs.
When she could not sleep, his wife lay waiting for this time, as for a period of peace. The only real rest seemed to be when he was out of the house.

He went downstairs in his shirt and then struggled into his pit trousers, which were left on the hearth to warm all night. There was always a fire because Mrs. Morel raked.

And the first sound in the house was the bang, bang of the poker against the raker, as Morel smashed the remainder of the coal to make the kettle, which was filled and left on the hob, finally boil. His cup and knife and fork, all he wanted except just the food, was laid ready on the table on a newspaper. Then he got his breakfast, made the tea, packed the bottom of the doors with rugs to shut out the draught, piled a big fire and sat down to an hour of joy. He toasted his bacon on a fork and caught the drops of fat on his bread; then he put the rasher on his thick slice of bread, and cut off chunks with a clasp knife, poured his tea into his saucer, and was happy. With his family about, meals were never so pleasant.

He loathed a fork; it is a modern introduction which has still scarcely reached common people. What Morel preferred was a clasp knife. Then, in solitude, he ate and drank, often sitting, in cold weather, on a little stool with his back to the warm chimney-piece, his food on the fender, his cup on the hearth.

And then he read the last night's newspaper – what of it he could – spelling it over laboriously. He preferred to keep the blinds down and the candle lit even when it was daylight; it was the habit of the mine.

At a quarter to six he rose, cut two tick slices of bread and butter and put them in the white calico snap-bag. He filled his tin bottle with tea. Cold tea without milk or sugar was the drink he preferred for the pit. Then he pulled off his shirt, and put on his pit-singlet, a vest of thick flannel cut low round the neck, and with short sleeves like a chemise.

He never took more than two slices of bread and butter to eat in the pit, so an apple or an orange was a treat to him. He always liked it when she put one out for him. He tied a scarf round his neck, put on his great, heavy boots, his coat with the big pocket that carried his snap bag and his bottle of tea, and went forth into the fresh morning air – closing, without locking, the door behind him. He loved the early morning and the walk across the fields. So he appeared at the pit-top, often with a stalk from the hedge between his teeth, which he chewed all day to keep his mouth moist, down the mine, feeling quite as happy as when he was in the field.

D. H. Lawrence, *Sons and Lovers* (1913)

At Easingden

The women (of Easingden) were morbidly ambitious about a perfect glitter on their fireside utensils. Angels in heaven haunting the blue ether, or treading rich fields of asphodel, were not happier than an Easingden woman exulting in a fireplace where the brasses and the copper ornaments shone with such lustre that you could see your image reflected in each shining object.

The fender, the fire-irons, spit-boxes and the brass dogs that glowed in their places, were all kept beautifully polished. The spit-boxes at each end of the fender shone with splendour. They were really too bright, too beautiful for everyday use. There was sawdust in them, all ready to soak up the yellowish spit that came from the chewing of thick brown twist; but except when there was a funeral, or a wedding, the brilliant gleaming spit-boxes were considered sacrosanct – like the rarer effigies of the angels that stood in gloomy isolation at each corner of the mantelpiece.

Whatever else might be disregarded, the brilliant fireplaces suffered no neglect. The dust that gathered on the angels was removed twice or thrice a week, but the fireplace utensils were made lucent daily. Pictures had their turn as time permitted. Pictures of a prize greyhound; the Pet Lamb being forcibly seized in lieu of debt; a fading chromotype of the Prince Consort and Queen Victoria on their wedding day; a Prize-fight showing the victor standing menacingly over his helpless, bleeding antagonist: Mary bringing in the Lost Sheep: and a head of Christ, where blood ran down the cheek, a white halo encircling all, except in the further distance in the drawing – and there the imaginative artist had carved a cloud carrying a host of quite likeable nymphs. Once a week was sufficient for the dusting of the Christ: the white halo of attainment, and the red blood, continued to gleam near the bed in the kitchen always.

So, funerals or weddings excepted, the men just spat in a free and easy fashion on the home-woven mats of many colours; mats deftly and artistically created from an accumulation of hundreds of bits of cloth assembled over long periods, and these aesthetic achievements were useful as well as beautiful.

The women put their souls into the hobby of mat-making.

J. G. Sinclair *Easingden,* (1926)

The Tiny Drawing Rooms

The tiny drawing rooms of miners' cottages, and their front doors, which opened directly on to the street, were used only on weekends, festive and ceremonial occasions. Ordinary weekday activity, with its frequent changing of work clothes and the consequent entry of pit dirt and pit smells into the house was confined to the large kitchen at the back. These drawing rooms contained the prided possessions of a miner's household – cheap pianos, gaudy carpets and plush furniture suites, the family album and family Bible; framed photograph enlargements of the preceding heads of the house, pictures of prize-winning whippets or of athletic members of the family, sentimental oleographs and illuminated mottoes, inscribed chinaware and holiday souvenirs crowded on the mantelpiece and corner fret-work shelves, and a rubber plant or other potted growth on a fancy metal tripod near the window.

Harry Carlisle, *Darkness at Noon* (1932)

In Lowood

In Lowood there were no sanitary conveniences of any kind, and it was a difficult matter for the women folk to keep a tidy house under these circumstances. But it was wonderful, the homeliness and comfort found in these single apartment houses. In such homes fine men and women were bred and reared, but the credit was due entirely to our womenfolk; for they had the fashioning of the spirit of the homes, and the spirit of the home is always the spirit of the people.

James C. Welsh, *The Underworld* (1926)

Geordie Comes Home

Geordie Shieldykes was the last of the shift to stagger home tonight. He swore all the way to keep his spirits up. The door of his house closed with a bang. That was how he wakened his dozing wife every night, for he made her serve him hand and foot whatever time it was.

Poor Jane jumped in her chair, like a startled fish. She proceeded to fill the foot-bath from innumerable pans and kettles, and swilled out the teapot ready for action.

Geordie continued to swear as he slung his clothes into the fender, where they started to steam with a pungent suggestion of sweat. The atmosphere was already thick and heavy with the smells of baking and washing. The bitter stench of soap, which could almost be tasted, the stenches of coal, yeasty bread and fish-and-chips — these constituted the usual amalgamated stink of a Hagger dwelling. He sat down in the bath, like a great striped toad. The swearing gave way to a hoarse continuous gurgle of sensuous satisfaction. Jane waited patiently upon him, without a word. She let him have time to recover; his wits were threadbare after the storm and the pit. He had spasms of shivering that rocked the water on to the floor. His teeth chattered. Great bleeding gashes glared on his arms and knees where the sharpfanged rocks had bitten and torn. How they stood forth on his lily-white flesh!

Jane took the floor brush and began to scrub between his shoulders and up and down his back. He purred like a cat and sometimes shrieked. His shoulder blades and rump were raw beef-steaks: he had been lying on his back, picking coal above his face. With her fingernails she scratched out the hard black crystals embedded in his skin. It seemed a hopeless task. Portions of his body were doomed to blackness because of the fragments of coal beneath the flesh. These he would never get rid of. The pit had actually permeated his body. He was coally, part of the pit. His blood, thronging with tiny black particles, was partly coal also. When he died and shrank to dust, it would be coal-dust, not just baccy ash.

She left him to soak while she poured out the tea. He smacked his lips as the hot liquid thawed his 'innards'. He felt all slushy inside. The pit of his stomach wallowed and he vomited between his knees into the tub.

J. C. Grant, *The Back to Backs* (1930)

Back to Backs

For the people of Hagger lived in rows of back-to-backs, like stalls in a byre; so that, if some drunkard crashed into the fender or blew his nose into the spitoon, the sound could be heard from the cottage near the pit to the cottage near the cemetery, as if the row of houses was nothing more than a megaphonic railway tunnel. But what a magnificently appropriate name to give to these parallel lines of hovels — back to backs!

There never was a better label attached to anything in Hagger. Not only did it embrace the rows of houses and closets, but also the whole life-course of the inhabitants themselves. Wherever one went in Hagger, this common word 'back' always kept cropping up in some connection or other. It was like the mud, everywhere, and ebbed and flowed on everybody's lips. The people in the strings of cottages lived literally back-to-back. With a numerous family, the boys and girls, lads and lasses, lay back-to-back in the same bed. The men who lay back-to-back at their hewing spoke of broken backs, as if that might happen to them any time. If there was a fall of stone at the pit, people would whisper, 'Is his back broken?' and, if so, they would continue, 'Poor chap! He will have to lie on his back for life'. If a wife wished to abuse another wife, she could not do better than say, 'Her husband has a dirty back', meaning of course, that the other woman did not scrub that difficult part of her man's anatomy and was, therefore, dirty and lazy. The men had raw torn backs, because they spent so much of their time upon them in the pit. They always felt their backs acutely, whether they lay in soft warm beds or rested in cosy armchairs. Whenever a wife was delirious with worry or disease she saw in front of her eyes a red, black, white mass that steamed and dripped and squirmed as she drove into it a huge steel piston with bristles of jagged wire.

And whenever a man was ill or dying, people would say, 'When is he going back to the pit?' as if he never ought to have stayed away from it. So too, if anyone left the village – ran away in desperation or could not restrain his ambitions – people would hold meetings in the street about it every hour of the day and night. One could hear them whispering to one another, 'When will he come back? He is certain to come back. Why doesn't he come back at once? He has stayed away long enough. It isn't right. Well, well, it doesn't matter much; he is sure to come back before long. Nobody ever leaves Hagger for good.'

J. C. Grant, *The Back to Backs* (1930)

The Maheu Family, Father, Sons and Daughter Return From Work and Wash Themselves

On returning from the pit they were always so hungry that they ate in their damp clothes, without even cleaning themselves....
In the meanwhile, beside the fire, they began to wash themselves in the half of a barrel transformed into a tub.

Catherine, whose turn came first, had filled it with warm water; and she undressed herself tranquilly, took off her cap, her jacket, her breeches, and even her chemise, habituated to this since the age of eight and having grown up without seeing any harm in it. She only turned with her stomach to the fire, then rubbed herself vigorously with black soap. No one looked at her, even Lenore and Henri were no longer inquisitive to see how she was made. When she was clean she went up the stairs quite naked, leaving her damp chemise and other garments in a heap on the floor. But a quarrel broke out between the two brothers. Jeanlin had hastened to jump into the tub under the pretence that Zacharie was still eating; and the latter hustled him, claiming his turn, and calling out that he was polite enough to allow Catherine to wash herself first, but he did not wish to have the rinsings of the young urchins, all the less since, when Jeanlin had been in, it would do to fill the school ink-pots. They ended by washing themselves together, also turning towards the fire, and they even helped each other, rubbing one another's backs. Then, like their sister, they disappeared up the staircase naked.

The father did not like washing *en famille*, as was practised in many houses in the set-tlement...

He was crouching before the tub quite naked, having first plunged his head into it, well rubbed with that black soap, the constant use of which discoloured and made yellow the hair of the race. Afterwards he got into the water, lathered his chest, belly, arms and thighs, scraping them energetically with both fists. His wife, standing by, watched him... (A conversation ensues about ways and means, with the possibility of having obtained a loan.) As usual, she was pulling up her sleeves to wash his back and those parts which he himself could not easily reach. Besides, he liked her to soap him, to rub him every-where till she almost broke her wrists. She took soap and worked away at his shoulders while he held himself stiff so as to resist the shock... From the back she had got down to the buttocks and was pushing into the folds, not leaving any part of the body with-out passing over it, making him shine like her three saucepans on Saturday: after a big clean. Only she began to sweat with this tremendous exertion of her arms, so exhausted and out of breath that her words were choked. Now she began to wipe him, plugging with a towel the parts that would not dry.

When he got up Maheu simply put on a dry pair of breeches. He liked, when he was clean and had taken his pleasure with his wife, to remain naked for a while. On his white skin, the whiteness of an anaemic girl, the scratches and gashes of the coal left tattoo marks, grafts as the miners called them, and he was proud of them, and exhibited his big arms and broad chest shining like veined marble. In summer all the miners could be seen in this condition at their doors. He even went there for a moment now, in spite of the wet weather, and shouted a rough joke to a comrade, whose breast was also naked, on the other side of the gardens. Others also appeared. And the children trailing along the pathways raised their heads and also laughed with delight at all this weary flesh of work-ers displayed in the open air.

Emile Zola, Germinal (from the edition translated by Havelock Ellis, 1894 and revised 1933)

The Maheus' Home

In the middle of the fields of wheat and beetroot, the *Deux-Cent-Quarante* settlement slept beneath the black night. One could vaguely distinguish four immense blocks of small houses, back to back, barracks or hospital blocks, geometric and parallel, separated by three large avenues which were divided into gardens of equal size. And over the desert plain one heard only the moan of squalls through the broken trellises of the enclosures.

In the Maheus' house, No. 16 in the second block, nothing was stirring. The single room that occupied the first floor was drowned in a thick darkness which seemed to overwhelm with its weight the sleep of the beings whom one felt to be there in a mass, with open mouths, overcome by weariness. In spite of the keen cold outside, there was a living heat in the heavy air, that hot stuffiness of even the best kept bedrooms, the smell of human cattle.

Four o'clock had struck from the clock in the room on the ground floor, but nothing yet stirred. One heard the piping of slender respirations, accompanied by two series of sonorous snores. And suddenly Catherine got up. In her weariness she had, as usual, counted the four strokes through the floor without the strength to arouse herself completely. Then, throwing her legs from under the bedclothes, she felt about, at last struck a match and lighted a candle. But she remained seated, her head so heavy that it fell back between her shoulders, seeking to return to the bolster.

Now the candle lighted up the room, a square room with two windows, and filled with three beds. There could be seen a cupboard, a table, and two old walnut chairs, whose smoky tone made hard, dark patches against the walls, which were painted a light yellow. And nothing else – only clothes hung to nails, a jug placed on the floor and a red pan which served as a basin. In the bed on the left Zacharie, the eldest, a youth of one-and-twenty, was asleep with his brother Jeanlin, who had completed his eleventh year. In the right hand bed two urchins, Lenore and Henri, the first six years old, the second four, slept in each other's arms, while Catherine shared the third bed with her sister Alzire, so small for her nine years that Catherine would not have felt her near her if it were not for the little invalid's humpback which pressed into her side. The glass door was open; one could perceive the lobby of a landing, and sort of recess in which the father and the mother occupied a fourth bed – against which they had been obliged to install the cradle of the latest come, Estelle, aged scarcely three months.

However, Catherine made a desperate effort. She stretched herself, she fidgeted her two hands in the red hair which covered her forehead and neck. Slender for her fifteen years, all that showed of her limbs outside the narrow sheath of her chemise were her bluish feet, as it were tattooed with coal, and her slight arms, the milky whiteness of which contrasted with the sallow tint of her face, already spoilt with constant washing with black soap. A final yawn opened her rather large mouth with splendid teeth against the chlorotic pallor of her gums; while her grey eyes were crying in her fight with sleep, with a look of painful distress and weariness which seemed to spread over the whole of her naked body.

Down below, Catherine had at first occupied herself with the fire, which was burning in the iron grate, flanked by two ovens. The Company distributed every month, to each family, eight hectolitres of hard slaty coal, gathered in the passages. It burnt slowly, and the young girl, who piled up the fire every night, only had to stir it in the morning, adding a few fragments of soft coal, carefully picked out. Then, after having placed a kettle on the grate, she sat down before the sideboard.

It was a fairly large room, occupying all the ground floor. Painted an apple green, and of flemish cleanliness, with its flags well washed and covered with white sand. Besides the sideboard of varnished deal the furniture consisted of a table and chairs of the same wood. Stuck on to the walls were some violently coloured prints, portraits of the emperor and the empress, given by the Company, of soldiers and of saints speckled with gold, contrasting crudely with the simple nudity of the room. There was no other ornament except a box of rose coloured pasteboard on the sideboard, and the clock with its daubed face and loud tick-tock, which seemed to fill the emptiness of the place. Near the staircase door another door led to the cellar. In spite of the cleanliness, an odour of cooked onion, shut up since the night before, poisoned the hot heavy air, always laden with an acrid flavour of coal.

Catherine, in front of the sideboard, was reflecting. There only remained the end of a loaf, cheese in fair abundance, and a fragment of butter and she had to provide bread and butter for four. At last she decided, cut the slices, took one and covered it with cheese, spread another with butter and stuck them together. That was the 'brick', the bread and butter sandwich taken to the pit every morning. The four bricks were soon on the table, in a row, cut with severe justice, from the big one for the father down to the little one for Jeanlin.

Catherine, who appeared absorbed in her household duties, must, however, have been thinking of the stories told by Zacharie about the head captain and the Pierron women, for she half opened the front door and glanced outside. The wind was still whistling. There were numerous spots of light on the low fronts of the settlement, from which arose a vague tremor of awakening. Already doors were being closed, and black files of workers passed into the night. It was stupid of her to get cold, since the porter at the pit-eye was certainly asleep, waiting to take his duties at six. Yet she remained and looked at the house on the other side of the gardens. The door opened, and her curiosity was aroused. But it could only be one of the little Pierrons, Lydie, setting out for the pit.

Now the lights in the settlement were extinguished, and the last door banged. All again fell asleep; the women and the little ones resuming their slumber in the midst of wider beds. And from the extinguished village to the roaring Voreux a slow filing of shadows took place beneath the squalls, the departure of the colliers to their work, bending their shoulders, and trying to protect their arms, while the brick behind formed a hump on each back. Clothed in their thin jackets they shivered with cold, but without hastening, straggling along the road with the tramp of the flock.

Emile Zola, *Germinal* (from the edition translated by Havelock Ellis, 1894 and revised 1933)

Morel 'Weshes'

'Shut that doo-er!' bawled Morel furiously. Annie banged it behind her and was gone.

'If tha oppens it agin while I'm weshin' me, I'll ma'e thy jaw rattle,' he threatened from the midst of his soapsuds. Paul and the mother frowned to hear him. Presently he came running out of the scullery, with the soapy water dripping from him, dithering with cold.

'Oh my sirs,' he said, 'Wheer's mi towel?'

It was hung on a chair to warm before the fire, otherwise he would have bullied and blustered. He squatted on his heels before the hot baking-fire to dry himself.

'F – ff – f!' he went, pretending to shudder with cold.

'Goodness man, don't be such a kid!' said Mrs. Morel. 'It's not cold.'

'Thee strip thysen stark nak'd to wesh thy flesh i' that scullery,' said the miner, as he rubbed his hair, 'now't b'r a ice 'ouse!'

'And I shouldn't make that fuss,' replied his wife.

'No, tha'd drop down still, as dead as a door-knob, wi' thy nesh sides.'

'Why is a door-knob deader than anything else?' asked Paul, curious.

'Eh, I dunno. That's what they say,' replied his father. 'But there's that much draught i' yon scullery as it blows through your ribs like through a five-barred gate.'

'It would have some difficulty in blowing through yours,' said Mrs. Morel.

Morel looked down ruefully at his sides.

'Me!' he exclaimed. 'I'm nowt b'r a skinned rabbit. My bones fair juts out on me.'

'I should like to know where,' retorted his wife.

'Iv'ry-wheer! I'm nobbut a sack o' faggots.'

Mrs. Morel laughed. He had still a wonderfully young body, muscular, without any fat. His skin was smooth and clear. It might have been the body of a man of twenty eight, except that there were, perhaps, too many blue scars, like tattoo marks, where the coal dust remained under the skin and that his chest was too hairy. But he put his hand on his sides ruefully.

It was his fixed belief that, because he did not get fat, that he was as thin as a starved rat.

Paul looked at his father's thick, brownish hands all scarred, with broken nails, rubbing the fine smoothness of his sides, and the incongruity struck him. It seemed strange they were the same flesh.

'Eh!' exclaimed the miner, glancing round, startled and timid, like a child.

'He had,' exclaimed Mrs. Morel, 'if he didn't hurtle himself up as if he was trying to get in the smallest space he could.'

'Me!' exclaimed Morel – 'me a good figure! I wor niver much more n'r skeleton.'

'Man!' cried his wife, 'don't be such a pulamiter!'

'Strewth!' he said. 'Tha's niver knowed me but what I looked as if I wor goin' off in a rapid decline.'

She sat and laughed.

'You've had a constitution like iron,' she said; 'and never a man had a better start, if it was body that counted. You should have seen him as a young man,' she cried suddenly to Paul, drawing herself up to imitate her husband's once handsome bearing. Morel watched her shyly. He saw again the passion she had had for him. It blazed upon her for a moment. He was shy, rather scared, and humble. Yet again he felt his old glow. And then immediately he felt the ruin he had made during these years. He wanted to bustle about, to run away from it.

'Gi'e mi back a bit of a wesh,' he asked her.

His wife brought a well-soaped flannel and clapped it on his shoulders. He gave a jump.

'Eh, tha' mucky little 'ussy!' he cried, 'cowd as death!'

'You ought to have been a salamander,' she laughed, washing his back. It was very rarely she would do anything so personal for him. The children did those things.

'The next world won't be half hot enough for you,' she added.

'No,' he said, 'tha'lt see as it's draughty for me.'

But she had finished. She wiped him in a desultry fashion, and went upstairs, returning immediately with his shifting-trousers. When he was dried he struggled into his shirt. Then, ruddy and shiny, with hair on end, and his flannelette shirt hanging over his pit-trousers, he stood warming the garments he was going to put on. He turned them, he pulled them inside out, he scorched them.

'Goodness, man!' cried Mrs. Morel, 'get dressed!'

'Should thee like to clap thysen into britches as cowd as a tub o' water?'

At last he took off his pit-trousers and donned decent black. He did all this on the hearthrug, as he would have done if Annie and her familiar friends had been present.

D. H. Lawrence, *Sons and Lovers* (1913)

Miners' Womenfolk

André Rassenfosse

George Bissill

'The Heckler' Upon Women-Folk

'Men are kittle cattle enough,' replied, 'the Heckler' oracularly, from his position of vantage on the top of a gate, to some question of mine concerning an indignation meeting held recently to protest against some matter about which no two people could give a like account; 'but they're nowt ti what womenfolk is. Ye can get roond most men easy enough if ye've a bit tax.'

'Tax?' I queried aloud, somewhat mystified. 'What tax? Not rates an' tax —'

'Gan on wi' thoo — rates an' tax be d——!' retorted the oracle swiftly. 'No, nowt ti do wi' them things; just tax, or tacts, mevvies it is, meanin' a pleasant way wi' ye, a bit touch o' the cap when the manager's vext wi' ye, a turn o' management when a drunken man wants ti fight ye for nowt at aal, ye ken, an' sae forth. Wow, but ye can fettle most things amangst men wiv a little o' that social lubricant, but wi' women it's different aaltigether; tax is nae use wi' them; it's just thowin' pearls before swine!'

'Halloa!' I interrupted again. 'What would the missus say to that?'

'Not hevin' heard it, she'll say nowt,' retorted 'the Heckler' severely.

'Well, as I was aboot to say when thoo forgot theeself and disturbed the meetin' wi' yor interruptions, most men has foibles — some's dog-men like myself, some's book-men, some's gardners, some's beer-barrils, and sae forth, an' if ye mind this ye can get what ye want usuallies oot o' them. But women's a different breed aaltigether. The divvn't care for the same things as men, an' ye cannet get roond them, I's warn'd, for the elwis gets roond ye instead. A man has no ambitions till he's married, Maister John. Nevvies he's keen aboot this an' that, an' 'tother thing but that's nowt. Noo, woman's just chockfull ov ambitions aal her life long, an's nivvor, no, nivver satisfied from her cradle tiv her grave, an' even then she's wanting fower horses tiv her hearse. Tak a wee girlie for instance: she's elwis wantin' new claes, then she's wantin' a man, then bairns, then a hoos ov her own, then a better cloak than Mariarann nex' door; an' when she gets them aal she's not satisfied, not one little bit, but's warse than ivvor.'

Howard Pease, *Tales of Northumbria* (1899)

Zay's Wife

And it was in the front bedroom of No. 3 Patchwork Row, where the cord had idly flapped, that, five nights later, George Rudd was born. Zay was at work, working overtime, and in the lamp-lit room strangers were about the labouring woman. Outside a perfect June night reigned in sedate, remote magnificence, the thin-worn floor of heaven loosing pin-pricked glimmers of light from the glorious day beyond, and the feet of passing angels again and again darkened the myriad tiny apertures. She could fancy the little lanes, may-bordered, moth-haunted, decked with foxgloves and guelder rose and wild parsley, winding through the night, and dreaming of a flowery wet dawn silent beneath the throstle's benison: and the gardens where cool airs moved after the heat of the day. Where yellow moths fluttered indecisively about the lupines, the pinks and the London Pride, where beneath the laburnum trees a scattering of cream, bleached petals grew wet and odorous with dew as the long night hours went by. And the woods where the grey cuckoo slept and in enchanted aisles bluebells shivered in the little night-wind and rang noiseless fairy peals too sweet for human ear: and the great amphitheatre of heath just beyond the houses opposite, a star-lit stage that eternally awaited actors' coming. And sometimes, in the pauses of her agony, the broken murmured threat of the pit-engines reached her. Again and again, as the slow hours wore on to dawn, pit-blowers moaned out in sudden unbearable melancholy, held on tenuously to their cheerless note, and then lugubriously faltered and failed, leaving the mysterious rumour of night to continue its everlasting whispering, leaving the murmurous pit-engines to their unquiet complaint. And when her agony returned she called out for her mother, for her husband, and would not hear their conventional reasonings and in the panting respites from pain, when the whole world seemed to pause for a moment, breathless, the murmur of the pit-engines rose up to answer her, to answer mockingly, suggesting in their broken mutterings a gigantic power for evil, conscious both of itself and of its menace. It seemed, in that time of lonely agony, as if the great pits out there in the quiet night lost their inanimateness, suddenly moved in dreadful life, like a circle of loathsome, watchful slobbering beasts. It seemed as if God had forsaken his world, giving it over to the whim and pleasure of nightmare creatures from the pit...

Just after dawn, as the first cocks crew, Zay arrived. He was pale beneath his coal-dust, and smelled of brandy. She clung to him and pleaded weakly, wildly, to be taken back to the country, the blessed quiet country. And he promised to take her, so that she was happy again.

But downstairs, to his sister Carrie, and his older brother Abe and the women gathered about Mrs. Jervis, he said:

'Ur want to goo whum, to Crawford.'

The women mowed at each other.

'Ah, they get funny fancies at times like these,' said Mrs. Jervis. 'I know; I 'ad eleven an' buried eight. Yow gotter 'umour 'em. Ur'll think different when ur gets on ur legs again.'

'Ah,' agreed Zay, feeling for his clay pipe and comfort. And then, with bravado: 'I conna fancy meself gooin' back theer, though, not for nobody,' he said. 'Why yow might as well be jead an' done for... Gimme summat to drink, missus. Drop o' that ale. I'm as weak as a babby.'

But up in the little bare room, watched over by the poor pictures that had come so far, the young mother slept with a smile on her pale, handsome face. Her baby lay beside her, and strident pain had gone, leaving in the room an atmosphere of almost suffocating silence and comfort. Outside the moon had risen in lone austerity, but dawn came, and pit-engines murmured fretfully in the dawn-light, like monsters baulked of their prey.

Bruce Beddow, *A Man of the Midlands* (1928)

Just Married

She was too good for him, everybody said. Yet still she did not regret marrying him. He had come courting her when he was only nineteen, and she twenty. He was in build what they call a tight little fellow; short, dark, with a warm colour, and that upright set of the head and chest, that flaunting way in movement recalling a mating bird, which denotes a body taut and compact with life. Being a good worker he had earned decent money in the mine, and having a good home had saved a little.

She was cook at 'Uplands', a tall fair girl, very quiet. Having seen her walk down the street, Horsepool had followed her from a distance. So, although he seemed a bit simple, without much intelligence, but having a sort of physical brightness, she considered, and accepted him.

When they were married they went to live in Scargill Street, in a highly respectable six-roomed house which they had furnished between them. The street was built up the side of a long, steep hill. It was narrow and rather tunnel-like. Nevertheless, the back looked out over the adjoining pasture, across a wide valley of fields and woods, in the bottom of which the mine lay snugly.

He made himself gaffer in his own house. She was unacquainted with a collier's mode of life. They were married on a Saturday. On the Sunday night he said:

'Set th' table for my breakfast, an' put my pit-things afront o' th' fire. I s'll be getting up at ha'ef pas' five. Tha nedna shift thysen not till when ter likes.'

He showed her how to put a newspaper on the table for a cloth. When she demurred:

'I want none o' your white cloths i' th' mornin'. I like ter be able to slobber if I feel like it,' he said.

He put before the fire his moleskin trousers, a clean singlet, or sleeveless vest of thick flannel, a pair of stockings and his pit boots, arranging them all to be warm and ready for morning.

'Now tha sees. That wants doin' ivery night.'

Punctually at half past five he left her, without any form of leave-taking, going downstairs in his shirt.

When he arrived home at four o'clock in the afternoon his dinner was ready to be dished up. She was startled when he came in, a short, sturdy figure, with a face indescribably black and streaked. She stood before the fire in her white blouse and white apron, a fair girl, the picture of beautiful cleanliness. He 'clommaxed' in, in his heavy boots.

'Well, how 'as ter gone on?' he asked.

'I was ready for you to come home,' she replied tenderly. In his black face the whites of his brown eyes flashed at her.

'An' I wor ready for comin',' he said. He planked his tin bottle and snap-bag on the dresser, took off his coat and scarf and waistcoat, dragged his armchair nearer to the fire and sat down.

'Let's hae a bit o' dinner then – I'm about clammed,' he said.

'Aren't you goin' to wash yourself first?'

'What am I to wesh mysen for?'

'Well, you can't eat your dinner –'

'Oh strike a daisy, Missus! Dunna I eat my snap i' th' pit wi'out weshin'? – forced to.'

She served the dinner and sat opposite him. His small bullet head was quite black, save for the whites of his eyes and his scarlet lips. It gave her a queer sensation to see him open his red mouth and bare his white teeth as he ate. His arms and hands were mottled black; his bare strong neck got a little fairer as it settled towards his shoulders, reassuring her. There was the faint indescribable odour of the pit in the room, an odour of damp, exhausted air.

'Why is your vest so black on the shoulders?' she asked.

'My singlet? That's wi' th' watter droppin' on us from th' roof. This is a dry un as I put on afore I come up. They ha'e gre't clothes-'osses, an' as we changes us things, we put 'em on theer ter dry.'

When he washed himself, kneeling on the hearth-rug stripped to the waist, she felt afraid of him again. He was so muscular, he seemed so intent on what he was doing, so intensely himself, like a vigorous animal. And as he stood wiping himself, with his naked breast towards her, she felt rather sick, seeing his thick arms bulge their muscles.

They were, nevertheless, very happy. He was at a great pitch of pride because of her. The men in the pit might chaff him, they might try to entice him away, but nothing could reduce his self-assured pride because of her, nothing could unsettle his almost infantile satisfaction. In the evening he sat in his arm-chair chattering to her, or listening as she read the newspaper to him. When it was fine, he would go into the street, squat on his heels as colliers do, with his back against the wall of his parlour, and call to passers-by, in greeting, one after another. If no one were passing, he was content just to squat and smoke, having such a fund of sufficiency and satisfaction in his heart. He was well married.

D. H. Lawrence, *The Prussian Officer and Other Stories* (1914)

Women's Utility

Woman's utility was wholly found in marriage; in offering her body for service as often as it was demanded; in breeding children; in darning stockings, repairing clothes, cooking meals whenever they were wanted; cleaning the pit boots and the Sunday boots; seeing that the children went regularly to school, and avoiding the stigma of the school-board officer coming in and looking under the bed in search of truants; keeping a good fire in the kitchen, and having the water ready to go into the zinc bathtub whenever it was wanted; nursing the sick, and, with skilled diplomacy, manoeuvring the temper of her man, sullenly emerging from the effects of a Pay-weekend bout, in the consciousness of having spent all his pocket-money, with another fortnight to wait before he got any more. These were superb responsibilities, in the carrying out of which married females found their essential utility; and the ways of God were justified to woman.

J. G. Sinclair, *Easingden* (1926)

A Kitchen in a House in Derbyshire

A kitchen in a house in Derbyshire,
A heap of pit-clothes by the fireside,
A few scraps of wood burning on the fire,
A woman crying. This is why she cried.

Her man working short-time, two days a week,
The last few shillings of her savings spent,
Credit stopped wherever she may seek,
An hour ago the landlord for the rent.

The greasy landlord who had sidled in
Heard her tale and leered like some great ape,
Ogled and slavered down his double-chin,
His rheumy eyes hard on her woman's shape.

'Let us make a bargain' he had cajoled,
'One that many a woman's made and kept;
Our little secret, eh.' This is why she wept.

Frederick C. Boden, *Out of the Coalfields* (1929)

A Woman Lies Awake

This winter's night a woman lies awake,
A widow woman without a mate or mite;
She cannot sleep at all for her son's sake
Who has begun on nightshift this same night.

She weeps for him so bitterly, poor fool,
Crying for fear something may be amiss,
Her only child, her one boy fresh from school,
Out with the nightshift on a night like this.

Down in a pit where coal is cut and filled,
Her little boy a labourer in a pit,
That dreadful place where men were maimed and killed —
The woman shakes with grief to think of it.

And in the darkness, with his tiny lamp
Glimmering faintly from a broken prop,
His schoolboy bones still with a strange new cramp
Until it seems each step will see him drop.

Her boy halts where the pass-by curves and dips,
Holding his tam back with his naked breast,
To wipe the coal-dust from his young red lips,
Closing his eyes, snatching a minute's rest.

There, fifteen hundred feet below the ground,
Alone, a sleepy stripling quite fordone,
His face black with the grime blowing around,
Grey streaks behind his ears where sweat has run.

He stands with shoulders bent, head hung awry,
Bought by a company for his body's worth,
A schoolboy in a tunnel four foot high,
There, fifteen hundred feet down in the earth.

Frederick C. Boden, *Out of the Coalfields* (1929)

The Collier's Wife

Somebody's knockin' at th' door
Mother, come down an' see!
– I's think it's nobbut a beggar;
Say I'm busy.

It's not a beggar, mother; hark
How 'ard 'e knocks!
– Eh, tha'rt a mard-arsed kid,
E'll gie thee socks!

Shout an' ax what 'e wants,
I canna come down.
– 'E says, is it Arthur Holliday's?
– Say Yes, tha clown.

'E says: Tell your mother as 'er mester's
Got hurt i 'th' pit—
What? Oh my Sirs, 'e never says that,
That's not it!

Come out o' th' way an' let me see!
Eh, there's no peace!
An' stop thy scraightin', childt,
Do shut they face!

'Your mester's 'ad a accident
An' they ta'ein' 'im i' th' ambulance
Ter Nottingham—Eh dear o' me,
If 'e's not a man for mischance!

Wheer's 'e hurst this time, lad?
—I dunna know,
They on'y towd me it wor bad—

Out o' my way childt! dear o' me, wheer
'Ave I put 'is clean stockin's an' shirt?
Goodness knows if they'll be able
To take off 'is pit-dirt!

An' what a moan 'e'll make! there niver
Was such a man for a fuss
If anything ailed 'im; at any rate
I shan't 'ave 'im to nuss.

I do 'ope as it's not so very bad!
Eh, what a shame it seems
As some should ha'e hardly as mite o' trouble
An' others 'as reams!

It's a shame as 'e should be knocked about
Like this, I'm, sure it is;
'E's 'ad twenty accidents, if 'e's 'ad one;
Owt bad, an' it's his!

There's one thing, we s'll 'ave a peaceful 'ous f'r a bit
Thank heaven for a peaceful house!
An' there's compensation, sin' it's accident,
An' club-money — I won't growse.

An' a fork an' a spoon 'el'll want — an' what else?
I s'll never catch that train:
What a traipse it is, if a man gets hurt:
I sh'd think 'e'll get right again. It would be so!

D. H. Lawrence, *Collected Poems* (1932)

Hermann Kätelhön

The Miner's Wife As Heroine

The miner's wife is one of the heroines of Great Britain. For at least ten years she has been pinching and scraping. Yet you never hear her complain. The outside world knows nothing of her or of her problems. She is obsessed by three thoughts: to pay the rent, to feed and clothe her family and to have hot water and food ready when her man comes home.

She knows perfectly well that the man who delivers coal to the cellars of London or Manchester gets more money than her husband gets for mining it. But she does not lose her temper about this. She has so often heard her husband talk about 'world-wide economic causes' that she regards living on the struggle line as a kind of disease.

In moments of optimism she will hope that some day things will be better – just as a patient passes a crisis in pneumonia. Suppose the Navy, with a generous gesture, scrapped oil and went back to coal? That would perhaps mean that one piece of meat would not have to drag its way in various disguises through the week, and that the children would not look so shabby in Sunday school.

Without such bright hopes it would be almost impossible to carry on. They may be illusions frail as rainbows, but they are necessary to the spiritual life of South Wales. One must believe in something...

'Come in,' said Mrs. Jones. 'I'm not too tidy, because I've been getting Mabel ready for the Sunday school outing at Barry. They're only young once and you must make them happy. I'm sure God never intended children to go short...'

On the table is a muslin dress which she had been cutting down to fit Mabel. If you look carefully at the children of South Wales you will see that almost miraculous things have been done for them with the garments of their elder brothers and sisters.

No matter how little money is coming in, appearances must be kept up. The miner and his wife during hard times are exactly like the public school man who dressed for dinner every night in the jungle in order to retain his self-respect!

The living room is bare, but the window curtains are snow white. You would never guess from the outside of this cottage how long and grim has been the struggle inside it. There is another room downstairs and three rooms above.

The house was designed about fifty years ago by some unknown woman-hater. There is nothing in it to help a woman who is always boiling water. Everything has got to be lifted up on an old fashioned kitchen grate. The rent is ten shillings a week...

'When our six girls came,' said Mrs. Jones, 'Bob was angry. He wanted sons. "I want boys," he used to say, "who can go down the pit and make good money." For his father and grandfather were colliers, and I suppose it's in the blood. But – hear him now! Girls are better than boys for South Wales now! Did you see the boys standing at the street corner on 'the dole'? That's where my boys would be if I'd had sons... What we should do without the girls I don't know. My three eldest are all in service in London – a place called Putney – and they're good to us when the pit's not working.'

'Bob hates going on 'the dole' but what can you do? It's two shifts one week, three the next, nothing the next and then a good week's work – up and down like that – so that I never know when I'm going to have thirty shillings or two pounds. But then it's no use grumbling. Mrs. Williams down the terrace was taken with consumption last week. And she's got seven children, the youngest only two. I might be worse off...'

A black man appears in the doorway. It's Bob home from the pit. The miner is the only man who always – always – in good times or bad, goes straight home. He enters his house, flings a small paper packet on the table without a word and goes into the back room. Mrs. Jones takes the paper packet, and says:

'Two pounds five.'

That is Bob's wage for hewing coal last week for forty-five hours.

He comes in, having washed his arms to the elbow. He is perhaps forty seven years of age, good looking in the monkish way of the Welsh miner. That may seem a strange thing to say. But it is a true one. I would guarantee to go into any Welsh mining village and in ten minutes pick thirty men whose faces suggest religion and poetry.

Bob sits down at the table. Mrs. Bob puts a soup plate on a clean newspaper, and ladles out some sort of Irish stew. He eats hungrily, and between his mouthfuls gives us the essential news of his day. Hugh Evans won something on a race. Young Willams hurt his foot in the pit, and had to be carried up. Then he gropes in his pocket and produces a thin strip of paper on which his 'stoppages' – the deductions from his wages – are indicated, a penny here and twopence there.

He finds a cigarette from somewhere and smokes moodily. His wife clears the table, chatting brightly all the time about Mabel's school outing at Barry. The child shall wear her Sunday shoes so that she'll be as smart as the others. She shows him Mabel's cut-down dress. Bob nods his head and looks out through the open door towards the mountain and the slag scab on the summit. He looks rather like a Trappist monk.

The woman brings in a galvanised bath and places it in front of the fire. One of the mysteries of South Wales is this: how do women manage to keep clean homes when every day husbands, sons or lodgers come in at different times black with coal dust and demand a bath? Even two hours in a coal mine fill your head with grit and blackens you – no matter what you are wearing – all over your body.

Bob strips and takes his bath. His wife cleans his back. He changes his clothes. He wears a blue suit, a soft collar and tie. Then, moodily, he goes to his pit clothes, gropes again in his pocket, and produces reluctantly a printed slip. It is a fortnight's notice. The pit is closing down.

H. V. Morton, *In Search Of Wales* (1932)

A Miner's Widow

Mrs. Bolton, Tevershall parish nurse… Mrs. Bolton was ready at any moment to talk. And she seemed so young, the way the passion would flush in her rather pale cheek! She was forty-seven.

Her husband, Ted Bolton, had been killed in the pit, twenty two years ago, twenty two years last Christmas, just at Christmastime, leaving her with two children, one a baby in arms. Oh, the baby was married now, Edith, to a young man in Boots Cash Chemists in Sheffield.

The other one was a school-teacher in Chesterfield, she came home weekends, when she wasn't asked out somewhere.

Young folks enjoyed themselves nowadays, not like when she, Ivy Bolton, was young.

Ted Bolton was twenty-eight when he was killed in an explosion down th' pit. The butty in front shouted to them all to lie down quick, there were four of them. And they all lay down in time, only Ted, and it killed him. Then at the enquiry, on the masters' side they said Ted had been frightened, and trying to run away, and not obeying orders, so it was like his fault really. So the compensation was only three hundred pounds, and they made out as if it was more of a gift than legal compensation, because it was really the man's own fault. And they wouldn't let her have the money down; she wanted to have a little shop. But they said she'd no doubt squander it, perhaps in drink!!! So she had to draw it thirty shillings a week. Yes, she had to go every Monday morning down to the offices, and stand there a couple of hours waiting her turn; yes, for almost four years she went every Monday.

And what could she do with two little children on her hands? But Ted's mother was very good to her. When the baby could toddle she'd keep both the children for the day, while she, Ivy Bolton, went to Sheffield, and attended classes in ambulance, and then in the fourth year she even took a nursing course and got qualified. She was determined to be independent and keep her children. So she was assistant at Uthwaite hospital, just a little place, for a while. But when the Company, the Tevershall Colliery Company, really Sir Geoffrey, saw that she could get on by herself, they were very good to her, gave her the parish nursing, and stood by her, and she would say that for them. And she'd done it ever since, till now it was getting a bit too much for her, she needed something a bit lighter, there was such a lot of traipsing round if you were a district nurse.

'Yes, the Company's been very good to me, I always say it. But I should never forget what they said about Ted, for he was as steady and fearless a chap as ever set foot on the cage, and it was as good as branding him a coward. But there, he was dead, and could say nothing to none of them.'

D. H. Lawrence, *Lady Chatterley's Lover* (1929) Paris Edition

Odour of Chrysanthemums

At a quarter to ten there were footsteps. One person! She watched for the door to open. It was an elderly woman, in a black bonnet and a black woollen shawl – his mother. She was about sixty years old, pale with blue eyes, and her face all wrinkled and lamentable. She shut the door and turned to her daughter-in-law peevishly.

'Eh, Lizzie, whatever shall we do, whatever shall we do!' she cried.

Elizabeth drew back a little, sharply.

'What is it, mother?' she said.

'I don't know child, I can't tell you!' – she shook her head slowly. Elizabeth sat watching her anxious and vexed.

'I don't know,' replied the grandmother, sighing very deeply. 'There's no end to my troubles, there isn't. The things I've gone through, I'm sure it's enough – !' She wept without wiping her eyes, the tears running.

'But, mother,' interrupted Elizabeth, 'what do you mean? What is it?'

The grandmother slowly wiped her eyes. The fountains of her tears were stopped by Elizabeth's directness. She wiped her eyes slowly.

'Poor child! Eh, you poor thing!' she moaned. 'I don't know what we're going to do, I don't – and you as you are – it's a thing, it is indeed!'

Elizabeth waited.

'Is he dead?' she asked, and at the words her heart swung violently, though she felt a slight flush of shame at the ultimate extravagance of the question. Her words sufficiently frightened the old lady, almost brought her to herself.

'Don't say so Elizabeth! We'll hope it's not as bad as that, no, may the Lord spare us that, Elizabeth. Jack Rigley came just as I was sittin' down to a glass afore going to bed, an' 'e said, "Appen you'll go down th' line, Mrs. Bates. Walt's had an accident. 'Appen you'll go an' sit wi' 'er till we can get him home." I hadn't time to ask him a word afore 'e was gone. An' I put on my bonnet an' come straight down, Lizzie. I thought to myself, 'Eh, that poor blessed child, if anybody should come an' tell her of a sudden, there's no knowing what'll 'appen to 'er. You mustn't let it upset you, Lizzie – or you know what to expect. How long is it, six months – or is it five, Lizzie? Ay!' The old woman shook her head – 'time slips on, it slips on! Ay!'

Elizabeth's thoughts were busy elsewhere. If he was killed – would she be able to manage on the little pension and what she could earn? She counted up rapidly. If he was hurt – they wouldn't take him to hospital – how tiresome he would be to nurse! – But perhaps she'd be able to get him away from the drink and his hateful ways. She would – while he was ill. The tears offered to come to her eyes at the picture. But what sentimental luxury was this she was beginning? – She turned to consider the children. At any rate she was absolutely necessary for them. They were her business.

'Aye!' repeated the old woman, 'it seems but a week or two since he brought me his first wages. Ay – he was a good lad, Elizabeth, he was, in his way. I don't know why he got to be such a trouble, I don't. He was a happy lad at home, only full of spirits. But there's no mistake he's been a handful of trouble, he has! I hope the Lord'll spare him to mend his ways. I hope so, I hope so. You've had a sight o' trouble with him, Elizabeth, you have indeed. But he was a jolly enough lad wi' me, he was, I can assure you. I don't know how it is…'

The old woman continued to muse aloud, a monotonous, irritating sound, while Elizabeth thought concentratedly, startled once, when she heard the winding-engine chuff quickly, and the brakes skirr with a shriek. Then she heard the engine more slowly and the brakes made no sound. The old woman did not notice. Elizabeth waited in suspense. The mother-in-law talked with lapses into silence.

'But he wasn't your son, Lizzie, an' it makes a difference. Whatever he was, I remember him when he was little, an' I learned to understand him and to make allowances. You've got to make allowances for them –'

It was half-past ten, and the old woman was saying: 'But it's trouble from beginning to end; you're never too old for trouble, never too old for that –' when the gate banged back, and there were heavy feet on the steps.

'I'll go, Lizzie, let me go,' cried the old woman rising.

But Elizabeth was at the door. It was a man in pit-clothes.

'They're bringing 'im Missus,' he said. Elizabeth's heart halted a moment. Then it surged on again, almost suffocating her.

'Is he – is it bad?' she asked.

The man turned away, looking at the darkness:

'The doctor says 'e'd been dead hours. 'E saw 'im i' th' lamp-cabin.'

The old woman, who stood just behind Elizabeth, dropped into a chair and folded her hands, crying: 'Oh, my boy, my boy!'

'Hush!' said Elizabeth, with a sharp twitch of a frown. 'Be still, mother, don't waken the children: I wouldn't have them down for anything!'

The old woman moaned softly, rocking herself. The man was drawing away. Elizabeth took a step forward.

'How was it?' she asked.

'Well, I couldn't say for sure,' the man replied very ill at ease. ''E wor finishin' a stint an' th' butties 'ad gone, an' a lot o' stuff came down atop 'n 'im.'

'And crushed him?' cried the widow, with a shudder.

'No,' said the man, 'it fell at th' back of 'im. 'E wor under th' face, an' it niver touched 'im. It shut 'im in. It seems 'e wor smothered.'

Elizabeth shrank back. She heard the old woman behind her cry:

'What? What did 'e say it was?'

The man replied, more loudly, ''E wor smothered!'

The old woman wailed aloud, and this relieved Elizabeth.

'Oh, mother,' she said, putting her hand on the old woman, 'don't waken th' children, don't waken th' children.'

She wept a little, unknowing, while the old mother rocked herself and moaned. Elizabeth remembered that they were bringing him home and she must be ready. 'They'll lay him in the parlour,' she said to herself, standing a moment pale and perplexed.

Then she lighted a candle and went into the tiny room. The air was cold and damp, but she could not make a fire, there was no fireplace. She set down the candle and looked round. The candle-light glittered on the lustre-glasses, on the two vases that held some of the pink chrysanthemums, and on the dark mahogany. There was a cold, deathly smell of chrysanthemums in the room, Elizabeth stood looking at the flowers. She turned away, and calculated whether there would be room to lay him on the floor, between the couch and the chiffonier. She pushed the chairs aside. There would be room to lay him down and to step round him. Then she fetched the old red tablecloth, and another old cloth, spreading them down to save her bit of carpet. She shivered on leaving the parlour: so, from the dresser-drawer she took a clean shirt and put it at the fire to air. All the time her mother-in-law was rocking herself in the chair and moaning.

'You'll have to move from there, Mother,' said Elizabeth. 'They'll be bringing him in. Come in the rocker.'

The old mother rose mechanically, and seated herself by the fire, continuing to lament. Elizabeth went into the pantry for another candle, and there in the little penthouse under the naked tiles, she heard them coming. She stood still in the pantry doorway, listening. She heard them pass the end of the house, and come awkwardly down the three steps, a jumble of shuffling footsteps and muttering voices. The old woman was silent. The men were in the yard.

Then Elizabeth heard Matthews, the manager of the pit, say, 'You go in first, Jim. Mind!'

The door came open, and the two women saw a collier backing into the room, holding one end of the stretcher, on which they could see the nailed pit-boots of the dead man. The two carriers halted, the man at the head stooping to the lintel of the door.

'Wheer will you have him?' asked the manager, a short white-bearded man.

Elizabeth roused herself and came from the pantry carrying the unlighted candle.

'In the parlour,' she said.

'In there, Jim!' pointed the manager, and the carriers backed round into the tiny room. The coat with which they had covered the body fell off as they awkwardly turned through the two doorways, and the women saw their man, naked to the waist, lying stripped for work. The old woman began to moan in a low voice of horror.

'Lay th' stretcher at th' side,' snapped the manager, 'an' put 'im on th' cloths. Mind now, mind! Look you now — !'

One of the men had knocked off a vase of chrysanthemums. He stared awkwardly, then they set down the stretcher. Elizabeth did not look at her husband. As soon as she could get in the room, she went and picked up the broken vase and the flowers.

'Wait a minute!' she said.

The three men waited in silence while she mopped up the water with a duster.

'Eh, what a job, what a job, to be sure!' said the manager, rubbing his brow with trouble and perplexity. 'Never knew such a thing in my life, never! He'd no business to ha' been left. I never knew such a thing in my life! Fell over him clean as a whistle, an' shut him in. Not four foot of space there wasn't yet it scarce bruised him.'

He looked down at the dead man, lying prone, half naked, all grimed with coal-dust.

"Sphyxiated,' the doctor said. 'It is the most terrible job I've ever known. Seems as if it was done o' purpose. Clean over him, an' shut 'im in, like a mouse-trap' – he made a sharp descending gesture with his hand.

The colliers standing by jerked aside their heads in hopeless comment.

The horror of the thing bristled upon them all.

Then they heard the girl's voice upstairs calling shrilly:

'Mother, mother – who is it? Mother, who is it?'

Elizabeth hurried to the foot of the stairs and opened the door:

'Go to sleep!' she commanded sharply. 'What are you shouting about? Go to sleep at once – there's nothing –'

Then she began to mount the stairs. They could hear her on the boards, and the plaster floor of the little bedroom. They could hear her say distinctly:

'What's the matter now? – what's the matter with you, silly thing?'– her voice was much agitated with an unreal gentleness.

'I thought it was some men come,' said the plaintive voice of the child. 'Has he come?'

'Yes, they've brought him. There's nothing to make a fuss about. Go to sleep now, like a good child.'

They could hear her voice in the bedroom, they waited whilst she covered the children under the bedclothes.

'Is he drunk?' asked the girl, timidly, faintly.

'No! No– he's not! He— he's asleep.'

'Is he asleep downstairs?'

'Yes – and don't make a noise.'

There was silence for a moment, then the men heard the frightened child again:

'What's that noise?'

'It's nothing, I tell you, what are you bothering for?'

The noise was the grandmother moaning. She was oblivious of everything, sitting on her chair, rocking and moaning. The manager put his hand on her arm and bade her 'Sh – sh!!'

The old woman opened her eyes and looked at him. She was shocked by this interruption, and seemed to wonder.

'What time is it?' – the plaintive thin voice of the child, sinking back unhappily into sleep asked this question.

'Ten o'clock,' answered the mother more softly. Then she must have bent down and kissed the children.

Matthews beckoned to the men to come away.

They put on their caps and took up the stretcher. Stepping over the body, they tip-toed out of the house. None of them spoke till they were far from the wakeful children.

When Elizabeth came down, she found her mother-in-law alone on the parlour floor, leaning over the dead man, the tears dropping on him.

'We must lay him out,' the wife said. She put on the kettle, then returning knelt at the feet, and began to unfasten the knotted leather laces. The room was clammy and dim with only one candle, so that she had to bend her face almost to the floor. At last she got off the heavy boots and put them away.

'You must help me now,' she whispered to the old woman. Together they stripped the man.

When they arose, saw him lying in the naïve dignity of death, the women stood arrested in fear and respect. For a few moments they remained still, looking down, the old mother whimpering. Elizabeth felt countermanded. She saw him, how utterly invio-lable he lay in himself. She had nothing to do with him. She could not accept it. Stooping, she laid her hand on him, in claim. He was still warm, for the mine was hot where he had died. His mother had his face between her hands, and was murmuring incoherently. The old tears fell in succession as drops from wet leaves; the mother was not weeping, merely her tears flowed. Elizabeth embraced the body of her husband, with cheek and lips. She seemed to be listening, inquiring, trying to get some connection. But she could not. She was driven away. He was impregnable.

She rose, went into the kitchen, where she poured warm water into a bowl, brought soap and flannel and a soft towel.

'I must wash him,' she said.

Then the old mother rose stiffly, and watched Elizabeth as she carefully washed his face, carefully brushing the big blonde moustache from his mouth with the flannel. She was afraid with a bottomless fear, so she ministered to him. The old woman, jealous, said:

'Let me wipe him!' – and she kneeled on the other side drying slowly as Elizabeth washed, her big black bonnet sometimes brushing the dark head of her daughter-in-law. They worked thus in silence for a long time. They never forgot it was death, and the touch of the man's dead body gave them strange emotions, different in each of the women; a great dread possessed them both, the mother felt the lie was given to her womb, she was denied; the wife felt the utter isolation of the human soul, the child with-in her was a weight apart from her.

At last it was finished. He was a man of handsome body, and his face showed no traces of drink. He was blonde, full-fleshed, with fine limbs. But he was dead.

'Bless him,' whispered his mother, looking always at his face, and speaking out of sheer terror. 'Dear lad – bless him!' She spoke in a faint sibilant ecstasy of fear and mother love.

Elizabeth sank down again to the floor, and put her face against his neck, and trembled and shuddered. But she had to draw away again. He was dead, and her living flesh had no place against his. A great dread and weariness held her: she was so unavailing. Her life was gone like this.

'White as milk he is, clear as a twelve-month baby, bless him, the darling!' the old mother murmured to herself. 'Not a mark on him, clear and clean and white and beautiful as ever a child was made,' she murmured with pride. Elizabeth kept her face hidden.

'He went peaceful, Lizzie – peaceful as sleep. Isn't he beautiful, the lamb? Ay – he must ha' made his peace, Lizzie. 'Appen he made it all right, Lizzie, shut in there. He'd have time. He wouldn't look like this if he hadn't made his peace. The lamb, the dear lamb. Eh, but he had a hearty laugh. I loved to hear it. He had the heartiest laugh, Lizzie, as a lad–'

Elizabeth looked up. The man's mouth was fallen back, slightly open under the cover of the moustache. The eyes, half shut, did not show glazed in the obscurity. Life with its smoky burning gone from him, had left him apart and utterly alien to her. And she knew what a stranger he was to her. In her womb was ice of fear, because of this separate stranger with whom she had been living as one flesh. Was this what it all meant – utter, intact separateness, obscured by heat of living? In dread she turned her face away. The fact was too deadly. There had been nothing between them, and yet they had come together, exchanging their nakedness repeatedly. Each time he had taken her, they had been two isolated beings, far apart as now. He was no more responsible than she. The child was like ice in her womb. For as she looked at the dead man, her mind, cold and detached, said clearly: 'Who am I? What have I been doing? I have been fighting a husband who did not exist. He existed all the time. What wrong have I done? What was that I have been living with? There lies the reality, this man' – and her soul died in her for fear: she knew she had never seen him, he had never seen her, they had met in the dark and had fought in the dark, not knowing whom they met nor whom they fought. And now she saw, and turned silent in seeing. For she had been wrong. She had said he was something he was not; she had felt familiar with him. Whereas he was apart all the while, living as she never lived, feeling as she never felt.

In fear and shame she looked at his naked body, that she had known falsely. And he was the father of her children. Her soul was torn from her body and stood apart. She looked at his naked body and was ashamed, as if she had denied it. After all, it was itself. It seemed awful to her. She looked at his face, and she turned her own face to the wall. For his look was other than hers, his way was not her way. She had denied him what he was – she saw it now. She had refused him as himself. – And this had been her life and his life. – She was grateful to death, which restored the truth. And she knew she was not dead.

And all the while her heart was bursting with grief and pity for him. What had he suffered? What stretch of horror for this helpless man! She was rigid with agony. She had not been able to help him. He had been cruelly injured, this naked man, this other being, and she could make no reparation. There were the children – but the children belonged to life. This dead man had nothing to do with them. He and she were only channels through which life had flowed to issue in the children. She was a mother – but how awful she knew it now to have been a wife. And, dead now, how awful he must have felt it to be a husband. She felt that in the next world he would be a stranger to her. If they met there, in the beyond, they would only be ashamed of what had been before. The children had come, for some mysterious reason, out of both of them. But the children did not unite them. Now he was dead, she knew how eternally he was apart from her, how eternally he had nothing more to do with her. She saw this episode of her life closed. They had denied each other in life. Now he had withdrawn. An anguish came over her. It was finished then: it had become hopeless between them long before he died. Yet he had been her husband. But how little!

'Have you got his shirt, Lizabeth?'

Elizabeth turned without answering, though she strove to weep and behave as her mother-in-law expected. But she could not, she was silenced. She went into the kitchen and returned with the garment.

'It is aired,' she said, grasping the cotton shirt here and there to try. She was almost ashamed to handle him; what right had she or anyone to handle him; but her touch was humble on his body. It was hard work to clothe him. He was so heavy and inert. A terrible dread gripped her all the while: that he could be so heavy and utterly inert, unresponsive, apart. The horror of the distance between them was almost too much for her – it was so infinite a gap she must look across.

At last it was finished. They covered him with a sheet and left him lying, with his face bound. And she fastened the door of the little parlour, lest the children should see what was lying there. Then, with peace sunk heavy on her heart, she went about making tidy the kitchen. She knew she submitted to life, which was her immediate master. But from death, her ultimate master, she winced with fear and shame.

D. H. Lawrence, *The Prussian Officer and Other Stories* (1914)

Revelation

The men of the day shift were threading their way out of the colliery. The cage had just clanked up into the daylight, the tightly packed men had poured out and deposited their lamps, the cage swishing down again for the next lot, and, hitching their belts and shaking themselves in the sunlight, those released workers of the underworld began their journey over the hill down to the squat grey town that was in the bed of the Valley. As he was passing the power-house, just before depositing his lamp, one of these colliers heard his name called from its doorway.

'Gomer Vaughan. A moment please.'

Gomer went over to the man who called him.

'You live near my house, don't you Vaughan? I wonder would you mind calling there to tell my wife I won't be home until about eight this evening? I've got a job on here, tell her, and I can't leave it. You see, she's expecting me now... Hope it's no trouble?'

Of course it wasn't. Gomer was glad to take the chief engineer's message. Montague was liked by all the miners. A chief engineer with sympathetic principles, though an Englishman. Gomer nodded and resumed his way, soon regaining the particular companions with whom he always walked home. They were all young men.

'What the blighter want?' asked one.

Gomer told him.

'She's a beauty, she is,' said another, meaning Mrs. Montague. 'Proud of herself too, strutting about and looking as though the world's no more than ninepence to her, whatever.'

'Got something to be proud of she had,' returned a short terrier-looking fellow, perking himself to have his say. 'A sprightlier bird never trod on two legs. Half French they say. Ach, she makes our lot look like a crowd of wet and panicky hens. Got something our skirts don't seem to have.'

'I wouldn't' said the eldest of them critically, 'swap her for my old 'ooman. Too much opinion of herself she has, by the look of her. A spirited mare she is in the house, I bet.'

Gomer said nothing. He was latest married of the company. He did not want to say anything on this subject of women. Though he could say a lot, by God he could. He could let flow some language — a lot of language. But he held himself tight, his eye glittering, while the others went on as men will, saying what they'd up and do if any woman had too much lip and bossiness. He had been married a year: and he was all raw and fiery from his encounters with Blodwen. God, he never thought a woman could be so contrary. Soft and simpering she before they married... Well, he'd show her yet... And as the colliers swung along together Gomer planked his huge nailed boots down on the pavement with a vicious firmness.

They had descended the hill, and as they reached the long dismal rows of dwellings that constituted the town they separated to climb to their different homes. Gomer lived in the last row reaching up the side of the greyish-green hill. At the end of this row was a detached house, where the engineer and his wife lived. The lonely bare hill swept up above it. Gomer had to pass his own cottage to climb to the villa.

It was a warm sunny summer's afternoon. There was a clear soft mist in the still air. Gomer wished there was a country lane of shady trees with a clean stream running near, in this part of Wales. He would have liked to stroll there in peace that evening. But no — after his meal and bath there would be nowhere to go but the street corners, the miserable pub or the bare uninviting hills. Ah, what a life! Gomer sighed. The same thing day after day. Down to the pit, up again, food, bath, quarrel with Blodwen, slam the door and then a miserable couple of hours trying to jaw to the fellows on the street corner — and back home to see Blodwen's face with the jibe on it still.

He cleared his throat and spat before opening the gate of the garden. Ach, he had had enough of her tantrums, and if she wanted a fight he was ready for her. Trying to dictate to him just as her mother had tried it on him. Save up to buy a piano indeed! And no one in the house who could play it. He'd give her piano!... He knocked the shining brass image on the villa door and glanced about. Natty house. Bright little garden — a rose garden. There were bushes and bushes of them: he'd never seen such big red and white roses. And such a smell! He almost snorted as he breathed in and emitted the perfume.

No one had answered his knock. He turned and knocked again. Where was the servant? Keeping him hanging about like this. He wanted his dinner. He knocked again. Then there came sounds of steps, upstairs it seemed, and as the steps sounded nearer, hurrying downstairs, a shrill voice called:

'Can't you wait a minute darling'

It was Mrs. Montague, of course, Gomer said to himself. She thought her husband was at the door. And there was laughter and excitement in her voice. Ah, that was the way to greet a tired husband coming home from work. An excited voice calling 'darling'. Made a man think a woman was worthy to be a wife... The door was flung wide open.

Gomer's tongue clave in astonishment to his mouth. The gaping silence lasted several moments. A naked woman stood before him, and then slowly, slowly retreated, her fist clenched in the cleft between her breasts.

'Mr... Mr... Montague asked me ...' Stammered Gomer and could not switch his rigid gaze from the apparition.

How lovely she was.

'... told me...' he went on humbly, '... said...' His voice dropped and he stared at her like one possessed.

She turned at the foot of the stairs... fled up: and it was like the flutter of some great white bird to heaven.

'... told me to tell you he couldn't come home at all until eight o'clock just...' suddenly bawled Gomer into the empty passageway.

He waited a few seconds wondering if she would answer. He heard her hurry about upstairs. Then she appeared again, wrapped now in a loose blue garment. Her face was flushed as she came down the stairs, but as she advanced to him she laughed. By God, how she laughed! Gomer felt his blood run. She wasn't ashamed, not she. And still her white feet were bare. They were bare and flawless and like lilies pressed on the floor.

'What is that about my husband?' she asked easily.

Gomer told her. Under the pit-dirt his cheeks burned.

She thanked him very prettily: and then she said:

'I thought it was he at the door. I'm sure you'll understand. I was having a bath. You are married, I expect?'

Gomer nodded. She looked up at his gazing eyes again in a queer laughing way and said in dismissal:

'Oh well, thank you very much for the message.'

He turned at last, and the door closed. He stepped out of the porch and, his eyes lifted in thoughtful amazement, made his way slowly to the gate. Never before had he seen a naked woman. Not a live one. Only in pictures. Respectable women – it had always been understood – kept themselves a mystery to men. But was that quite right? Ought they to keep themselves such a mystery? When they were so beautiful. Surely Mrs. Montague was respectable enough! Her husband was a fine respected man too. He wouldn't have things done that weren't right... Gomer suddenly made a decision that it was quite natural for a woman to meet her husband naked. It was lovely too.

As he opened the gate he saw a rose bush stretched up the wall. There were several curled pink-flushed roses. One bloom wouldn't be missed. His hand immediately snatched a flower, and, when he got outside the gate, he laid it in his food tin.

Gomer's shoulders seemed squared and defiant as he went down at a quickened pace to his cottage. He was going to make his peace with Blodwen. But he was not going to be a namby-pamby fool either. After all, she was his wife; and he was not an unreasonable man. He had been quite fond of her too; and there were times when he thought her handsome enough for any man.

II

'You're late,' she said accusingly. And before waiting for him to reply she went on shrilly, 'Don't blame me if the dinner's spoilt.'

'Which means it is I suppose!' he said. But he smiled at her, his good white teeth shining out in his blackened face.

'Come in at your proper time then,' she rapped out, prodding the meat viciously.

He leaned forward and playfully slapped her on the back. She uttered a scream and the meat slid off the plate, hesitated on the edge of the table and fell on the floor. His action and the ensuing accident had an exaggerated effect on Blodwen. She arched up her long neck in a tight rigid fashion, her face flamed and she darted out into the little scullery like an infuriated turkey.

'I've had enough,' she screamed, 'and more than enough.'

And she banged some crockery about.

'Now then,' Gomer called to her soothingly, 'now then my pet. What's the damage? A bit of dust on the old meat! Look, it's all right. Now, Blod, behave yourself. Where's the taters? I'm hungry.'

He knew she'd find his gentle coaxing astonishing. Another time he would have hurled abuse at her. But she remained in the scullery. He sighed and went in there. She turned her back on him and went to the tap. He followed her and whispered in her pink ear.

'Now, now. What's got you my darling? That's no way to treat a tired working man who's been working hard as he can to get you a bit of dough! Turn about Blod — and show me your chops laughing, the same as you used to! Look, look what I've got you —'. He lifted his hidden hand and tickled her ear with the rose, then reached it to her nose. 'Smell! Put it in your blouse.'

She turned and said angrily: 'What do I want with a rose in my working blouse? Where did you get it whatever?' She was relenting.

'Ah! My secret that is.'

'Oh well,' she said, tossing her head, 'put it in a cup on the table.'

During the meal she reverted again to the piano controversy. 'A catalogue came today from Jones & Evans. Cheaper they seem than anyone else. There's one that works out at seven and six a week.'

His brows were drawn in wrathfully for a moment. He did not speak. She went on talking and at last he cropped in:

'We'll see. We'll see.'

The meal finished, a big wooden tub was dragged in to the place before the fire, the mat rolled up. Blodwen, sturdy enough, lifted the huge pan of boiling water from the fire and poured it in the tub. Gomer stripped. The pit-dirt covered his body. Blodwen added cold water and Gomer stepped in the tub. While he washed she cleared away the dinner things. She was quick and deft enough in her work, and the house was bright and neat.

'I'm ready for my back,' Gomer called.

'Wait a minute,' she said coldly, taking the remainder of the dishes into the scullery.

So he had to wait standing in the tub with a patch of coal dust beneath his shoulders glaring on the whiteness of the rest of his body. He knew she was exercising her own contrary will again. He might have yelled at her, but today he didn't want to. He was holding himself tight in glowing anticipation. When she came at last to rub the hand cloth over his back and swill him down, he said nothing. Only grunted when she had finished.

'Not much respect have you got for a man's naked skin, Blod. You rub me as though

I'm a bit of old leather.'

'Bah!' said Blodwen – 'a nice little powder puff I'll get for you.'

He laughed, lingeringly, and good temperedly. He wanted to get her in a good mood. 'Ach,' he said with affection, 'one of these days, Blod fach, perhaps you'll come to know what a nice skin your husband's got on him.'

'Conceit!' she said, and would not look as he vigorously towelled himself.

Early that evening, when he sat comfortable and easy by the fire, he said to her, as she was about to go upstairs and change:

'You're not going out this evening are you Blod?'

'Yes. I'm going to the chapel.'

'Don't you go this evening, if you please', he said.

Amazement was now evident on her face. This politeness and interference with her arrangements was quite unusual. 'Oh, indeed!' she began, ready for a battle.

He cocked his tight-skinned sturdy young head up at her. His eyes gleamed, there was an odd smile on his lips. 'Well, go and change first,' he said.

She shrugged her shoulders and went upstairs.

He sat waiting for her. She appeared in a peach-coloured silky dress. Her face shone clean. She was prepared for the women's meeting in the chapel. He looked at her appraisingly and said softly:

'Come here Blod.'

'What d'you want now?' she demanded, withheld in spite of her coldness. She moved near to his chair – but apparently to the mantelshelf looking for something.

'You're looking nice tonight,' he said. And he suddenly leaned out of his chair and caught her. She cried out, disliking this horse-play in her best silk dress. But he held her and she had to keep still. Then he whispered a few words in her ear.

She suddenly wrenched herself free and slapped his face. He sprang up. Her face and slender tightened neck were mottled.

'Indeed,' she breathed, 'indeed! You rude ruffian. What d'you take me for, indeed? Please to remember I'm you wife will you? I'll teach you to respect me Gomer Vaughan.' Yet there was an undercurrent of fear in her breathed words of contempt and horror.

But he had caught fire. His head lurched towards her, his eyes like flame-lit glass, he shouted:

'That's just it my fine lady. Remember you are my wife I'm doing. Look here you. Enough of your silly airs and graces I've had. A lodger in this house I might be. You do what I tell you to, now.'

'Never!' she screamed. 'Such rudeness I've never heard of.'

'What's in it?' he demanded furiously. 'You see me don't you, when I wash?'

She was retreating from him in obvious fear now.

'Never have I heard of such a thing!' she exclaimed. Her face was contracted, her eyes were strange and haunted. 'Never. A woman is different from a man... And never do I look at you... not in that way.'

He was advancing to her. She saw the clear determination burning in his eye. With a sudden quick movement she darted out of the room and he sprang too late. She was out of the house. He heard the front door slam.

III

He knew where she had fled to. Twice before, after their more furious clashings, she had hurried off to her mother's – Mrs. Hopkins, a widow, who kept a sweet shop. Mrs. Hopkins had come up 'to see him about it' afterwards. No doubt she would come this evening. He hated her.

She arrived half an hour later. Directly Gomer saw her pale aggressive face, he buckled in his belt and thrust out his chin.

'What's this I hear from my Blodwen, Gomer Vaughan?' she began with shocked asperity. She looked startled this time too.

He uttered an exclamation of contemptuous ire.

'That daughter of yours got no right to be a wife at all, Lizzie Hopkins' he fumed. 'Running to her mother like a little filly! And don't you come here poking your nose in this business either. You go back and tell your silly daughter to return at once to the man she's married. See?' And he turned his back on her abruptly.

'Well you might look ashamed' Mrs. Hopkins replied in a rising voice – 'well you might. Scandalous is the thing I have heard from Blodwen now just. Advice she has asked me. Gomer Vaughan a respectable man I thought you. Please you remember that my daughter is a religious girl, brought up in a good family that's never had a breath of scandal said about them. And now you want her to be a party to these goings-on.' Her voice reached a dangerous pitch. 'Dreadful is this thing I have heard. Surely not fit to be married to a respectable girl you are! Shame on you man, shame on you. What my poor dead Rowland would have said I can imagine. Why, Gomer Vaughan, for forty years I was married to him, and never once was I obliged to show myself in that awful way! Don't you fear the wrath of God, man, don't you think of His eye watching?'

Gomer retained an admirable silence through this tirade. His thumbs stuck in his belt, he spat in the fire and said:

'Pah, you narrow minded old bigot, you.'

Mrs. Hopkins began to breathe heavily.

'Insult and rudeness! Would my poor Rowland was here! And would my dear girl was single again!'

Gomer lost his balance then. He turned and shouted:

'You be quiet, jealous old cat! What do you understand about young married people today? Interfering! Turning Blodwen's ideas the wrong way. A girl she is, isn't she then? Nothing extraordinary was it that I asked her. Only today was it I saw such a thing.'

Mrs. Hopkins said quickly, 'Who?'

In his ire Gomer incautiously answered, as though to strengthen his case, 'Mr. Montague's wife. I . . .'

But Mrs. Hopkins broke in with a loud exclamation:

'Ha! So that's it then. Ha! Now I understand well enough. She is the one, is it? Long have I had my feelings about her . . . Very well, Gomer Vaughan, very well . . .' And she began to back out of the room, her heavy head nodding with hidden menace, her pale eyes fixed on him triumphantly.

Gomer shouted at her:

'You send Blodwen back here at once.'

Mrs. Hopkins whisked her bulky figure out of the doorway in a surprisingly swift way. 'We'll see young man,' she darted back over her shoulder, 'we'll see.'

But Gomer had no doubts that Blodwen would return.

IV

And so she came back — sooner than he expected. Mrs. Hopkins scarcely had time to reach home and impart whatever she had to say, and Blodwen was dashing into the room where her husband sat in brooding wrath.

'You,' she panted — 'you been seeing that woman!'

She looked as though she wanted to leap on him. But like an enraged hound on leash she stood prancing and glaring wildly. 'That's where you been, when you came home late! That's your monkey's game is it – '

'Now, now Blodwen' – he began. Then he was silent, and he did not attempt to deny her accusation. There was a wolfish grin about his mouth. Blodwen continued to heap vituperation upon him. She became wilder and wilder. Her mouth began to froth, her eyes to protrude. And he liked her fierce, savage beauty. She had a splendour thus. His cunning wolfish grin widened. She became desperate.

'Not another night will I spend in this house! Gladly will my mother welcome me back – '

He decided she had reached the pinnacle of fear. He got up and went to her. She shrunk away and he followed. He took her arms firmly and with power.

'Long enough I've listened to your insults, Blod. Where did you get that idea from that I've been running loose? Eh? Has that old bitch been lying to you then?'

'You told her you been seeing Mrs. Montague naked – '

'Well, well and so I have – '

Blodwen struggled to be free. 'Oh, oh!' she cried aloud.

'Some women there are,' he said, 'who are not so mean as you about their prettiness! Mrs Montague's got very good ideas how to make her husband happy. Listen, my silly little pet . . .' And he told her of the afternoon's event.

She became quiet. Surprise, astonishment and amazement leaped successively to her wild-coloured face. And, also, there came a slow and wondering dawn in her eyes...

'There now,' Gomer finished. 'See how ready you are to think evil of me. And here I came home wishing to see a better sight than Mrs. Montague could give me. And well I could have it too, only you been brought up wrong. That's where the mischief is. Too much shame you have been taught, by half.'

Blodwen's head was a little low. The curve of her healthy red-gold cheek filled him with tenderness. And magnanimity. He said softly:

'I tell you what, Blod. We'll strike a bargain. You want that piano bad, don't you? Well, say now, we'll give way to one another —'

She hung her head lower. Some threads of her rust-brown hair touched his lips. He quivered. His hand slipped over her shoulder. But she would not speak.

'— and be nice to each other,' he continued, not always squabbling as your mother and father used to do! Live in our own way we must, Blod... There now, isn't she a sweet one... there, ah! Sweet as a rose, my darling, a better pink and white than any rose's!... there, my pet, my angel!'

Rhys Davies, *A Pig in a Poke* (1931)

Hermann Kätelhön

The Collier's Wedding

André Rassenfosse

The Collier's Wedding

I sing not of great Caesar's might,
How brave he led his men to fight;
Now shew how haughty Cato dy'd
Or what could make him satisfy'd,
Nor do I here attempt to tell
How Michael fought or Satan fell –
I choose to sing in strains much lower,
Of Collier Lads, unsung before;
What sport and feasting doth ensue,
When such like mortals buckle to.

In former days when trade was good,
And men got money, clothes and food;
When landlords were not too severe,
And tenants broke not every year;
But liv'd in plenty, knew no need,
And had enough to do their deed:
Then country lads went neat and clean,
And lasses comely to be seen;
Strove with each other ev'ry day,
Who should excel at work or play;
Were honest servants, virtuous wives,
Led harmless, inoffensive lives:
Their greatest pride was just to know
When corn was ripe, or grass would mow;
How cows, and sheep, and butter sold,
Or who got married, when grown old.
Then COLLIER LADS got money fast;
Had merry days while it did last;
They lov'd to feast, drink, play and game,
And swore without a sense of shame;
They went to church but very rare,
But miss'd not when a bride was there;
Yet rested on the Sabbath day
From ev'ry thing, but drink and play,
And slept that day; but not before
Their muddl'd heads could bear no more;

Then like true cocks that won each main,
They'd rise and drink, and sleep again.

Their wives could drink, as people say,
And hold as much, or more, than they;
Wou'd have their menseful penny spent,
With gossips, at a merriment:
Those homely females drank no tea,
Nor chocolates, nor ratifea;
They made no visits, saw no play,
But spun their vacant hours away.
And thus the Colliers and their wives,
Liv'd drunken, honest, working lives;
Yet still were fond of one another,
And always married thro' each other.

The sons and daughters of this sort,
Delighted in each country sport;
And all the young unmarried fry
Strove one another to outvie;
And would on hopping-days be drest
Genteel, and in their very best;
Look smart, be clean from top to toe,
As all that would be marry'd do.

So have I seen poor fishes caught,
By curious bait which men have wrought;
And from their wat'ry region bore
By some small hairs to die on shore;
So women, when they fish for men,
Use ev'ry bait that will trepan;
And women's bait draws more than theirs,
They've brighter charms and stronger hairs.

A Collier's daughter, brisk and clean,
Once at a country wake was seen;
The maid was born in Benwell town,
Was not too fair, nor yet too brown;
Of beauty she had got her part,
Enough to wound a Collier's heart;

And then her name was up for this,
She lov'd to spin, but blush'd to kiss:
Her pliant limbs, when music play'd,
Could humour every thing it said;
For when she tripp'd it on the plain,
To Jockey's lost his fellow swain,
Her easy steps, and airy wheels,
Shew'd she had music in her heels;
She danc'd so well, so very long,
She won the smock and pleas'd the throng.

A Collier lad was standing by,
And view'd her with a lover's eye;
He scratched his head, and then he swore,
That none had danc'd so well before;
Then made a brush up to the maid,
'How do you lass?' the lover said;
'I'm glad to see ye, by my saul,
'For sink my heart, thou bangs them all;
'Thou's warm'd their stomachs for them now,
'By Jove, thou is a tuing sow!
'Zoons lass, come gan, I'll warr'nt thou's dry;
'Come fool, what makes ye luik se shy?'
He seized her hand, and being strong,
He lugg'd the willing maid along;

She had not many words to say,
But hung her head, the country way;
Then shew'd a modest blush, and so
In silence gave consent to go.
He led her to a house hard by,
Where drink was good, if she was dry;
In private they were o'er a pot,
With other cheer the house had got.
The lad must now declare his mind,
And try to make the lass inclin'd;
He gap'd, and stretch'd himself, and then
He rubb'd his eyes, and stretched again,
And thus began: 'My comely Jenny,
'I love thee better far than any;

'If thou'll have me, faith I'll have thee,
'And love thee till the day I dee;
'I'll work my banes to make thee easy,
'Do every thing in life to please thee;
'Baith day and night I'll do my duty;
'Come speak, I cannot leeve without thee.'
She sighed and made him this reply:
'Come, let me gan, for shame, oh! Fy!
'Do, lad be quiet, pray give ower,
'The folks are peeping thro' the door.
'I cannot hear, ye squeeze so hard;
'For heaven's sake have some regard:
'How can ye use a body so?
'Take off your hand, and let me go.
'May you be happy in some other,
'For I mun wed to please my mother:-
'But call, if you should come our way,
'And hear what the awd wife will say:
'Fareweel, and thank you for this treat,
'I'll rest your debtor till we meet.'

He flew to catch her when just rising,
For he was keen and past advising;
He clasp'd her close, and held her fast,
And wonder'd at her mighty haste;
Then stretch'd himself, and loll'd upon her,
And swore like any man of honour.

Thus country 'squires, and merry blades,
Hug fresh unthinking chamber-maids;
Will kiss them till their breath blow short,
Then swear, and lie, and seldom part,
Without a maiden-head or heart.
Like them our furious country lover,
Made use of every art to move her.
He ply'd her all the afternoon,
And kept her warm to melt her down;
He strok'd her neck, and squeez'd her hand,
And press'd her till she could not stand:
And then she struggled in his arms,

With sweet disorder'd, homely charms,
Till fear and love with equal grace,
Varied the colours in her face;
Her pulse beat quick – her breath went slow,
She just could say, 'Oh! – let me go:-
'I'm spent, undone, oh! lack-a-day!
'What can I either do or say?
'Was ever lass in my condition?
'For heaven's sake hear my petition;
'Unfold your arms and give me air,
'And let me rest upon my chair:
'I faint, oh! – Tommy cut my lace,
'And thraw my apron o'er my face.'

And when in wars great generals fight
For honour, victory, or right;
When they storm citadel or town,
And blow the forts and bulwarks down;
When those within can hold no longer,
Because the enemy is stronger,
The signal's made that they surrender,
By colour dropt, or some such tender;
So now, our conquer'd, yielding maid,
Drops both her colour and her head;
The woman works in every vein,
And life, not spent, returns again;
A rising blush spreads o'er her face,
But fear at first denies it place;
With languid looks, and downcast eyes,
She sees her lover in surprize;
Is griev'd to think she makes him smart,
Yet fears to tell he's won her heart;
Her face with modest blushes burns,
And smiles increase as life returns;
Then struggling hard to shew her mind,
Her looks declare she would be kind;
Yet dar'd not speak to let him know, –
Young modest maids are always so.
With am'rous looks he call her jewel,
And says, 'How can you be so cruel;

'Come ease my mind, and speak my life,
'And give consent to be my wife;
'For I can never love another,
'Come, I'll gan with you to your mother;
'Have her consent, hear what she'll say,
'And then we'll fix our wedding day.'
Before she spoke she look'd about,
For she could hold no longer out;
And when she saw that none was nigh,
She thus broke out; 'I do comply;
'You hug, and kiss, and squeeze me now,
'But what will wedding make you do?
'I never thought to marry any;
'But Tommy, thou hast conquer'd Jenny;
'My heart and every thing that's mine,
From henceforth, Tommy, shall be thine;
'I'll love, and cherish, and obey,
'And strive to please thee night and day;'
He kiss'd, she leer'd, and seemed fain,
And rose and bush'd, and kiss'd again:
Then arm and arm away they went,
To gain old Bessy's blithe consent;
For now they'd nothing more to do,
But make the mother buckle to;
Which must be done, or else the bargain
Would not be worth a single farthing.

They trudg'd along, got home at last,
And found old Goody at her blast;
Plac'd on a cracket near the fire,
Her spinning wheel was standing by her.
Her coats lay up for fear of burning,
She lov'd all warm, but hated turning,
An earthen pot with humming beer,
Stood on a little table near;
Our old wife turn'd her head about,
And spy'd at last her daughter out;
She'd cry, 'Lass, where the de'il hae ye been?
'I thought thou wou'd no more be seen;
'You've got your belly, full of play,

'I'll warrant ye've had a merry day;
'For now it will be twelve o'clock
'And more, for I've spun off my rock.
'Whe's that wi' ye?' – 'Whe should it be?'
'Sit still,' says Tom, 'it's on'y me;
'I came to have a little clash.'
'Hout lad, get hame, ye're nought but fash;
'My pipe's just out, then we'll to bed;
'So Jenny, come and loose my head,
'And get some coals and rake the fire,
'And lay my cods a little higher;
'And Tom, be sure that ye get hame,
'And give my sarvice to your dame?
'De'il scart you're a-e, what brought ye here?
'Ye've kept our daughter up I fear.'

Tom rose, and went where Bessy sat,
And fann'd the fire up with his hat;
Play'd with her pipe till it was broke,
And grinn'd and laugh'd, and then he spoke.

'Your Jenny is my heart's delight;
'De'il rive their sark gans home tonight;
'I'll have her, had she not a smock;
'If ye'll consent we'll call up Jock,
'And raise up Doll to fetch a drink;
'Come, Bessy, speak, what do you think?'
The old wife cock'd her chin and spoke,
'Why surely, Tom, you do but joke:
'If ye're sincere, as ye are warm,
'And mean to do my bairn nae harm,
'Ye knew our Jenny's on'y young,
'And easily may be o'ercome;
'So court her first, hear what she'll say,
'We'll have a drink and fix the day.'
Her daughter Jane, with modest grace,
And fingers spread before her face,
Cry'd 'Mother, Tommy's won my heart,
'If ye'll consent we'll never part;
'I love him as I do my life,

'And would like weel to be his wife.'
When Bessy heard her daughter Jane
Declare herself so very plain,
The house was in an instant rais'd
Grey-beard was wash'd, the fire soon blaz'd;
Strong beer was fetch'd, tobacco too,
Old Bessy drank till she was fou;
Then reel'd to Tom with her consent,
Threw up her liquor as she went;
Old Jock and Doll lay on the floor,
For they could drink and talk no more.
Our lovers now have all the play,
They smack and fix their wedding day:
Things were concluded for the best
And drunk and sober go to rest.

Now all the country lads around
That get their living underground,
To have themselves prepar'd are told
When Tommy's wedding day will hold:
The maids have warning, friends besides
Must all be there to mense the bride;
At Benwell, at her mother's house,
For Tommy gave the bride her choose,
The wedding dinner must be there
Provided with the greatest care.
Great joy in ev'ry face is seen,
The lads are pleas'd, the lasses keen:
Old men and women all agree
To share good fare, and merry be.

The farmer waits not with more pain,
For former or for latter rain;
Nor does the moser more desire
His coffers full, or int'rest higher;
Nor landlords wish the quarter-day,
When tenants are prepar'd to pay;
Nor those that in suspense await,
More anxious for the birth of fate;
Nor longing mother's passion more,

For child, or joy unfelt before;
Than do our lovers for the day,
To sport it and the night away:
Their breasts are fir'd with equal flame,
They wish for what they blush to name;
They long the balmy joys to reap,
And kiss each other in their sleep.
The wish'd for day is come at last,
In early hour the bride is dress'd;
The music makes the village ring,
The children shout, the old wives sing.
Tom comes in triumph o'er the plain,
With collier lads, a jolly train;
They dash along the dusty way,
Whips crack for joy, the horses play.
The bridegroom rides in state before,
'Midst clouds of dust the bagpipes roar.
The echoes borne on wings of air,
Make all the Benwell folk prepare:
Like streamers in the painted sky,
At ev'ry breast, the favours fly.
The blithesome, buxom, country maids,
With knots of ribbons on their heads,
And pinners flutt'ring in the wind,
That fan before and toss behind,
Came thither from each neighb'ring place,
With proofs of health in ev'ry face;
To do their honours to the bride,
And eat, and drink and dance beside.

Now each prepared and ready stands,
With fans and posies in their hands.
But hark! A distant noise they hear,
And some fore-riders now appear,
Proclaim with an exalted voice,
The bridegroom near, – they all rejoice;
Loud shouts and acclamations rise,
The sound of joy in echo dies.
The bridegroom now appears in sight,
And all receive him with delight;

Clap hands, and bid him welcome there,
And place him in the elbow chair,
Old Bessy, glad at his approach,
Cries, 'Doll, be quick: the barrel broach!
'Bring on the ale, the cakes, and cheese;
'Then eat and drink, folks, as ye please.'
Then Tommy goes and kisses Jenny,
And says to her, 'How do you, hinny?
'Pluck up your heart, and never fear;
'What makes you be se sad, my dear!
'The priest will tell us what to say,
'Tis nothing but a perfect play;
'I have the ring and all things ready,
'And faith thou's buss'd like any lady;
'Thou looks so brisk, it does me good,' –
'Be quiet Tom, thou'll cramp my hood:
'Come let us rise and gan away,
'We'll may be make the parson stay;
'And that ye know's not fit to be,
'Because we are not quality.'

To leave the house now all incline,
And haste to church; the clock struck nine;
Two lusty lads, well dress'd and strong,
Stept out to lead the bride along;
And two young maids of equal size,
As soon the bridegroom's hands surprize;
The pipers wind and take their post,
And go before to clear the coast;
Then all the vast, promiscuous crowd,
With thund'ring tongues, and feet as loud,
Toss up their hats, clap hands, and hollow,
O'erjoy'd like Bedlamites, they follow:
Some shout the bride, and some the groom,
Till just as mad, to church they come;
Knock, swear, and rattle at the gate,
And vow to break the beadle's pate;
Sad scene of wickedness, and strife,
When some e'en curse the beadle's wife;
They rive, and tear, and make a noise,

Like rude distracted fools or boys.
Now some slip out as sure as fate,
To tell the priest the people wait;
He smiles and hobbles, pleas'd to know,
By age worn out, he wanders slow.
The gates fly open, all rush in,
The church is full with folks and din;
And all the crew both great and small,
Behave as in a common hall:
For some perhaps that were threescore,
Were never twice in church before;
They scamper, climb and break the pews,
To see the couple make their vows.
With solemn face the priest draws near,
Poor Tom and Jenny quake for fear;
Are singled out from all the band
That round about them gaping stand.

When they're in decent order got,
The priest proceeds to tie the knot;
The hands are join'd, and loos'd again,
And Tommy says, 'I take thee, Jane,' —
Then Jenny looks a little shy,
And kneels, and says, 'I take Tom-my;' —
But here's the blessing or the curse,
'Tis done for better or for worse;
For now they're fairly in for life;
The priest declares them man and wife.

Our couple now kneel down to pray,
Much unacquainted with the way;
Whole troops of Colliers swarm around,
And seize poor Jenny on the ground:
Put up their hands to loose her garters,
And work for pluck about her quarters;
Till ribbons from her legs are torn,
And round the church in triumph borne:
As when a conquest great was won
By Caesar or by Philip's son;
They had the honour of the prize,

And all the shouts that did arise;
So now the fame and praise attend
The garters and the bridegroom's friend.

The wedding now is fairly o'er,
The fees are paid, but nothing more;
The bridegroom swaggers foremost out,
He cocks his hat and looks about;
The pipers play for victory.
I'll make thee fain to follow me.
Four rustic fellows wait the while,
To kiss the bride at the church stile;
The vig'rous mount their felter'd steeds,
With heavy heels and clumsy heads;
They smartly scourge them head and tail,
To win what country folks call hail;
Spruce Tommy now leads first away,
For Jenny's bound and must obey:
But most wives think't a sad disaster,
To have the man be one day master;
And must be rid, or they submit,
With whip and spur, and temper'd bit,
Must taste the sweets and plagues of marriage,
Before they have an easy carriage.
Yet here our bride must have her due,
She stuck as close to Tom as glue;
Tuck'd up her coats to mend her pace,
And walk'd 'till sweat ran down her face;
Sturdy she rak'd along the plain,
To keep in view her fellow swain;
And kindly follows Tommy's lead,
That she at night on joys may feed.
If he prepares, when things are drest,
I'll pawn my life she'll be his guest;
Close to him stick, and round him twine,
Till Phoebus through the curtains shine,
Surround their pillows with his rays,
And wish them many happy days.

Now they arrive all in a foam,

Old Bessy bids them welcome home;
Salutes her daughter and her son –
So now begins the merry fun.

The busy, greasy cook appears,
And thunders mischief in their ears;
She scolds and brawls, and makes a noise,
And throws her fat among the boys;
Now runs to see the kettle boil,
Meanwhile she lets the butter oil;
Then boxes her who turns the spit,
And cries, 'you jade you'll burn the meat.'
Fire, smoke, and fury round her goes,
'She's burnt her apron, greas'd her clothes;
'The dinner will be spoil'd' she cries;
'Good God! The baker's burnt the pies.
'That goose will not be half enough;
'The beef is old and will eat tough;
'Here, lass – some flour to dredge the veal;
'I wish your dinner at the de'il:
'Come take your seats and stand away,
'My ladle has not room to play:-
'The hens and cocks are just laid down:
'I never thought you'd come so soon:' –
And thus, with such-like noise and din,
The wedding banquet does begin.
Impatient for the want of meat,
They feak and cannot keep a seat;
Play with the plates, drum on the table,
And fast as well as they are able;
Then count the number of the knives,
And who is there that has not wives;
Unfold the napkins, lay them down,
Then tell the letters on a spoon:
Some eat the bread, – some lick the salt:-
Some drink, – and other some find fault.
Disorder is in every place,
And hunger sharpens every face:
In short they could no longer put,
For belly thinks the throat is cut:

They damn, and sink, and curse the cook,
And give her many a frightful look;
She's call'd a lazy jade, and sow;
Yet says she does what fire can do:
The empty guts disturb and vex 'em,
And want of patience this perplex 'em;
'Tis want of patience causeth strife,
In ev'ry sphere of human life.

Thus hungry, raw, unthinking youth,
Run home from school with open mouth;
Anxious for meat, and wild for play,
Impatient at the maid's delay;
Will dip their bread in dripping-pan,
With all the eagerness they can;
Disturb the house, and teaze their mother, —
Fight with their sister or their brother;
Roar, punch, and kick, and play the fool,
And cry 'they'll be too late for school.'
Bum plates — and discompose the table,
Do all the mischief they are able;
Abuse the maid, climb on the chairs,
And dirty all the new clean'd stairs:
Till Tray with his machine descends,
When Peggy draws and makes all friends;
For dinner's serv'd, they eat, — are pleas'd,
March off to school; the house is eas'd.
At last the beef appears in sight,
The groom moves slow the pond'rous weight;
The haste is made, the table clad,
No patience till the grace is said:
Swift to the smoking beef they fly;
Some cut their passage through a pye:
Out streams the gravy on the cloth;
Some burn their tongues with scalding broth:
But rolling spices make them fain,
They shake their heads, and sup again,
'Cut up that goose,' cries one below,
'Hand down a leg, or wing, or so:'
An honest neighbour tries the point,

Works hard, but cannot hit a joint:
The bride sat nigh, she rose in prim,
And cut and tore her, limb from limb,
Now geese, cocks, hens, their fury fee,
Extended jaws devour the veal:
Each rives, and eats what he can get;
And all is fish that comes to net;
No qualmish appetites her sit,
None curious for a dainty bit.

The bridegroom waits with active force,
And bring them drink 'twixt ev'ry course;
With napkin round his body girt,
To keep his clothes from grease and dirt;
With busy face he runs about,
To fill the pots as they're drunk out.

Old Bessy, dress'd in all her airs,
Gives her attendance in the stairs,
There she received the broken meat,
Just when it is not fit to eat;
Plates, knives, and spoons about are tost,
The old wife's care's that naught is lost:
By her the borrow'd things are known,
She wishes folks may get their own.

Now all are full, the meat away,
The table drawn, the pipers play
The bridegroom first gets on the floor,
And dances all the maidens o'er;
Then rubs his face, and makes a bow,
So marches off — what can he do?
He must not tire himself outright,
The bride expects a dance at night.
In ev'ry room, both high and low,
The fiddlers play, the bagpipes blow:
Some about the bride, and some the groom,
They roar the very music dumb,
Hand over head, and one through other,
They dance with sister, and with brother:

Their common tune is, 'Get her, Bo!'
The weary lass cries, — 'Music so;'
Till tir'd in circling round they wheel,
And beat the ground with toe and heel.
A Collier lad of taller size,
With rings of dust about his eyes,
Laid down his pipe, rose from the table,
And swore he'd dance while he was able;
He catch'd a partner by the hand,
And kiss'd her first to make her stand;
And then he bade the music play,
And said, 'Now lass, come dance away;'
He led her off; just when begun
She stopt, cry'd 'Houts — some other tune;'
They whispered in the piper's ear,
So loud, that ev'ry one might hear,
'I wish you'd play me Jumping John'
He tried his reed, and tuned his drone,
The pipes scream out her fav'rite jig,
She knack'd her thumbs and stood her trig;
Then cock'd her belly up a little,
And wet her fingers with her spittle:
So off she goes; the Collier lad
Sprung from the floor, and danc'd like mad:
They sweep each corner of the room,
And all stand clear where e're they come:
They dance, and tire the piper out.
And all's concluded with a shout.

Old Bessy next was taken in,
She curl'd her nose, and cock'd her chin;
They held her coats on either side,
And boo'd, and cried, 'Up with the bride;
'Come piper,' sayd the good old woman,
'Play me The joyful days are coming;
'I'll dance for joy, upon my life,
'For now my daughter's made a wife'
The old wife did what limbs could do;
'Well danc'd, old Bessy,' cried the crew:
The goody laugh'd, and shew'd her teeth,

And said, 'Ah! Sirs, I have no breath;
'I once was thought right good at this,'
So curtsying mumbl'd up his kiss.

And thus the day in pleasure flies,
Till shining Phoebus quits the skies:
The gladsome night 'gins to approach;
Bit not one barrel left to broach;
There's but a pipe for every one,
The dear tobacco's almost gone:
The candles in their sockets wink,
Now sweal, – now drop, – then die and stink:
Intoxicating fumes arise,
They reel and rub their drowsy eyes:
Dead drunk some tumble on the floor,
And lay in what they drank before:
'Hick-up,' cries one, - 'reach me your hand,
'The house turns round, I cannot stand:'
So now the drunken senseless crew,
Break pipes, spill drink, save but a few,
Who would, to vice, to folly blind,
Laugh at the weakness of mankind.

The sleepy neds now mount the balk,
Ducks quack, flap wings and homeward walk.
Quite sick and weary some become,
Now welcome night, and quick trudge home.

The posset made, the bride is led,
In great procession to her bed;
The females with an order come,
That all the men depart the room,
On pain of scandal and disgrace,
If any one stay in the place.

Their proclamation is obey'd,
The men walk out till she be laid;
But with this cautious reprimand,
The posset should have leave to stand
Be unmolested, feel no lip,

Nor any one attempt to sip;
For all declare they'll be accurs'd,
If bride and bridegroom drink not first:
When young and old are all gone out,
They shut the doors and spy about;
A gen'ral search is quickly made,
Lest any lie in ambuscade:
So when they think all places sure,
And holes and corners are secure,
That none could see, or none could hear,
Or none rush in to make them fear:
Then one, far wiser than the rest,
Who knew their way of bedding best,
Steps up to Jenny, bath'd in tears,
And thus with counsel fills her ears:
'Come, wipe your face, for shame, don't cry,
'We all were made with men to lie;

'And Tommy, if I guess but right,
'Will make you have a merry night;
'Be courteous, – kind – lie in his arms,
'And let him rifle all your charms;
'If he should rise, – do you lie still,
'He'll fall again – give him his will;
'Lie close and keep your husband warm,
'And as I live you'll get no harm;
'Be mannerly in ev'ry posture:-
'Take this advice from Nanny Forster.'

Thus said she ran, and catch'd the bowl,
Where currant cakes in ale did roll;
Then with a smile, said, 'Jenny, lass,
'Come here's thy health without a glass;'
Her arms supports it to her head,
She drinks, and gobbles up the bread;
So ev'ry one their courses took,
Some watch, for fear the men shou'd look:
Their hasty promise soon was broke,
For they must either drink or choke.

Now some prepare t' undress the bride,
While others tame the posset's pride;
Some loose her head, and some her stays,
And so undress her sundry ways;
Then quickly lay her into bed,
And bind a ribbon round her head:
Her neck and breasts are both display'd,
And ev'ry charm in order laid,
Now all's prepared for Tommy's coming,
The doors are open'd for Tommy's coming,
The doors are open'd by the women;
Impatient Tommy rushes in,
And thinks that they have longsome been:
The maids unwilling to withdraw,
Are told they must, for that's the law.
Now Tommy next must be undrest,
But which of them can do it best? –
It is no matter, all assist,
Some at his feet, some at his breast:
Soon they undress the jolly blade,
And into bed he's fairly laid.

Between the sheets now view this pair,
And think what merry work was there;
The stocking thrown, the crowd all gone,
And Tom and Jenny left alone;
No light was there but Jenny's charms,
And Tom had those within his arms.

Now he is master of his wishes,
Treats Jenny with a thousand kisses:
And hopes, no doubt, her heart to glad
With nine-months hence – a thumping lad.

Edward Chicken. Written c.1710, published 1773

The poem contains the first known record of Geordie dialect. It has been put to music and was a popular song in the mid eighteenth and early nineteenth century.

An abridged version appears in *Come All Ye Bold Miners: Ballads and Songs of the Coalfields* (1952), compiled by A. L. Lloyd. Lloyd also notes that the poem appeared in mid-eighteenth and early nineteenth-century editions, for example, J. White and Saint, M. Angus, George Angus, John Marshall and other printers of Newcastle Upon Tyne.

Pit Lads and Lasses

Hermann Kätelhön

George Bissill

The Pit Girls of Montsou

At Requillart, around the old ruined mine, all the girls of Montsou prowled about with their lovers. It was the common rendezvous, the remote and deserted spot to which the putters came to get their first child when they dared not risk the shed. The broken palings opened to every one the old yard, now become a nondescript piece of ground, obstructed by the ruins of the two sheds which had fallen in, and by the skeletons of the large buttresses which were still standing. Derelict trams were lying about, and piles of old rotting wood, while a dense vegetation was re-conquering this corner of ground, displaying itself in thick grass, and springing up in young trees that were already vigorous. Every girl found herself at home here; there were concealed holes for all; their lovers placed them over beams behind the timber, in the trams; they even lay elbow to elbow without troubling about their neighbours. And it seemed that round this extinguished engine, near this shaft weary of disgorging coal, there was a revenge of creation in the free love which, beneath the lash of instinct, planted children in the bellies of these girls who were yet hardly women.

Emile Zola, *Germinal* (from the edition translated by Havelock Ellis, 1894 and revised 1933)

The Maiden in Trousers

Lettice Forrester was attired after the fashion of the females who work about the Lancashire mines. A soft print bonnet rested on her fair hair, and fell on her shoulders, which were covered by a loose blouse of some dark stuff; and under this jacket a short shirt hung, being looped up in front, and displaying a pair of cord trousers, which, coming down within a few inches of her dainty little clogs, with thin bright buckles of brass, afforded a glimpse of a pair of finely moulded ankles, clad in dark blue hose.

The girl's soft refined features bore only faint traces of the grime which occasionally covers the faces of pit-brow girls when they labour in the screens and shootes among the black dust of the coal; and her few month's residence in the village had driven that sick pallor from her comely countenance which had rested upon it the day of the rustic festival.

Her slim, graceful figure was alert, lissom, and easy moving as any maiden's could be.

J. Monk Foster *The Watchman of Orsden Moss* (1897)

Catherine Underground

They were seven hundred and eight metres to the north in the first passage of the Desiree seam, which was at a distance of three kilometres from the pit-eye. When they spoke of this part of the pit, the miners of the region grew pale, and lowered their voices, as if they had spoken of hell; and most often they were content to shake their heads as men who would rather not speak of these depths of fiery furnace. As the galleries sank towards the north, they approached Tartaret, penetrating to that interior fire which calcined the rocks above. The cuttings at the point at which they had arrived had an average temperature of forty-five degrees. They were there in the accursed city, in the midst of the flames which the passers-by on the plain could see through the fissures, spitting out sulphur and poisonous vapours.

Catherine, who had already taken off her jacket, hesitated, then took off her trousers also, and with naked arms and naked thighs, her chemise tied round her hips by a cord like a blouse, she began to push again.

'Anyhow, that's better,' she said aloud.

In the stifling heat she still felt a vague fear. Ever since they began working here, five days ago, she had thought of the stories told her in childhood, of those putter girls of the days of old who were burning beneath Tartaret, as a punishment for things which no one dared to repeat. No doubt she was too big now to believe such silly stories; but still, what would she do if she were suddenly to see coming out of the wall a girl as red as a stove, with eyes like live coals? The idea made her perspire still more.

At the relay, eighty metres from the cutting, another putter took the tram and pushed it eighty metres further to the upbrow, so that the receiver could forward it with the others which came down from the upper galleries.

'Gracious! You're making yourself comfortable!' said this woman, a lean widow of thirty, when she saw Catherine in her chemise. 'I can't do it, the trammers at the brow bother me with their dirty tricks.'

'Ah, well!' replied the young girl. 'I don't care about the men! I feel too bad!'

She went off again, pushing an empty tram. The worst was that in this bottom passage another cause joined with the neighbourhood of Tartaret to make the heat unbearable. They were by the side of old workings, a very deep abandoned gallery of Gaston-Marie, where, ten years earlier, an explosion of firedamp had set alight the seam; and it was still burning behind the clay wall which had been built there and was kept constantly repaired in order to limit the disaster. Deprived of air, the fire ought to have become extinct, but no doubt unknown currents kept it alive; it had gone on for ten years, and heated the clay wall like the bricks of an oven, so that those who passed felt half roasted. It was along this wall, for a length of more than a hundred metres, that the haulage was carried on, in a temperature of 60 degrees.

After two journeys, Catherine again felt stifled. Fortunately, the passage was large and convenient in this Desiree seam, one of the thickest in the district. The bed was one metre ninety in height and the men could work standing. But they would rather have worked with twisted necks and a little fresh air.

Catherine had painfully decided to fill her tram, then she pushed it. The gallery was too wide for her to buttress herself to the timber on both sides; her naked feet were twisted in the rails where she sought a point of support, while she slowly moved on, her arms stiffened in front, and her back breaking. As soon as she came up to the clay wall, the fiery torture again began and the sweat fell from her whole body in enormous drops, as from a storm cloud. She had scarcely got a third of the way before she streamed, blinded, soiled also by the black mud. Her narrow chemise, as though dipped in ink, was sticking to her skin, and rising up to her waist with the movement of her thighs; it hurt her so that she had once more to stop her task.

What was the matter with her then, today? Never before had she felt as if there were wool in her bones. It must be the bad air. The ventilation did not reach to the bottom of this distant passage. One breathed there all sorts of vapours, which came out of the coal, with the low bubbling sound of a spring, so abundantly sometimes that the lamps would not burn; to say nothing of the fire-damp, which nobody noticed, for from one week's end to the other the men were always breathing it into their noses throughout the seam. She knew that bad air well; dead air the miners called it; it was below the heavy asphyxiated gases, above the light gases which catch fire and blow up all the stalls of a pit, with hundreds of men, in a single burst of thunder. From her childhood she had swallowed so much that she was surprised she bore it so badly, with buzzing ears and burning throat.

Unable to go farther, she felt the need of taking off her chemise. It was beginning to torture her, this garment of which the least folds cut and burnt her. She resisted the longing, and tried to push again, but was forced to stand upright. Then quickly, saying to herself that she would cover herself at the relay, she took off everything, the cord and the chemise, so feverishly that she would have torn off her skin if she could. And now, naked and pitiful, brought down to the level of the female animal seeking living in the mire of the streets, covered with soot and mud up to the belly, she laboured on like a cab-hack. On all fours she pushed onwards.

But despair came; it gave her no relief to be naked. What more could she take off? The buzzing in her ears deafened her; she seemed to feel a vice pressing in her temples. She fell on her knees. The lamp, wedged into the coal in the tram, seemed to her to be going out. The intention to turn up the wick alone survived in the midst of her confused ideas. Twice she tried to examine it, and both times when she placed it before her on the earth, she saw it turn pale, as though it also lacked breath. Suddenly the lamp went out. Then everything whirled around her in the darkness; a millstone turned in her head, her heart grew weak and left off beating, numbed in turn by the immense weariness which was putting her limbs to sleep. She had fallen back in anguish amid the asphyxiating air close to the ground.

Emile Zola, *Germinal* (from the edition translated by Havelock Ellis, 1894 and revised in 1933)

Pit-Girls

They did not look like women, or at least a stranger new to the district might easily have been misled by their appearance, as they stood together in a group by the pit's mouth. There were about a dozen of them there – all 'pit-girls', as they were called. Women who wore a dress more than half masculine, and who talked loudly and laughed discordantly, and some of whom, God knows, had faces as hard and brutal as the hardest of their collier brothers and husbands and sweethearts. They had lived among the coal-pits and had worked early and late at the 'mouth', ever since they had been old enough to take part in the heavy labour. It was not to be wondered at that they had lost all bloom of woman-ly modesty and gentleness. Their mothers had been 'pit-girls' in their time, their grand-mothers in theirs. They had been born in coarse homes; they had fared hardly, and worked hard; they had breathed in the dust and grime of coal, and somehow or other, it seemed to stick to them and reveal itself in their natures as it did in their bold unwashed faces...

On the particular evening of which I speak, the group at the pit's mouth were even more than unusually noisy. They were laughing, gossiping and joking – coarse enough jokes – and now and then a listener might have heard an oath flung out as if all were well used to the sound. Most of them were young women, though there were a few older ones among them, and the principal figure in the group – central figure about whom the rest clustered – was a young woman.

But she differed from the rest in two or three respects. The others seemed somewhat stunted in growth; she was tall enough to be imposing. She was as roughly clad as the poorest of them, but she wore her uncouth garb differently. The man's jacket of fustian, open at the neck, bared a handsome sun-browned throat. The man's hat shaded a face with dark eyes that had a sort of animal beauty, and a well-moulded chin.

Frances Hodgson Burnett, *That Lass O' Lowries* (1877)

Rab and Mysie

'We've left the school the day, Mr. Walker, an' Mysie an' me want to ken if ye can gie us a job on the pitheid?' and Walker noted with amusement the manly swagger in the boy's voice and bearing.

'We dinna' usually start lasses as wee as Mysie,' replied Walker, eyeing the children with an amused smile, 'but we need two or three laddies to the tables to help the women to pick stones.'

Mysie's face showed her keen disappointment. She knew that it was not customary for girls to be employed as young as she was; and Robert noted her disappointed look as well.

'Could ye no' try Mysie, too?' he asked, breaking in anxiously. 'She's a guid worker, an' she'll be able to pick as many stanes as the weemen. Willn't ye Mysie?' and he turned to the girl for corroboration with assurance.

As Mysie nodded, Walker saw a hint of tears in the girl's eyes, and the quivering of the tiny mouth; and as there is a soft spot in all men's hearts, even he had sympathy, for he understood what refusal meant.

'Weel, I micht gie her a trial,' he said, 'but she'll hae to work awfu' hard,' and he spoke as one conferring an especial concession upon a girl.

'Oh, she'll work hard enough,' said Robert. 'Mysie's a guid worker, an' you'll see...'

'Oh, then,' said Walker hurriedly breading in upon Robert's outburst of agreement, 'ye can both come oot the morn, and I'll try and put ye both up.'

'Six an' sixpence a week,' said Mysie, as they tramped home. 'My, that's a lot o' money, Rab, isn't it?'

'Aye, it's a guid lot, Mysie,' he replied, 'but we'll hae to work aufu' hard, or we'll no' get it. Guid night!' And so the children parted, feeling that the work was about to be good to them, and all their thought of care was bounded by six and sixpence a week.

'Take a wee rest, Mysie,' he said, 'are ye no' aufu' dizzy?

Mysie heard, but 'six and sixpence a week' was still ringing in her head. Indeed, the monotonous swing of the tables ground out the refrain of their harsh clamour, as they swung backwards and forwards. 'Six and sixpence a week' with every leap forward; 'six and sixpence a week' as they receded. 'Six and sixpence' with every shake and roar, and with each pulsing throb of the engine; and 'six and sixpence a week' her little hands, already cut and bleeding, kept time with regular beat, as she lifted the stones and flung them aside. She was part of the refrain – a note in the fortissimo of industry. The engines roared and crashed and hissed to it. They beat the air regularly as the pistons rose and fell back and forth – thump, thud, hiss, groan, up and down, out and in: 'six and sixpence a week'.

Mysie tried to straighten herself, as Robert had advised, and immediately a pain shot through her back which seemed to snap it in two. The whole place seemed to be rushing round in a mad whirl, the roof of the shed coming down, and the floor rushing up, when with a stagger, Mysie fell full length upon a 'bing' of stones, bruising her cheek and cutting her little hands worse than ever. This was what usually happened to all beginners at 'pickin' sklits'.

One of the women raised Mysie up, gave her a drink from a flask containing coal tea, and sat her aside to rest a short time.

'Just sit there a wee, my dochter,' she said with rough kindness, 'an' you'll soon be a' richt. They mostly a' feel that way when they first start on the scree.'

Mysie was feeling sick, and already the thought was shaping in her mind that she would never be able to continue. She had only worked an hour as yet, but it seemed to her a whole day.

———————

The great wheels groaned and swished like the imprisoned monster of Robert's imaginings, and at last came to a halt at the end of the shift; but in the pattern which they had that day woven into the web of industry, there were two bright threads – threads of great beauty and high worth – threads which the very gods seemed proud of seeing there, twisted and twined, and lending colour of richest hue to the whole design – threads of glorious fibre and rare quality, which sparkled and shone like the neck of a pigeon in the sunshine. These threads in the web of industry, which had shone that day for the first time, were the lives of two little children.

James C. Welsh, *The Underworld* (1920)

The Collier's Ragged Wean

He's up at early morning, howe'er the win' may blaw,
Lang before the sun comes roun' to chase the stars awa';
And 'mang a thousan' dangers, unkent in sweet daylight,
He'll toil until the stars again keek through the chilly night.
See the puir wee callan' 'neath the cauld clear moon:
His knees oot through his troosers, an his taes oot through his shoon,
Wading through the freezing snaw, and thinking ower again
How happy every wean maun be that's no' a collier's wean.

His cheeks are blae wi' cauld, and the chittering winna cease
To gi'e the hungry callan' time to eat his morning piece;
His lamp is burning on his heid wi' feeble, flickering ray,
And in his heart the lamp of Hope is burning feebly tae.
Nae wonner that the call's sweert to face his daily toil,
Nae wonner he sae seldom greets the morning wi' a smile,
For weel he kens he's growing up to face the cauld disdain
That lang the world has measured oot to every collier's wean.

The poor wee hirpling laddie! How mournfully he's gaun,
Aye dichting aff the ither tear wi' 's wee, hard, hackit haun'!
Sair, sair, he's tempit' mang the snaw to toom his flask o' oil,
But, ah! ae flash o' faither's ire were waur than weeks o' toil.
In vain the stars look on the youth wi' merry twinkling een,
Through clouds o' care sae dense as his their glory is nae seen;
He thinks 'twad been a better plan if coal had 'boonmost lain,
And wonners why his faither made a collier o' his wean.

Oh! Ye that row in Fortune's lap, his waefu' story hear,
Aft sorrows no sae deep as his ha'e won a pitying tear,
And lichter wrangs than he endures your sympathy ha'e won –
Although he is a collier's, mind he's still a Briton's son.
And ye wha mak' and mend oor laws, tak' pity on the bairn,
Oh bring him sooner frae the pit, and gi'e him time to learn;
Sae shall ye lift him frae the mire 'mang which he lang has lain,
And win a blessing frae the heart o' every collier's wean,

David Wingate, *Select Poems and Songs* (1890)

The Collier Lad

My lad he is a collier lad,
And ere the lark awakes
He's up and away to spend the day
Where daylight never breaks.
But when at last the day has pass'd,
Clean washed and cleanly clad,
He courts his Nell, who loveth well,
Her handsome collier lad.

Chorus
There's not his match in smoky Shields;
Newcastle never had
A lad more tight, more trim, nor bright
Than is my collier lad.

Though doomed to labour under ground
A merry lad is he,
And when a holiday comes round
He'll spend that day in glee;
He'll tell his tale o'er a pint of ale,
And crack his joke, and bad
Must be the heart who loveth not
To hear the collier lad.

At bowling matches on the green
He ever takes the lead,
For none can swing his arm and fling
With such a pith and speed.
His bowl is seen to skim the green,
And bound as if right glad
To hear the cry of victory
Salute the collier lad.

When 'gainst the wall they play the ball,
He's never known to lag,
But up and down he gars it bound
Till all his rivals flag;
When deftly — lo! he strikes a blow

Which gars them all look sad,
And wonder how it came to pass,
They play'd the collier lad.

The quoits are out, the hobs are fixed,
The first round quit he flints
Enrings the hob; and lo! the next
The hob again enrings.
And thus he'll play the summer day,
The theme of those who gad,
And youngsters shrink to bet their brass
Against the collier lad.

When in the dance he doth advance
The rest all sigh to see
How he can spring and kick his heels
When they a-wearied be;
Your one-two-three, with either knee,
He'll beat, and then, glee-mad,
Aheel-o'er-head leap crowns the dance
Danced by the collier lad.

Besides a will and pith and skill
My laddie owns a heart
That never once would suffer him
To act a cruel part;
That to the poor would ope the door
To share the last he had;
And many a secret blessing's pour'd
Upon my collier lad.

He seldom goes to church, I own,
And when he does, why then,
He with a leer will sit and hear
And doubt the holy men;
This very much annoys my heart,
But soon as we are wed,
To please the priest, I'll do my best
To tame my collier lad.

Joseph Skipsey, in Rt. Hon. Robert Spence Watson, *J. Skipsey: His Life and Works* (1909)
Also found in J. Skipsey, *Poems* (1871)

Joe Tarrant Starts Work

He had reached the colossal age of fourteen. With school children it is a momentous age. It is the last of their school lives, the time when all the fetters are snapped. At four o'clock that day Joe Tarrant stepped out of the playground of the Stanhope Toad Schools, Shielding, a free person. He was free. School-life was ended. He was a hero, for his mates of the classroom had known this day. All the week they had envied his good fortune. They had made their secret comparisons. In so many weeks they would be equal to him. Then…

Joe had been proud when the schoolmaster had called him out in front of the class.

'This will be your last day, Tarrant?' he had said.

'Yes, sir.'

'Where do you intend on working?'

'Hunton pit, sir.'

———————

At half past five he was ready. There was a can upon the table containing tea, and a red handkerchief wrapped around some food. He picked it up and went to the door. He halted. His mother was sleeping now in the bed. She snored loudly. He felt a desire to kiss her, and he wondered if he dare. It was a long time since he had kissed his mother. It was most unusual for him to want to kiss his mother. His courage failed him and he went on. He went out into the street. The door banged.

———————

Joe groped his way along the narrow path between the two slowly moving belts until he came to where Bailey stood.

'Mister Bailey!'

Jim Bailey was the Head Keeper at Hunton Colliery. He was the foreman of all the unskilled labour attached to the pithead, and had charge of the loading of the cages, the tipping of the coal tubs and the subsequent screening of the coal and truck-loading. He was responsible directly to the engineer.

'You the new lad?' he yelled.

'Yes.'

'See that man over there?' he shouted. Joe looked and nodded, for his eyes were beginning to grow accustomed to the gloom of the place. "E'll tell you w'at to do.'

Joe stumbled and floundered in the semi-darkness until he arrived at the man to whom he had been directed. His new master proved to be very human, and directed him to his duties. Soon he found himself collecting cans of tea that were standing about and carried them out to a cabin where a huge brazier was glowing. His duties for that day were simple. He had to keep the brazier burning and the cans warming.

Joe found his new master instructing him in the duties that were required of him after the warm tea had been consumed by the various owners. This fellow, Abe Rotherfold, a kind and sympathetic soul, went to great lengths to explain the mechanism and functions of the screening house. He explained to Joe that when the tubs arrived at the surface they were taken to the weighing machine, weighed and checked. They were then emptied down the chute, which was so arranged that the small coal slid through the bars and the larger pieces of coal slid down and came through the aperture near which they were sitting, to do a trip along the belt. Joe realised how cunningly the arrangements worked, for he could see that the small coal was not lost, but came along a belt of its own. Boys made it their business to pick the pieces of stone, shale or rubble from the appliance. At the end of the process the coal fell into the trucks below.

For the rest of the eight-hour shift Joe was diligent in his task. He grew accustomed to the noise and gloom, and very soon he was able to pounce upon the pieces of stone that came his way. When he had a lot of stone to contend with, and being near the beginning of the belt, he began to wonder why a young man should be so busy writing upon a board, shouting out numbers, and continually stopping the belt. Joe asked him the nature of his job.

'I lay tubs out,' he explained. 'When a tub of coal comes with a lot of stone in it I take its number and the chap who filled it is fined.'

'Very much?'

'About fourpence generally.'

Joe failed to appreciate the justice of this.

'If we didn't they'd fill a lot of stone,' said the young man.

And the first day ended.

Harold Heslop, *The Gate of a Strange Field* (1929)

Hermann Kätelhön

Mother Wept

Mother wept, and father sighed;
With delight aglow
Cried the lad, 'Tomorrow,' cried
'To the pit I go.'

Up and down the place he sped –
Greeted old and young;
Far and wide the tidings spread;
Clapt his hands and sung.

Came his cronies; some to gaze,
Wrapt in wonder; some
Free with counsel; some with praise;
Some with envy dumb.

'May he,' many a gossip cried,
'Be from peril kept,'
Father hid his face and sighed
Mother turned and wept.

Referenced by William Maurice as Memoir of Joseph Skipsey but not identifiable.
Found in *Poems* (1871)

They Lifted You Gently...

They lifted you gently from the dripping, sludgy cage,
And wrapped you in bagging to hide your sodden clouts;
But watching you mangled and bleeding I guessed at your age.
And knew you a very boy, fifteen or thereabouts.

You never knew happiness, little fellow dead,
You lived in sad times and toiled and suffered so,
And runaway trams have torn and crushed your head,
So even tho' times alter you never will know.

Frederick C. Boden, *Out of the Coalfields* (1929)

To A Pithead Lass

I watch you passing down the street
These grey days,
Grey houses, grey skies, and the pit smokes
Grey haze.

Jauntily humming in April air,
And the morning sun
Floods with its gold an ancient street
of Babylon.

And Thisbe, robed in virgin white,
Gaily doth pass,
Innocent of the tragic eyes
Of Pyramus.

I watch you passing down the street,
These grey days,
And thinking of your mother's fate,
My heart prays.

Joe Corrie, *The Image O' God and Other Poems* (1937)

Willy and Jenny

Duskier than the clouds that lie
'Tween the coal pit and the sky,
Lo, how Willy whistles by
Right cheery from the colliery.

Duskier might the laddie be
Save his coaxing coal-black e'e,
Nothing dark could Jenny see
A-coming from the colliery.

Joseph Skipsey, *Poems* (1871)

My Collier Laddie

'O, WHARE live ye, my bonnie lass,
And tell me how they ca' ye?'
'My name,' she says, 'is Mistress Jean,
And I follow the collier laddie.

'O, see you not yon hills and dales
The sun shines on sae brawlie?
They a're min, and they shall be thine,
Gin ye'll leave your collier laddie!

'An' ye shall gang in gay attire,
Weel buskit up sae gaudy,
And ane to wait on every hand,
Gin ye'll leave your collier laddie!'

'Tho' ye had a' the sun shines on,
And the earth conceals sae lowly,
I was turn my back on you and it a'
And embrace my collier laddie.

'I can win my five pennies in a day,
An' spend it at night fu' brawlie,
And make my bed in the collier's neuk
And lie down wi' my collier laddie.

'Loove for loove is the bargain for me,
Tho' the wee cot-house should haud me,
And the warld before me to win my bread –
And fair fa' my collier laddie!'

Referenced by William Maurice as Robert Burns in *Johnson's Musical Museum Vol IV*, 1792.
Also published in *Robert Burns Poetry Vol III*, songs (1897)

Youth

Lumbering down the grade, the full tubs run
On clanking trolleys towards him where he stands
At the crossways of the pit, and with huge hands
He grips them and unhooks and slews them round
And sends them trundling down the tramway, bound
For the cage that carries them to the pithead.
Unerringly till his six-hour shift is done,
As they bear down on him, he stops them dead,
Grips and unhooks and heaves them, all the while
Checking the empty tubs as they come back
And sending each up the right gallery
To the putter who awaits it; easily,
The tensile muscles 'neath the silky black
Skin of his glistening torso rippling, thews
Of arms and shoulders knotting taut, he slews
Each truck, while 'neath his grimy brow burn bright
The undefeated eyes of youth, as he
Lets none of his mates go by without a smile
Of strong white teeth that glitter in the light
And a chuckling word of chaff. Still fresh and fit
In the pride of youth's resilient health, nightlong
He heaves and swings to keep things going, and keep
Life coursing through the arteries of the pit,
As though his full-charged veins the blood runs strong,
Till the shift ends, and he, released, at length
Relaxes, trudging home; and in sound sleep,
Hard-earned, renews his inexhaustible strength.

Wilfrid Gibson, *Fuel* (1934)

The Pitman's Courtship

Quite soft blew the wind from the west,
The sun faintly shone in the sky,
When Lukey and Bessy sat courting,
As walking I chanc'd to espy;
Unheeded I stoke close beside them,
To hear their discourse was my plan;
I listen'd each word they were saying,
When Lukey his courtship began.

'Last hoppen thou won up my fancy,
Wi' thy fine silken jacket o' blue;
An' smash if thor fine Newcassel lyedys
Cou'd marrow the curls o' thy brow;
That day aw whiles danc'd wi' lang Nancy,
She couldn't like thou lift her heel,
My grandy likes spice singing hinnies
Ma comely, aw like thou as weel.

'Thou knaws, ever since we were little,
Together we've ranged through the woods,
At neets hand in hand toddled hyem,
Varry oft wi' howl kites and torn duds;
But now we can tauk aboot marriage,
An' lang sair for wor weddin'-day:
When married we'll keep a bit shop,
An' sell things in a huickstery way.

'An' to get us a canny bit leevin',
A' kinds of fine sweetmeats we'll sell—
Reed harrin' broon syep, and mint candy,
Black pepper, dye-sand, an' sma' yell,
Spice hunters, pick-shafts, farden candles,
Wax dollies wi' reed leather shoes,
Chawk pusscats, fine curly-greens,
Paper skyets, penny pies, and huil-doos.

'T'se help thou to tie up the shuggar,
At neets when frae wark I get lowse!
An' wor Dick that leeves owr by High Whickham
He'll myek us broom bussums for nowse;
Like an image thou's stand owr the coonter,
Wi' thy fine muslin, cambricker goon;
An'te let fokes see thou's a lyedy
On a cuddy thou's ride to the toon.

'There's be matches, pipe-clay, an' broon dishes,
Canary seed, raisins and fegs;
And, to please the pit laddies at Easter,
A dishful of giltey paste-eggs;
Wor neibors, that's snuffers an' smokers,
For wor snuff an' wor backy they'll seek,
An' to shown them we deal wi' Newcassel,
Twee blackies sal mense the door cheek.

'So now for Tim Bodkin I'se send,
To darn my silk breeks at the knee,
Thou thy ruffles and frills mun get ready,
Next Whit-Sunday married we'll be.
Now I think it's high time to be steppin'
We've sittin tiv aw's about lyem;'
So then, wiv a kiss and a cuddle,
These lovers they bent their ways hyem.

William Mitford, in J. Stokoe (ed) *Songs and Ballads of Northern England* (1899)

André Rassenfosse

George Bissill

Colliers and Collieries

Conrad Felixmüller

George Bissill

Coal

A valley, narrow as the pit,
Without a blossoming thing in it:
Raw and dirty, an unwashed wound.
In the midst, insurgently rise
Wheels, sharp-fretted traceries,
Chimneys that score with smoke the skies.
It is a cancer spot, a fane,
A mass of hovels, a city of men,
A mart of mud and blood and gold,
A thing that clings to earth's bosom cold
And sucks the last drops from her breasts running dry,
Gorging the coal as it comes from the mine.

Grind of wheels and clank of pumps
Make the thick air twitch and shrink
Like broken nerves, throughout the day.
As dawn throws his torch in the soot-hung sky
An aimless procession shuffles by:
The men march out for another day
Of darkness in the pits below.
When the dusk swoops swiftly down,
Like a black vulture on the town,
They shamble back the self-same way,
Towards the mocking bedazzling glow
Of bar-rooms, seeking with hungry eyes
Over the streets for their victories.
But they have borne their prize away;
Black, but with life-blood dripping red,
It fills their wastes with sense and soul;
It makes all love and hate and strife,
Fairer than song, better than bread,
The harvest hope, the life of life,
Coal!
Downwards suddenly plunge the cages
From the daylight, to the vast
Abysmal silence of the night:
Now the thick earth holds them fast:
The slaves who sell life for death's wages,

Risking indifferently the blast
Of gas exploding, that choking death.
They tumble into iron carts
Their grimy bodies, as they start,
An echo follows them behind
Through the mean tunnels which drearily wind
Onward and on.
Clanking, clattering, bumping, grinding,
The carts roll through them, onward and on.

At last, they make a sudden stay.
Lo now, beneath a spluttering ray,
The half-stripped bodies at their toil!
Backs that gleam as wet with oil;
Picks alternately aswing,
Crashing with dull and sullen ring;
Hewing the thick tough carbon out.
These men strive stoutly there, no doubt,
At the sacred shrine of their joy and despair!
One of them, weary and loath,
Yawns, an mutters an obscene oath:
Another spits, and one agape
Grins, expectant of some jape.
But the steel picks rise and fall, –
Relentless pendulums, – through it all.

Blood of it and bone of it,
Above on earth, are men in towns;
Statesmen, churchmen, rogues and clowns,
Doing all things fit, unfit:
Palaces and hairpins making,
Pamphleteering, loafing, baking.
Black, but with life blood dripping red,
It fills their breasts with sense and soul:
It makes all love and hate and strife,
Fairer than song, better than bread,
The harvest hope, the life of life –
Coal.

Referenced by William Maurice as John Gould Fletcher, *The Poetry of Tril* but not indentifiable.

The Welsh Miner

So in Heartbreak Valley you will see pits whose chimneys no longer smoke and the men who want work, and can only stand about at street corners because they were born and bred to mine coal and cannot conceive of any other employment, will tell you stories of the water rising in the mines.

Heartbreak Valley is stranded by what is called the 'post-war depression'. Town after town can only sit idly watching the pits that once gave them bread.

Beneath these towns, if you take the trouble to find it, is the beauty of pride and endurance. The beauty of North Wales is the beauty of hill lying against hill, the coming of dawn and the fall of the mists at night. But in the South you have woman struggling to keep her home together and man hoping against hope that the tide will turn.

If the thousands of people who go gaily through the mountain passes of Snowdonia and haunt the ruins of dead castles would spend only a few days in the South talking to the people, trying to understand their situation, attempting to visualise the hard facts of their lives, the nation might in time bring a little more sympathy and understanding to the problems of the Welsh coal-field. The miner is misunderstood and misrepresented. At the moment he is down and out. If he is not living on the 'dole', he lives in fear of living on it. His work is shamefully paid. Hundreds of thousands of families are existing – you cannot call it living – on marvellously fractional variations of £2 to £3.10s.

The Welsh miner is a proud, sensitive – I use the word with deliberation and in true sense – gentleman. I have met him in crowds; I have met him individually. I have seen him at work; I have sat at his fireside and talked to him for hours. I would like to think, if I had entered a pit at the age of fourteen and had grown to manhood in it, that I would retain the outlook and the intellectual curiosity of the average Welsh miner.

His intellectual interests are remarkable. At a street corner in Tonypandy I heard two young miners discussing Einstein's Theory of Relativity. I know this was exceptional, but it is significant; and it is true.

It will not seem out of the way to anyone who knows South Wales. It will be believed by the manager of Smith's bookshop in Cardiff who recently delivered Murray's Oxford English Dictionary, which cost £45, to the Workman's Institute at Ton-yr-efail. This £45 was saved by miners in twopences! And they followed it up by saving £39 for the Encyclopaedia Britannica!

I have met miners whose culture and gift of self-expression seem to me nothing short of miraculous. These men know how to think. They have a queer mental curiosity which leads them into all kinds of queer paths. Music is one of their passions. It does not consist of putting a record on a gramophone. In one miner's home there are four framed objects on the wall, and three of them are L.R.A.M. certificates!

I was introduced to a miner who had taught himself to play music by studying the

Welsh hymn book. This has the tonic sol-fa on one page and opposite is the ordinary notation. He translated them painfully and became proficient.

How can you withhold admiration from a community in which this is not an exceptional achievement? It is going on every day.

'Hugh So-and-So,' said an ex-miner, 'was so mad on music that he could hear it in the rhythm of the wheels of the journey.' (The 'journey' is the line of loaded coal 'trams' which travels, often for miles, from the coal seam to the pit bottom.) 'The wheels make different sounds on the gradients. Hugh heard music in this, and he used to keep a bit of chalk in his pocket and write melodies on the ventilating doors. They made wonderful blackboards.'

Imagine that! Think of a man hearing music in the darkness of a pit and writing melodies by the light of a safety lamp!

'Where is Hugh now?' I asked.

'Teaching music in America.'

I asked this man to explain to me the exceptional interests of the miner.

'Every miner has a hobby,' he said. 'Some are useful; some are not. Some miners take up hobbies as amateurs; some study to escape from the pit. I did. Even now I sometimes marvel that it is possible to earn money except with my hands. Why do we do so many things? It's difficult to say. It may be a reaction from physical strain. The miner works in a dark strange world. He comes up into light. It is a new world. It is stimulating. He wants to do something. It may be, in good times, pigeon racing, fretwork, whippet racing, carpentry, music, choral singing or reading. Think what reading means to an active mind that is locked away in the dark for hours every day! Why, in mid-Rhondda there are 40,000 books in a month in circulation from four libraries...'

Meanwhile, Heartbreak Valley watches the pits. Its people stand at the side of the road as if waiting for something to happen. Men wander over the immense slag heaps, which years of prosperity have vomited from the earth, wondering if salvation lies in something called by-products. Perhaps at this moment, they think, some scientist in a laboratory is bending over his test-tubes and his flames with a discovery that will once more make it possible to live decently.

But Heartbreak Valley is off the map. No visitors go there from choice. Even the long tables where the commercial travellers used to eat are half empty in the hotels.

I hope some people will take my advice. These mining valleys do not want compassion or charity. But they are worth understanding; and they are very friendly, and their beauty is not that of sun or moon, but of the human heart.

H. V. Morton, *In Search of Wales* (1932)

Fire of Coals

Behold I have litten a fire and I am warmed thereby,
The splendid thing delights me, seeming to be alive,
With ruddy countenance and a husky tongue
That lisps insatiable greed.

I can smell the hot thick breath of molasses giant-treed,
First fruits of the damsel earth when she enter'd the
    sun's harém,
When first she cast her virgin veil aside
    of torrent rains and thunder cloud.

It is the heart, the heart, of the Earth, the Sultan's bride,
That burns so bright and so hot, and the whisper is her sigh,
And all things burning passion ever vow'd
Mount upwards as from Dido's pyre.

O this is the poem of things, a song immortally sung
By the world itself for the stars, when they glow'd and
were glad and young,
Which Time, once having written in his book,
Turn'd down the pages one by one.

And I will make mention of those we heed not, who delve
    the seam,
My Miner, the bondman of death, in pledge for our lumps
    of coal,
The Genie prison'd in the jagged pit,
The Worm that tunnels in Time's leaves.

In him the passions of Earth still this way and that are flung,
In the last most beautiful lamp that ever was torn from it;
And still the white flame struggles to survive
On oil that seeps in scanty dole.

EARTH! We have foul'd your lamp and the flame is
sootish and dun,
And the glaze is rubb'd and grime occludes the delicate
frieze,

And hark — the black ash tinkles, which forsook
The flagrant purity of fire.

J. P. Angold, first published in *The New English Weekly*, March 15th 1934.
Also published in *Collected Poems* (1952)

Get up

'Get up,' the caller calls, 'Get up!'
And in the dead of night,
To win the bairns their bite and sup,
I rise a weary wight.

My flannel dudden donn'd, thrice o'er
My birds are kissed, and then,
I with a whistle shut the door,
I may not ope again.

Joseph Skipsey, *Poems* (1871)

Pit Bus

Here in the Spring twilight, sprawling and slithering,
Down the way to the colliery comes the pit bus;
Inside it a scrum of labouring men,
Close packed, inchoate:
Good fellows enough, average Englishmen;
But in the dim light of one wretched lamp
Their faces are blurs, and their bodies writhe,
Shifting and twisting in one working mass,
Like torn bowels of some horrid beast
Hurt unto death; which dragging its inwards
Crawls, growling and whimpering,
Hither in agony home to its lair;
Eager to hide away deep in the dark;
Where it will stretch itself,
Snapping impotent jaws, gnawing the earth;
Waiting in misery surcease of pain.

Kenneth H. Ashley, *Up Hill and Down Dale* (1924)

The Mineshaft

To feel like one who's sinned and earned the wage,
And hears on earth the tolling of his knell...

To feel like one who enters in a cage
Defies the mineshaft, and, as in a spell,
Hears them shout All Clear; hears the bell,
Then seems to dream he's falling; seems an age
Uneasily descending, hears the foreman yell,
And through a long tube sees the equipage
Of circling constellations come to shine
Bluely up above; hears the cable whine,
The whimpering of the ropeway, and the rage
And friction of the kibble 'gainst the well,
Its grim hydraulic cadencies, the fine
High-pitched responses of the line;
And sees the shaft-wall like a donjon cell,
Dripping, oozy; feels his cheeks as well
With drippings scalded, smarting, saline...

And sniffs at crimson stenches as they swell
Like lava from the entrails of the mine;
Tar and timber, coal dust, fungus smell;
Some firm as faith, some lewd and infidel,
And some unindividualised, condign
And sharp but not familiar to define;
Some trembling upwards like a solenelle,
Some subterranean, others fresh as brine...

So dreams he's falling, feels the pit confine
And bandage him about; himself supine
Spreadeagled, powerless to rebel...
Then wakes to hear the grimy gaffer tell
The headwaysman to hew more parallel
And thinks those level accents sound divine;
And think him how that flimsy cradle fell
And shot on sooty pinions down the line,
Straight as a demon down the flues of Hell,
Or Hell's own image in a Durham mine.

A. E. Tomlinson, *Candour* (1922)

A Cage Load of Men

Just like a truck load of cattle,
Sixteen rushed on at a time,
The yawning abyss beneath them,
Awaiting the 'bottomer's' chime,
To leave all the glories to nature,
And toil in the muck and the grime.

Hard-handed stalwarts of labour,
Nurtured to grin and to bear,
Seldom a thought of the danger
That haunts every corner down there,
Praying to Christ it was 'lowsing',
But not in the language of prayer.

Nipper so proud to be working,
Grandad with hair like the snow,
One with his eyes on the heavens,
One with his eyes on below,
Free to stay up if they wishit,
But hunger, ah! both of them know.

One with the cares of a household,
Weary and sick of it all,
The best of his years he had given,
And now with his back to the wall.
Haunted with fears of the future,
Dreading how far he will fall.

Clang! goes the 'bottomer's' signal,
Down, strangely silent, they go,
In comes another mixed cage-load,
Each with a number to show,
Cogs in the wheel of Corruption,
Grinding so sure and so slow.

Referenced by William Maurice as Joe Corrie, *The Image O' God and Other Poems* (1937), but not identifiable. Printed in a slightly different form in, Joe Corrie, *Poems by Joe Corrie* (1955)

Cavilling Day

Cavilling day came every three months, bringing a thrill, anticipation; for some laughter, for others – long faces. The future would be easier or life a little leaner from that day. Piece wages were determined quarterly by the luck of the ballot – a piece of paper with a name and number written thereon called a 'cavil'. The apparently schemeless world below was mapped out in numerous small portions of coal, hewers allotted to each section, putters to a small district serving several hewers. In three seams some seventy cavils for the hewers, four to a cavil. A game of chance played in a small room; a small slip of paper with a name and number deciding the issue. But it gave a certain independence, for it was better than being subject to officials who might choose their friends for good working places, and penalise men who dared to speak of wrong or injustice, or were too lively in Union matters.

The cavil is a gamble. It gives laughter to the winner and gloom to the unfortunate. True, piece rates are fixed by agreement, properly argued by the workers' representatives and assented to by the men after discussion. And a weighty technical business it is. But even then there is hard coal and soft coal and many things that bring much trouble and little money. So the cavil decides who shall have the good and who endure the evil. And everyone knows which is which, and just where, in that world below – even the women.

Jabez Sill sat in the little office near the window, beside him Overman Ralph Strawn, and between them a basin holding the fateful slips of paper.

The hewers had drawn their lots earlier in the day and now everything was ready for the drawing of the putters' cavils. One by one they came, dipped a hand in the basin, took out a slip, handed it to Jabez who read out aloud what was written thereon. Seam, district and pony. Ralph Strewn wrote the name on the sheet before him, next to the details of the area set down. Faces lit up, others fell, as Jabez read. 'Straight back. Another three months in the – hole,' growled one to whom the ballot meant no change. Another grinned and that was eloquence. Drivers shouted the news to each other, sidled up to the youth who was coming to his flat an told that person of the vices or virtues of his new pony, assuming airs of knowledge with a kind of 'we've got to work together' look. But the putter, as became a mighty man of valour, took no notice of his midget partners.

One by one they came. 'Piper's Drift; First West Flat; Tinker the Pony,' read Jabez Sill. The excitement of the table, the thrill of the race, the zipp of the Cup Final – it was all there as the lottery was drawn. Good luck, bad luck, hard, grinding work for all, a little better wages for some, worse wages for others. But some kind of work for all, and no favouritism. Thus were many working fates settled for another three months in Westburn.

Jack Lawson, *Under The Wheels* (1934)

Geordie's Marrow

It was just six o'clock on a bitter winter's morning at Wenley-on-the-Hill. The sky was still covered with night, but starless; and the earth seemed to throw up against it a pale reflection from her own deep snows. The smooth white roofs of the village, showing clear above the invisible walls, gave the houses a look of children's toys. Dark as it was, a few dark figures could be seen slowly stealing up the snowy street, on which there was as yet no track of wheels or footprints. They were the cold and sleepy miners on their way to the pits for day-shift. Under the gaunt and gallows-like stack at the mouth of the Trigger Pit, Shadow was trampling the snow impatiently, and trying to fan a warmth in his bosom by whistling 'The Campbell's are Coming' as a pibroch, with long intervals of groaning accompaniment. All the time he kept a general lookout for the mustering of his forces. It was the custom for all hands to go down the pit by half-past six, even though they knew they would be at once sent up again to 'play', because orders were slack. This was thought a salutary discipline for the spirit, like the eight o'clock services in the warmed and lighted chapels of the universities.

As usual, the first to appear at the stack was a powerful, clean-shaven collier with a surly or taciturn manner and a strange look of defiance in his eyes. He was a pikeman from the North – a hewer, he called himself – and as he came from Durham, of course his name was Geordie. Close behind him trudged a queer slip of a boy, his inseparable companion – his 'marrow', as the miners had learnt to call him, slightly perverting the strict use of the Northern word. For by 'marrow' they simply meant partner, or 'half-stent', as they themselves would have said. The boy was tallish and very slim. He had his hair cropped close till it was brown and velvety as the back of a field-mouse. He always wore enormous boots, much too loose for him, and a bluish shirt, which it was supposed he never took off. Certainly he had no need to strip down in the pit like the rest, for he was only a driver as yet, and in consequence that shirt was rather to be called black than blue. Yet it harmonised well with his face and arms, which look black past washing, and were as black in the morning as at night. Only once had a streak of white skin been visible through the cloud of coal dust, and Shadow had called it the hope of Sunlight. But it never reappeared, and the boy was known as Dirty Dick.

This was the more strange because Geordie was quite indecently clean, and when he stripped did not even show the 'collier's ring', or line of natural demarcation where clothes leave off and washing begins, but, like those superior people in the North, washed all over every day. He practised other nasty Northern customs as well – sat on his heels to pick, rather preferred the narrow workings, and was indifferent to pigeons. The Butty only kept him because he was short of hands for a contract, and found that Geordie could send up sixteen tubs to any other pikeman's fifteen. Besides, he never drank, and always volunteered for remote or dangerous workings, where he would be likely to be posted alone with his 'marrow'. When the day-shift came up at four o'clock, they were always the last, and they went straight home to their cottage at the top of the hill. They kept house for themselves, and late at night Dick came out to shop, still black as sin. Through the chinks in the blind it could be seen that they had very little furniture. The bed was placed right opposite the street door, as is the Northern custom, and the door was always kept shut and bolted. Well, if they did not wish to be sociable, no one could object. An Englishman's house is his prison, locked on the inside.

'Hullo, Zulu!' said Shadow, swinging his safety-lamp in the boy's face. 'What soap's that you're advertisin' this mornin'?'

'Same as your old woman washes the blood off yer carvin' sword with,' retorted Dick, knowing Shadow's martial soul and single estate. But as he spoke he saw Geordie shiver and look behind him.

'All right, ole man,' he said, as all three stepped together on to the cage. 'You've got a bit of a chill on you from us workin' yesterday with the water bleedin' through out of the pound on us. We'll get old Job to stick us in a warmer place today.'

'Steady up, Geordie,' cried Shadow, as he gave the signal for the engineman to lower away. 'You jolly well keep 'old on that there chain, or in 'alf a minute you'll be in a warmer place nor ever old Job can give yer.'

The bands were already moving, and the wheels spun round this way and that under them, when suddenly a figure raced up out of the darkness, and seemed to be calling to the party to stop. But neither Shadow nor Dick saw it. The railings fell clattering into their place round the pit's mouth, and the figure was left staring over them at Shadow's lamp, which grew fainter and fainter as the cage rushed down, bumping now and then against the uneven brickwork of the shaft.

'You're nigh on 'alf an hour afore time, as you will always be. There's only the Doggies down as yet,' said Shadow, as they lighted their tallow dips and plastered the ends round with balls of wet clay. 'You'd best get along to the black hole, seein' you've took a fancy for it. I'll tell Job, and send the Marshal after yer', afore you've got two tubs loaded. The old pit's goin' full gate today.'

'Forward the Light Brigade!' cried Dick, and away he went along the gallery, teaching the groves of pit-props to resound the name of Annie Laurie. Geordie followed him in silence along the dusty track between the rails.

As soon as they were out of sight and hearing, Dick turned and said in a low voice, 'Why, what was the matter, Geordie?'

Geordie looked up with a wild terror in his eyes, and then tramped on in silence.

'Sorry I said that about the sword,' Dick continued.

'Oh, it wasn't that,' said Geordie. 'Didn't you see it?'

'No. See what?'

'Why, something black ran up to the pit's mouth as we started down. It looked over at me. I've never seen it so plain before.'

'Oh, Geordie, there was nothing there!'

'No, there was nothing there, of course. That's just the worst of it.'

'There, Geordie, there.' said Dick soothingly.

'You slept badly last night. It'll pass. In time it won't come again – in time.'

'The thing has often been done before. Do you think all the others have suffered like me?'

'You mustn't think about it at all, Geordie. It's driving us mad. Of course it's been done before. It's quite common. It doesn't count. Besides we're safe now.'

'Oh Dick, I almost wish we weren't. I wish I was caught, and all over.'

'Doesn't us count for nothink, then?' said Dick, with a pitiful attempt at a smile on his black face, where a line of white teeth showed for a moment.

There was no answer, and they crept along the branching galleries in silence – two flames of human life, so deep below the fields and rivers. As they went on, the workings became narrower, and Geordie had to stoop low to avoid the slabs of timber across the top. Where the dips were steep, they had to wade through water and black slush. Sometimes they came to a door against which the current of air was beating with the noise of a torrent stream. As they violently pushed it open the noise ceased, and then began again behind them. Sometimes the heat made the sweat start from their skins, and next moment an icy wind chilled them to the bone through their wet clothes.

At last they turned from one of the main air-ways down a new gallery, which was being cut for ventilation as well as for coal. This was the black hole Shadow mentioned, and it had now been carried forward for about seventy yards. Along the left side for part of the distance ran a made-up fire-rib to protect the mine from a fire which had been kindled by the friction of some ancient workings falling in, and was now always smouldering. In spite of the dam an almost imperceptible greenish smoke would sometimes curl through the crevices, and lie coiled along the top of the gallery – 'clinging to the rough', as the miners say – till it could be carried off by a draught. But the air along the gallery itself was so stagnant now, that before Geordie and his marrow had gone twenty yards their candles began to burn dim, the heat was intense, and the silence in their ears almost terrible. When they reached the 'face', Geordie took off his clothes and began the daily toil without a word. As soon as enough coal had fallen they set about loading up the tubs side by side with forks and shovels, and before the second tub was full, a low rumble was heard approaching.

'That's the Marshal coming,' said Dick, wiping his dripping face with his shirt-sleeve, and substituting a new layer of grime. The Marshal was one of Shadow's favourite ponies. Hearing Dick's answer to the shout of the driver who had brought him down with others for that part of the mine, he came of his own accord for a short distance along the stifling gallery. He was a tiny little creature, old, nearly blind, and covered with the glorious scars and wounds of service. In the happy days when he had roamed the field beside his mother, he had perhaps been a bay. Now he was the colour that veterans wear when the long battle is nearly over. Meeting Dick on the way, he stopped, and breathing hard with the delight of recognition, rubbed his nose against his chest, taking the dirty shirt playfully between his lips in petition for the accustomed bit of sugar.

'Nice beast,' said Dick, bringing the sugar from his pocket and stroking the soft curve of furry nose between the nostrils. 'There's something still glad to have me here, anyhow.'

He hooked the Marshal to the full tubs, and drove them away, seated on an iron step low down in front, with his legs stretched over the chains on each side of the pony's body. He had to take the tubs far away to a main working, where he could hook them to a continuous rope which ran to the shaft. Then, after calling in at another station, he returned with empty tubs to help Geordie with the loading. And so the work went on hour after hour; hewing, loading and driving. In heat and sweat and bitter winds and blackness; the tubs rumbling along the galleries; the Doggies going their rounds; the naked pitmen cursing and clamouring for drink; the boys yelling bold metaphors at all objects living or inanimate. But in all the pit there was not a boy so wildly eloquent as Dirty Dick. It was an artistic pleasure to listen to him.

'Drink time' came half-past twelve. Geordie and Dick emerged into the air-way, and throwing their jackets over their shoulders, sat huddled together upon a dusty scrap of sacking to devour the bread and dried haddock out of a knotted handkerchief.

'Sorry I was such a fool this morning,' said Geordie. 'I'm all right now. Fear runs out of me with the sweat, and so does remorse. I suppose it was nothing after all.'

'Of course it was nothing,' said Dick. 'And never talk about remorse and things like that. It's no good thinking about the past. That doesn't matter. We've got our day's work to do. Have some more coffee. I've made it rather nice today.'

'Most men have got something against them, I suppose,' Geordie went on, taking no notice of the consolation. 'It must be common enough.'

'Of course it's common,' Dick answered, as cheerfully as if he said it for the first time. 'A man ought to be very glad if he has only one thing against him. By the time I'm a man I'll have a lot more than one, I'm pretty sure.'

'Oh Dick, he gave me such a look as he fell to the ground,' said Geordie, shivering. 'He was always so happy. Everybody liked him. You knew him, didn't you Dick?'

'Of course I knew him,' said Dick, dropping his head wearily between his knees. 'What does it all matter now?'

A small party of miners went merrily by, and there was a rapid interchange of miner's wit and compliment. When their laughing at Dick's shameless retorts had died away, Geordie said, 'He doubled himself together all over the place and cried out —. You know what he cried out?'

'Oh Geordie,' Dick moaned in answer, 'why will you be always talking about it? Why can't you forget it like me? What does one man more or less matter? Look here, now — if his spirit covered with blood came and stood here, I'd go up to him and curse him to his face for making you unhappy.'

Laying his hand hastily upon Dick's shoulder, Geordie peered round into the darkness. 'Come along,' he said at last, 'let's get to work again. A man like me need be afraid of nothing – nothing real.'

He threw off his coat, revealing the great muscles of his arms and chest. Dick rolled up his own shirt-sleeve, and laughed at the contrast. They groped their way back to the 'face', their candle now showing little more than the blue of the flame.

'You'd better keep in the air-way with the pony,' said Geordie. 'It's getting a bit too thick up here. I'll shout when the tubs are ready. I've got to finish the stint. They shan't say I couldn't work, anyhow.'

'Nor me either,' said Dick.

'You won't ever leave me, Dick?'

'Leave you? What will you say next, I wonder? How could I leave you now?'

There was a pause, and then Dick drove the tubs away, kindling the Marshal's ardour with the chorus –

A little sup of milk, and a little bite of bread,

A mighty lot of labour, and a blessed time in bed,

A little bit of loving, and a stone above your head;

Then, cheer up! You'll soon be dead,

And it's over.

For two hours the work went on as before, and the time to 'loose' was drawing near. Without moving to breathe the fresher air, Geordie was labouring to finish off his last two tubs. He had squatted down to 'undergo' his last fall of coal. The dim candle glimmered at his side. His brain seemed numbed, and a dizzy sickness rendered him incapable of thought or memory. The world beyond that yard or two of coal had become blank, and he vaguely wondered whether he was feeling happier than usual. In the midst of his labour a new sensation came over him, but it seemed to be a very long time before he was really conscious of it. He then felt that he was being watched; that there was something looking at him from behind. The sensation seemed to come through his back. At last he stopped his pick and listened. There was no sound but the creeping of the coal. Not daring to look round, he went on with his work. Then something made him stop again, and again he listened. A lump of coal crunched behind him. 'Dick,' he cried, 'is that you?'

There was no answer and no sound. Again he drove his pick into the coal, but he could not pull it out. There was certainly something present close behind him.

Very slowly he turned his head to look. He knew what he would see. There it was, standing motionless and watching him. The candle's tiny light showed that it was naked to the waist. Geordie gazed at it without moving.

'It's me,' it said. 'I knowed you from the first. Maybe you'll know me best by this.'

It laid a finger on a short brown slit in its side.

'Think I'm afraid?' Geordie gasped, springing up so that his head struck against the low roof. Instinctively he lifted his candle too. It went out at once, and he was in utter darkness. He had just strength to fling his pick down the gallery and he heard it fall without striking anything. Then a dizziness took hold of him. His limbs trembled, and he fell heavily beside the half-filled tub. The 'damp' disturbed from its lurking-place, fell with him and lapped itself round his head in invisible coils and currents.

When Dick came back with the Marshal, he saw no light at the end of the working and there was a peculiar smell in the stagnant air. Suddenly the pony stopped dead and stood shaking. Dick sprang from his seat and ran forward with a cry, but before he had taken three steps his candle went out. He threw it away, and groped along, stretching out his hands before his face. At last his boots struck against something soft and he stumbled and fell upon it. He felt at it with his hands. It was a man's body naked to the waist.

'Geordie!' he screamed – 'wake up! Give me your arms and I'll drag you out.'

The man only uttered a comfortable sigh of sleep. Dick put his hands upon the chest and face.

'It isn't Geordie!' he cried, throwing himself backwards, and violently shaking the body. 'Here, you, whoever you are, tell me where Geordie is?'

'There isn't a feller called Geordie in these parts,' murmured a sleepy voice. 'The feller alongside me was taken bad through me havin' a game with 'im.'

At the sound of the voice Dick shivered in the hot air and shrank away. He stared into the darkness, but his eyes might just as well have been shut.

'I knowed you too,' the voice went on more drowsily still. 'Just you stick your arm round my neck and I'll go off sweet as heaven.'

'Don't speak, only tell me where he is,' whispered Dick.

'Climb over me then. You've no call to move your arm.'

Dick felt himself trembling all over from the poison of the air. He had hardly strength to creep across the body, but close on the other side he found him for whom he was seeking. With a last effort he wound his right arm under the head, and laid his face beside it.

'Haven't you a word left for me?' he whispered, and, with the deep breath of a child going to sleep, he stretched himself full length upon the motionless form of his comrade.

'Damn them furreigners!' cried Shadow, impatiently stamping the quick mark-time in the stable far away. 'What's the good of 'em always workin' overtime and keepin' my poor 'osses from their comfortable 'ome? I can't see no call for furreigners myself, never could, neither French nor German, North nor Welsh, nor nothink. The Marshal will be fair bustin' with emptiness for his corn and drinks.'

He listened from the door, and imitating a bugle, he sang the infantry kitchen-call, which all the ponies knew as well as German boars know the sound of forester's potatoes pattering on the frozen earth. But no rumbling of wheels answered; and taking his lamp, he set out in search, cursing the perversity of all the human race that was not born in Wenley.

Arrived at the black hole, he called again, and a feeble whinney replied. He found that the Marshal had tried to back down into the air-way, but had got jammed athwart, and now stood quivering, whilst the sweat dripped from his sides. Shadow cut him loose, and he staggered slowly away, like one on whom the Fury has for a moment gazed and then passed on.

'My God, if it ain't the fire-stink!' said Shadow, ceasing to storm, and crouching close to the ground as he ran quickly forward. The 'damp' was gradually rising again, and his lamp showed one little spark. Suddenly he stopped, and drew in his breath.

'Why, it's a perfect battlefield!' he said.

He felt the three bodies turn. Two gave no sign, but Dick moaned.

'What, Dick, you dirty little devil!' cried Shadow. 'Wake 'oop can't yer, and coom along wi' me. Wake oop, you young cuss! Do ye know yer've pretty nigh killed the Marshal?'

'Take the other man,' murmured Dick, 'and leave me with my mate.'

But Shadow had already uncoupled an empty tub and let down the side. One by one he dragged the bodies up, and shoved and lifted them into it. They lay there limp and jammed together like slaughtered carcasses. By the time he had run the tub out of the working, Shadow himself was quivering and ready to drop. But pushing with all the strength left in him, he made his way towards the sump. The Marshal feebly ambled behind him with legs as unwarlike as a new-born lamb's.

'What's thee got there, Shadow?' said old Job who was left alone at the foot of the shaft.

'I don't rightly know what to call 'em now,' Shadow answered; 'but two on 'em was Geordie and Dick, and t'other looks to me like the Kinestead unemployed as was took on yesterday. I told the butty 'ow it 'ud be if he kep' on turnin' the old pit into a Casual Ward; and now they've gone and pretty nigh killed one of my 'osses!'

'Why, man alive! Them's dyin' of the fire-stink,' said old Job, peering into the tub, aghast.

'I'd ought to know that much for myself,' said Shadow, 'see me shakin'! Quick with it! We must damp 'em down now afore the fresh air carries 'em off. Here's two corn sacks for them two men. Lay hold, and I'll damp down Dick with his shirt and my old jacket.'

They lapped the sacks tightly round the heads, and taking Dick's shirt, they turned it back over his face, old Job holding up a lamp.

'Oh, look 'e, Shadow, - look 'e! he cried. Dick don't seem to be the kind of thing as he gave 'imself out for!

'Oh Job, Job, don't yer take no notice for what you see! You look the other way. Who'd 'ave thought such things could 'appen in the Trigger Pit? It is clean agen the Abstract of the Regulation Act for his Lordship's Mines.'

As Shadow spoke he was binding up Dick's head in his own jacket, and with trembling fingers was trying to button his own waistcoat round the naked body, and all the time he cried and sobbed, like a soldier who, in the midst of a battle, finds that he has driven his bayonet home between a woman's breasts.

They rang the signal four times, and then once more to show that men were coming up. At the top the miners, seeing the terrible load, came running out of the hovel where they were drinking their allowance of beer. The bodies were caught up and carried off to the engine-house.

'Gord's truth, her's a female!' cried the giant Manasseh who had Dick in his arms.

At the word the miners gathered round, uttering the most complex oaths and catching hold of her hands and feet, or trying to touch her grimy clothes, as though she had been a mediaeval saint with power to stop a pestilence.

Hour after hour the bodies lay stretched out side by side in the engine-house. The doctor came. The whole village came. The black crowd stood in the snow murmuring conjectures, though evening and night fell. At last there were sounds of moving and talking in the shed. Shadow appeared at the top of the steps swinging both arms as signals. The crowd hummed with expectation. A few minutes later Geordie and the Kinestead unemployed were seen being helped through the door. No one paid much attention to them. Behind them came the doctor, carrying Dick. All drew in their breath, and then the long cry of joy went up, and it was the women's turn to weep.

Henry W. Nevinson, *In the Valley of Tophet* (1896)

George Bissill

Red Shean is Worried

Red's head was in a whirl when he reached the lamp-cabin. A thousand devils were press-ing minute spears to the back of his eyeballs. He took his lamp and proceeded auto-matically toward the cages in the wake of his shift-mates. As he reached the middle of the ramp he paused and looked intently at the countryside visible beyond the shoulder of the pit superstructure. Sunshine flooded the fields, except in places where breeze-driv-en clouds cast moving shadows. He remembered how as a child he had often run across fields to escape such shadows. He bit his lip now, gripped by an unutterable yearning for the life of his youth. From behind him came the persistent snuffles and gasps of the engines.

'Men on!' The cry came from the banksman. A rapper rose and fell with a metallic clink. Men hurried past Red, who slowly turned and followed them. He stepped into a cage and squatted, his head once more falling onto his chest. The swift drop of the cage brought a queer sensation to his disordered stomach, causing him to look up in alarm. It was a feeling he had experienced when he first entered the mine – as though his stom-ach were forcing its way upwards through his body. He clenched his teeth as he stared with half closed eyes at the greased skids which guided the cage into the depths. The cage shivered at times, as though the skids clutched it too tightly. It sounded a staccato clatter and a vibrant moan. The skids steadily swished upwards, their greased surfaces gleaming from the dim light of the lamps. Then came a scream of suddenly compressed air as the ascending and descending cages passed. One thousand feet – the halfway mark. The down cage hurtled past a huge cavity in the shaft side, from which sounded a sud-den gasp. Down… down… down. It seemed to Red that an age had passed since that first falling sensation. Would the cage never stop?

'Cage brok away at Hufton last neet and crashed into the sump,' came a voice at Red's elbow.

'Aye,' responded someone, 'it dropped fra the Main Coal and brok the sump timbers. The stone men were waiting to descend. Lucky.'

'Aye, they're laid off for three days.'

Silence again, but for the rattling of the cage and the soughing of displaced air. Red stared sullenly at the swiftly ascending walls of the shaft, slimy surfaces dripping water. A shrill whistle came from timber buttresses. From the lower deck of the cage came a raucous laugh, followed by a line from a popular song which seemed to break and echo wearily from various directions. Then came a loud jeering and blurting as the cage hur-tled past the electrically lit, whitewashed, cloisterlike cavity of the uppermost coal-seam. The noise was flung back, together with a hollow, booming rush of air which ended in a swish and a sigh. The speed of the cage was checked, it slowed to a stop at Red's seam. Gates were flung open, and he stepped from the confining space and straightened his aching back.

He shaded his eyes from the electric light while his lamp was inspected. Then he took his place in the long file of men who set off in-bye. They found stout ash sticks, or whittled blackthorns, which they had hidden behind the props near the shaft, and one by one they entered the low places and adopted a mechanical pace, throwing the weight of their torsos, which were bent almost parallel to the floor, onto their sticks. Their lamps were shielded with pieces of tin behind, so as not to dazzle those in the rear, and the lights lit up the legs of the man in front. When they reached 'The Heavy', Red dropped out and squatted in a refuge hole, watching the legs of the bent men filing past. The deputy overman in charge reached him and paused. He always walked in the the rear, to see that the men got safely in.

'Is tha tired, Red?'

'Nay…' Red stood up and walked out the where he could stand upright. He looked out-bye, where he could see the faint circle of light which represented the shaft. 'I'm just lookin',' he said simply.

'Aye, but we'd better be gittin' in,' said the deputy.

Red reached high into the 'cloisters' of the timbered space with his stick, then started walking up the steep incline.

'It's high here,' he said.

'Aye,' came the voice from behind. 'We had a hell of a time timbering her. Many a fall we had afore we used t' iron girders. There's a hole up there reet to the seam above. Walled wi' brick it is, for an escape. Never had t' use it, though, but once.'

They plodded on in silence. Red was enraged when they reached the low timbers again and had to bend double. They progressed steadily for two miles, without a word being spoken. He stopped when they had reached a driver's flat and douched his throbbing head in a drinking trough for the ponies. Soon he reached Taffy Evans, who chatted happily of their luck in striking soft coal.

'Give her hell, Red,' he said as he left the caval. 'Use up all thy tokens.'

Red took his trousers off his shoulders and rolled them up, placing them on a pile of shale and stone; he hung up his bunch of tokens on a prop near the end of the rails; drove his lamp nail into a prop where it would serve his purpose best. He placed his tools ready to hand, and with a mell hammered flat a curled section of the coal shovel. Then he struck the tub standing there to see if it was full: it gave forth an empty sound. He sat down then, not on his heels, but flat on his backside, with his legs thrust out in front of him. He looked at and beyond the heap of coal which the relieved man had left lying. He was in misery.

The putter came to a curve some distance away and shouted in to Red, asking if he had a full tub ready. Red, without turning his head, answered that he'd be ready in two minutes. He rose, and even though he was bent almost double his red crop rubbed against the cold damp stone ceiling.

Then he started shovelling the coal hurriedly, as though to overcome his pain and mental confusion by work. The coal struck the stone roof with clicking, brittle sounds, and thundered into the wooden tub. Soon the tub was full. The putter came in and took away the full tub, then ran in an empty. He spoke to Red but got no answer. Then he said: 'Had a fight with thy woman?' Red paid no attention to the customary witticism. He mechanically started shovelling again; and again waited for the putter, sitting with his shovel across his knees. Soon the caval was cleaned up. With precision of long habit Red started hewing. Presently he paused and looked for his water-bottle. Then he remembered that he had walked out of the house without either food or water. He cursed aloud, his rage rising. His throat was parched, and he made vain efforts to spit out the coal dust. He returned grimly to his work, swinging his pick wildly to express his rage, aiming at the points of light reflected by the coal facets, which he associated with the mocking light of Mary Ann's eyes.

When the deputy came to fire, Red asked if he had a nip of water to spare. The deputy said he would send some in with the putter. He fired his shot and departed. A good four tubs laid loose, and Red swung his shovel and filled tubs as fast as the putter brought them. Each time the putter came in he had a remark for Red. 'Tha's doin' fine Red. Tha'll get a score at this rate.' Or: 'Mad at thysel' Red? Better leave some coal for t'others.' Or: 'Tha'll hole through into the sea afore laowse.' Red ignored him, excepting to ask if the deputy had sent some water. Only once he responded to the putter's chaffing; when Mary Ann's name was mentioned. He swore savagely and flung the shovel at the putter, who dodged behind the tub just in time, then yelled in derision as he slipped on to the low limbers of his pony and urged him out.

Red's throat was burning, his eyes were burning; he felt fevered and savage. The putter brought him another empty in and cried that there was a message on it for Red. Red dropped his shovel and lounged to the tub. He pressed his head sideways against the top near the tub so that he could look inside, knowing that a tin bottle would reflect the light. There it was! He groped inside with his long arm, and drew forth the near-empty bottle. Quickly he took out the cork and gulped, gargling his dusty throat. He shook his head to wash the dust from his mouth. His cheeks bulged with the water. Then he stopped, electrified by what he saw chalked on the tub. 'WATER FOR RED SHEAN – RIGHT 3RD GATE'. And underneath was a crude limerick, reading:

There's a lass in a pub, called Mary Ann
Who has on the string a red-headed man.
While he works in the pit
Or his drinking his bit,
She's having some fun with a gentleman.

Red could hardly believe his eyes as he goggled at the puerile but vicious rhyme. Powerful emotion surged through him. He read the thing over and over. The writing was blurred in parts, and double strokes, one set fresher than the other, indicated that some wag in the pit had re-chalked it. Red spat out his mouthful of water at it, then lunged forward and struck the tub with his fist. He winced with pain. He sat back, seething with fury, and spoke aloud, unaware of the hollow booming of his voice: 'Buggers of hell! Thou swine... swine... swine.

Thought whirled, torturing him. 'Gentleman... Mary Ann... Mary Ann... having some fun with a gentleman.' How long had this message been going through the pit? He could imagine the belt-boys and drivers singing it to a limerick-tune recently made popular by a music-hall comedian. Probably the whole pit-crew were chuckling over it. He broke into a cold sweat at the thought of his humiliation. He spat again to obliterate the thing, but the chalk remained, a dull grey. He rubbed his wet hand on the bottom amongst the coal dust, then scrubbed the tub until the message was gone. He took his lamp and circled the tub, looking for other chalk marks. There was an 'OXO' game, unfinished; a crudely drawn profile; and an almost obscured statement that 'God is love!' He stumbled wearily back into his caval and jammed his lamp spike into the prop, driving it securely in with the palm of his hand. He squatted with his back to the lamp, feeling sick at heart. His eyes closed, and his head bent wearily forward on to his knees.

Who could they mean?

It never occurred to him to question the truth of the message. He was only conscious of being made a fool.

Gentleman?... One of the Sunday crowd! That was it – a fool not to have thought of it before!

And now every suspicious circumstance flashed through his mind: There was the day he saw Mary Ann pulling her hand away from one of the young pups who was tipsily following her downstairs: There was the night he had been in bed, and had heard her whispering outside the bedroom. She had explained that – she was giving instructions for the morning, whispering so as not to disturb a guest sleeping in the room opposite.

Who was it? One of the jolly, flirtatious drinkers – one of the prosperous ones?

Last night – by God!

Last night – where did she come from when he saw her shadowy figure suddenly appear in the corridor? Whose door opened and closed just then?

This morning – when she came from Mr. Keith's room. What did that mean? It must have been Keith's money that started the pub going. Because of her obligations to Keith she had made a fool of her husband. Aye, he remembered now that Toby had been trying to warn him about something fishy going on. And she had kept him in the pit all along against his wish because of Keith and her damned greed. Damn the bitch to blazes! He'd twist her head off her shoulders!

And with that satisfactory conclusion, he thumped his knee. He clasped his throbbing head and sat listening to the wild pulsing of his heart. Then he stretched his long arms over his head without rising from his haunches, and touched the stone ceiling, pressing upwards as though to force his way upwards through the immense thickness of rock – to sunlight – and to freedom through the throttling of Mary Ann.

A groan escaped him, and his arms dropped limply to his sides. His hands trailed on the floor, and one of them touched a shovel and closed convulsively on the handle.

Work! He could forget for the moment in work. He rose so quickly that his head cracked against the stone top. He shook his head to kill the pain. Light danced madly across his eyeballs. Then he shovelled frantically. Coal crackled and skidded as it struck the roof near the gaping mouth of the tub, then thudded and boomed as it fell inside. The raucous sounds drove into his disordered mind with crude rhythm: Mary Ann... Mr. Keith... Mr. Keith... Mary Ann.

The putter came and changed the tubs. Red cleaned up the loose coal. Mechanically he laid out his tools only opening his eyes at intervals, and wagging his head slowly like a horse in its stall. He started hewing. Mary Ann... Mis-ter Keith... Mar-ee Ann... Mis-ter Keith. His pick swung back and forth. He opened his eyes each time he was ready to strike, then closed them as the blow struck home and he swung his pick back. His tired mind became fearfully imaginative. He saw a jumbled picture of bright spots of colour, the faces of Mary Ann and Mr. Keith, the procession of dead bodies from the mine after a disaster, white-faced women at bank, waiting to claim those bodies. Every experience of strong emotion brought its imagery to him – jumbled flashes without sense, which faded quickly each time he opened his eyes, then returned, changed and distorted, when he closed them again.

His pick struck the ribbon of shale, and set up a musical vibration. He opened his eyes wide then, and paused. Suddenly panic gripped him. The coal face started to revolve! It went slowly at first; then quickly, until it was merely a blur of rapid movement. Red dropped his pick and rubbed his eyes with sweaty, grimy fingers. Keeping his eyes closed, he reached out and felt the coal with trembling fingers. It was still. He cautiously opened his eyes, snapping them closed as soon as the face moved again in his vision. He shuddered. Nystagmus, the feared eye disease of miners was upon him. Often he had seen stricken men, the victims of insane fear, rush madly out from the face, lunging blindly and shrieking with rage when encountering a direct light, which made them stop dead and cover their eyes. Sometimes, when reaching bank, the sudden contrast of darkness with brilliant sunshine had made them blind – often resulting in insanity.

Red moaned. For the moment he had forgotten his rage at Mary Ann. He only wanted to get out of the mine and never to re-enter it. The last shift! He'd laowse, he thought, before his eyes got worse. He rose to gather his things, and the direct rays of his lamp flame struck his tortured eyeballs; everything whirled again! With a curse he swung wildly at the lamp and knocked it off the prop. When it struck the bottom the glass shattered and the flame went out.

He was now in merciful darkness. Gloom closed about him like a cloak. His steel-studded boots shuffled uncertainly, cracking little pieces of brittle coal as he moved. He decided to rest his eyes; to stay in the darkness for a while. He stretched on the floor, brushing away the sharp pieces of coal with his hand, which encountered the halt of his stonepick and thrust it aside. He laid down, pressing his fingers to his eyes. Soon the cold stone struck a chill into his nude torso. He groped for his shirt and put it on, then made a pillow of his long trousers. He settled back. His thoughts recommended. He became lost to the menace of the roof above – lost to the world of coal. He could hear his heart slowly pounding – Mary Ann... Mister Keith...

Harry Carlisle, *Darkness at Noon* (1932)

The Ancient Miner

He sits the image of a life of toil;
The strength of age is his through age of strength
For him is long since past; and now at length
His outworn frame seeks rest; his native soil
No more shall feel his tread; the dreary moil
Of nights and days the treach'rous earth beneath,
Doomed to the damps that fouled his panting breath
And gave him poison for his sweat the while –
'Tis o'er; and yet to him denied is ease;
His mask-like face all wretched is and pale;
His sunken eyes roam round his mean abode;
Locked in the dreaded grasp of fell disease,
He waits and waits with wasted limbs and frail
To rush unto the bosom of his God.

Chas. MacCarron, in *The Cornhill Magazine*, March 9th 1934

The Flight of the Lodger

We were standing round 'Tommy's' bedside, waiting for the end; his forecast had proved true, and the doctors, having discovered that he was suffering from cancer in the stomach, had sent him home to die, being unable either to alleviate or extirpate that fatal malady.

The quiet of the room was broken at intervals by the sobs of his wife and his two children, and occasionally 'Tommy' himself spoke in a dreamy way a few words to his 'marrer', whose hand was fast in his own.

After a long pause in which we though he had fallen asleep, 'Jack,' he said suddenly 'is that thoo?' 'Ay, lad,' came back the thick response from his mate beside him. 'I's makin' sharp for the other side, Jack.'

'Ay, thoo's ap-proachin'.'

'But it's alright, Jack, I's comfortable; I's got Christ i' my heart, an' the clay's nearly done. So long, hinny!' And therewith he fell into a doze. The sound of his wife's sobs, I think, recalled him to a brief consciousness, for he feebly tried to draw her nearer to him with his other hand, then sank still further back upon his pillows with a groan.

'I wud be vary much obliged for a wee suck at an orange,' began 'Tommy', but a renewed burst of weeping from his wife – it was mid-August and no orange was procurable – at once diverted him from his own torment, and he turned to comfort and rebuke her at one and the same time.

'Whist, then, whist, Mary lass; thor's no call ti greet, it's nowt but the clay that's leavin' ye, the lodger cannot die, an' there he'll be to meet thoo on the other side o' the river.'

The effort had exhausted him; he sank back with closed eyes on to his pillow. Then suddenly he opened them shining brightly and triumphant, and – with a 'Ho-way, Lord' upon his lips – the gentle lodger departed to his rest.

How long we stood there in the solemn silence, I knew not, but gradually we bethought us of the widow and the children, and so came out quietly together.

The doctor, I noted, held his hand to his eyes as though he wished none to observe him, and I heard the Vicar, who also had come to bid 'Tommy' farewell, murmur to himself as he passed me by: 'Verily I have not found so great faith, no, not in Israel'.

Howard Pease, *The White-Faced Priest and Other Northumbrian Episodes* (1896)

A Pitman's Epitaph

He lived underground, now he's dead underground,
His cogs could not hold up the squeezing of age.
He knocked many 'props' out, his own prop is knocked out,
He withered in earning a wage.

He turned away gas, now he's turning to gas,
A sheet he oft wound, now he's wound in a sheet:
The Jim Crow of Death had bent out his breath,
And the parting is for every complete.

He sweated the salt of his tears in work,
All life was a jest, and death but a joke;

And fastioned with pain for but little gain
Monuments that ended in smoke.

Huw Menai Williams, *The Passing of Guto and Other Poems* (1929)

The Hodder

Joe Burt was Geordie's mate in days gone by. They worked side by side in the pit, hacking at the same chunk of coal, filling the same tub and sharing their earnings equally. Even when they were boys, they had been harnessed to the same truck, harnessed as the ponies were now, with great, hard, heavy leather trappings, chains and metal fittings. Geordie's harness still hung in the shed outside. He felt rather proud of it now, as men feel proud of extracted shrapnel which had given them trouble and pain enough at some time or other in their lives. He liked the children and young people to ask him questions about it. 'That's the harness I used to wear when I was a donkey', he would tell them.

Conditions were different now…

The human harness had gone, but the marks remained. They could be seen when Geordie was having his tub. There was a ruddy, crinkled belt around his waist over the thigh bones, as if someone had branded him with a red hot ring. And diagonally and vertically across his body were similar marks, made by the harness when his body was soft, pliable, tender – at the age of eight or thereabouts. He was a living relic of a period, only a few years distant, when man in certain spheres of life was treated like a beast of toil.

J. C. Grant, *The Back to Backs* (1930)

'Dudleys'

'Dudleys', those round and corded tin receptacles holding just a quart of water and slung around the shoulder as one slings a haversack in the 'Dudleys' most of all! The epic of the 'Dudley'! Who will write it? This round and battered water tin, faithful, companionable and of the mine. Oh! Most lovable 'Dudley'!

How often have my lips closed round about your welcome mouthpiece, cleaving, loving, insistent, longing never to let thee go?

Ambassador of healing spring, of coolly laving water, of meadows and repose –

Roger Dataller, *A Pitman's Notebook* (1925)

'Pitmatik'

The local miners (East Durham) have a curious lingo of their own, which they call 'pit-matik'. It is, you might say, a dialect within a dialect, for it is only used by the pitmen when they are talking among themselves.

The women do not talk it. When the pitmen are exchanging stories of colliery life, usually very grim stories, they do it in 'pitmatik', which is Scandinavian in origin, far nearer to the Norse than the ordinary Durham dialect.

J. B. Priestly, *English Journey* (1934)

The Tyneside Accent

The people were not bad once you got to know them, though even to a Yorkshire lad they appeared uncouth... To my ears it still sounds a most barbarous, monotonous and irritating twang. Every short phrase rises in exactly the same way, almost to a scream: taw taw ta ta tee tee ti ti. The constant 'Ay-ee, mon,' or 'Ay-ee, b...' of the men's talk and the never-ending 'hinnying' of the women seem to me equally objectionable.

J. B. Priestley, *English Journey* (1934)

George Bissill

The Pitman's Pay

I sing not here of warriors bold,
  Of battles lost or victories won,
Of cities sack'd or nations sold,
  Of cruel deeds by tyrants done

I sing the pitmen's plagues and cares,
  Their labour hard and lowly lot,
Their homely joys and humble fares,
  Their pay-night o'er a foaming pot.

Their week's work done, the coaly craft,
  These horny-handed sons of toil,
Require a 'right gude willie-waught',
  The creaking wheels of life to oil.

See hewers, putters, drivers too,
  With pleasure hail this happy day –
All, clean washed up, their way pursue
  To drink, and crack, and get their pay.

––––––––––

'Here's just a swatch of pitmen's life,
  'Frae bein' breek'd till fit te marry:
'A scene o' ceaseless pain and strife,
  'Hatch'd by wor deedly foe, AWD HARRY:

'For there's ne imp iv a' his hell
  'That could sic tortur heve invented:
'It mun ha'e been AWD NICKY'S sel –
  'He likes te see us se tormented.

'Then ye that sleep on beds o' doon,
  'An niver JACK THE CALLER dreedin' –
'Gan finely clad the hyell year roun',
  'And a'ways upon dainties feedin' –

'Think on us, hinnies, if ye please,

'An it were but te show yor pity;
'For a' the toils and tears it gi'es,
    'Te warm the shins o' Lunnon city.

'The fiery 'blast' cuts short wor lives,
    'And steeps wor hyems in deep distress;
'Myeks widows o' wor canny wives,
    'And a' wor bairns leave faitherless.

————————

'We labour hard to myek ends meet,
    'Which baffles oft the gentry's schemin';
'And though wor sleep be short, it's sweet,
    'Whilst they're on bums and bailies dreamin'.

'There's a charm aw cannot nyem,
    'That's little knawn to quality:
'Ye'll find it in the happy hyem
    'Of honest-hearted poverty.

'Yor high-flown cheps oft fyel and brick,
    'But we hev a'ways yet been able
'Te keep the wheelband i' the nick,
    'Though oft wi' but a barish tyeble.

'O dear! but they lead wicken lives,
    'If a' be true that's i' the papers:
'Oft kissin' yen anothers wives,
    'And cuttin' other idle capers.

'The run up debts they cannot pay —
    'Whiles pay off PAUL wi' robbin' PETER;
'But, thank God, JACK, there's nyen can say
    'We iver wrang'd a leevin' creetur.

'Aw dinnet mean te brad o' this —
    'It's but the way we a' should treed;
'But where the greet se often miss,
    'We may luick up when we succeed.

'For raither sic disgrace te share,
  'An bring a stain upon wor friends,
'We'd work, on breed-an-waiter fare,
  'Till blood drops frae wor finger ends.

'Besides, when a' is fadin' fast
  'That cheer'd the droopin' spirits here –
'When we luick backwards at the past,
  'Te see how we'll at last appear –

'Twill form a breet and sunny place
  'On which the mind may rest wi' pleasur
'An' then de mair te help wor case,
  'Than hoarded heaps o' yearthly treasur.'

Thomas Wilson, in *Mitchell's Magazine* (1830)

'Mining Royalties'

'Five miles under the sea
We slave from morn till night,
With never a ray of the blessed sun
To cheer us with its light.
With frames bent down by toil,
With lungs beclogged by dust,
We miners work in the seams below,
For the wage that brings a crust.

'Pick – Pick – Pick,
In the tunnel's endless gloom,
And every blow that our strong arms strike
But helps to carve our tomb.
But what is that to those
Who live by our grim toil?
For 'mining royalties' must be made
To glut the landlord's spoil!

'O ye who sit by the coals
As they glow in the cheery grate,

Do ye ever think of our fearsome lives
Or bemoan our children's fate?
Our children reared in rags;
Our wives but drudges and slaves,
While all our days are turned to night,
Five miles beneath the waves?

'They tell us in the books
No Briton is a slave,
But we are owned, both body and soul,
Five miles beneath the wave.
We toil from morn to night,
But not for our own gain,
For 'mining royalties' must be wrung
From out our sweat and pain.

'They tell us there's a God
Who loves his children dear,
But he's our god who owns the sod,
For whom we work in fear;
He lives in a palace fine,
Bathed in the sun's sweet light,
While we sweat blood in the coal black mine,
Where all our days are night.

'O, Ye who see the Light,
And know that God is just,
Will ye not help to put things right?
Claim for us more than a crust?
O, not the crust of toil,
But the fullness of our OWN;
For now our children ask for bread,
And they give them but a stone.

'Yes; open your purses wide
To aid our present need –
But more we ask than this alone:
The death of private greed.
O, free for us the land;
Restore to us our own,

So that our children who ask for bread
May not receive a stone.'

Referenced by William Maurice as W. B. Northrop, *Contrasts Poems of Poverty* (1911), but not identifiable

Tony Hallbauer-Wagner

George Bissill

Pit Ponies and Colliery Horses

Hermann Kätelhön

George Bissill

Pit Ponies and Colliery Horses

On the way back from the 'front line' I asked to be shown the 'pit ponies'.

'There are no pit ponies in Wales,' I was told. 'They are colliery horses.'

I was taken to the mine stables near the pit bottom. There were six stalls well lit by electric light. A man was whitewashing them. The horses not on duty were being groomed. I noticed that above every stall was written the name of its occupant, as in racing stables. Each pit horse is christened before it goes down a mine. No colliery horse is under 14.2 hands high. They cost between £55 and £60 each. One colliery values its horses at over £7,000.

"Warrior' has been underground for fifteen years,' said the farrier. 'Does he look unhappy? Does he look ill-fed?'

He did not.

'How many of these horses are blind?'

'I have never met a blind pit horse,' said the farrier. 'It is true that after a number of years a horse taken above had defective sight: but they are never totally blind. They get the best of food, good quarters and work which is not so strenuous as that of a London dray horse...'

'What about injuries?'

'After every shift the haulier is forced to report any injury no matter how trivial. The slightest scratch must be reported. The vet then visits the horse at once and treats him if necessary. Cruelty? We never meet it. But there are very strict regulations in every colliery to guard against it. If a haulier is cruel to his horse then a red mark goes down against his name. This is against him even if his action might have been accidental. Three red marks and a man is instantly sacked. There is no argument. Out he goes!'

The live-stock in a coal mine is interesting. A fat black cat was sitting in these stables on a bale of hay. All mines have cats on the ration list. They keep down the mice which gets into the fodder. Colliery books contain dozens of entries like this:

Milk...1s. 6d.

The haulier has charge also of the stable cat and its milk.

'Some of these cats are funny,' said the farrier. 'They will go to the pit bottom and wait for the cage like a man. They walk in, go to the surface, take a look round to see it's raining and wait for the next cage down again! Sometimes the hauliers have taken them home for a weekend.'

We watched the hauliers bringing their horse to stables after the shift. The pit horse has a journey of perhaps 200 yards from the coal face to the junction. He draws 28cwt of coal in a 'tram' on rails. He works six or eight shifts a week, but he is never allowed to work two consecutive shifts. He never works on a Saturday or Sunday.

People who think that a pit horse just pulls a 'tram' have never seen these animals at work. The horse, like the haulier, knows his job. Every haulier keeps to his own horse, and would very much resent any other man working him. And the reason is that in taking coal from the seam to the junction there are various little difficulties which can only be easily avoided by a sympathy between man and beast.

When, for instance, a 'tram' runs off the line or fouls the points, a man and horse who know each other's methods of work can rail it again in a few seconds and with a minimum expenditure of energy. If you or I tried to do this we should confuse the horse and fail to get the tram back. But watch a haulier and his horse. He has a special word of command. The horse knows that he has to give one sharp pull while his man put his back to the 'tram' and guides.

The pit horse is intelligent and understanding. He knows his man. His man naturally cares for him. Even if the miner were not notoriously fond of animals; even if he were an inhuman creature he would be complicating his work by neglecting his horse or failing to establish contact with him.

Coal haulage is not one man's job; it is man plus horse. You have only to see — as you will always see in a mine — the haulier with his arm round his horse's neck, talking to him and patting him, to know that the Welsh pit horse is not a mere beast of burden.

'And,' said the farrier, 'in the morning most hauliers take something down for their horses. It may be only a lump of sugar; but there is generally something in their pockets — even in these hard times.

I went 'down the line' with a new idea of the miner and with the knowledge that I can never again look at a bucket of coal without remembering him, black as pitch and wet with sweat, bracing his body against the coal wall half a mile from daylight...

'Well, and what do you think of it?'

A set of white teeth and two white eyeballs gleamed at me.

'You are always in the firing line...'

'We get used to it. It's got to be done! I wish a few more people would come and see us work. Cheriol!...'

The cage moved and shot up towards the world. It was like a resurrection. I did not mind how it banged or rattled. I knew that above was sunlight and green grass! Water began to drip into the cage. The darkness of the shaft lightened. The cage leapt up and stopped.

I had to close my eyes. Daylight was blinding. It was as if my eyes had been turned inwards. But when I opened them I saw that it was raining. But how good it looked; how clean and marvellous!

And when I walked out of the cage a friend laughed at my black hands and my black face; and I knew again why the men coming up have no time for the men going down.

H. V. Morton, *In Search of Wales* (1932)

Gals

Pitponies were called 'gals' in Lancashire, possibly because waggoning was done by women until the year 1842... Most of the pit shafts were so small that the ponies had to be trussed up in a network of strips, with their legs drawn tightly against their bodies, before being lowered. These ponies often remained down for years, but fortunately for them they were generally petted by the colliers. Some of them even acquired a taste for tobacco and learnt to search for it in the pockets of their friends' jackets.

Lawrence Pilkington, *Tattlefold — A Tale of a Lancashire Colliery Village in Mid-Victorian Times* (1926)

The Stables

Time was when the Company had forty ponies in its stalls; shiny, hefty little customers with attendant drivers and the requisite equipment; to wit, a heavy bridle or bonnet fortified along the eyes and nose rather like a lumbering Norman helmet, a leather collar and a pair of chains for attachment to the corves. Now only a pathetic muster occupies the long straight line of cubicles. In many instances the names of former animals remain painted upon neat little rectangular boards, each one of which is set above the manger of the stall. Alack! Alas! 'Turpin' and 'Jubilee' and 'Gordon' and 'Tartar' and many another will never clatter along these stones again; the mystic alchemy of endless ropes and electric engines have filched away their occupation.

———————

Unforgettable the atmosphere, itself substantial, in which the odours of urine, chop and oats, leather oil and sawdust are variously constituent.

The odours of near Eastern cities (so they tell us), particularly Constantinople, are in a sense unique. And so it is with our stable underground. There is nothing quite like it in all the multitudinous catalogue of the odours. It is absolutely unique and an infallible key to remembrance.

Roger Dataller, *A Pitman's Notebook* (1925)

173

The Ponies

During the strike, the ponies were brought up
From their snug stables, some three hundred feet
Below the surface – up the pit's main shaft
Shot one by one into the light of day;
And as each stepped, bewildered, from the cage,
He stood amongst his fellows, shivering
In the unaccustomed freshness of free air,
His dim eyes dazzled by the April light.
And then one suddenly left the huddled group,
Lifted his muzzle, snuffed the freshness in,
Pawed the soft turf and, whinneying, started trotting,
Across the field; and one by one his follows
With prickling ears each slowly followed him,
Timidly trotting: when the leader's trot
Broke into a canter, then into a gallop;
And now the whole herd galloped at his heels,
Around the dewy meadow, hard hoofs, used
To stumbling over treacherous stony tramways
And plunging hock-deep through black steamy puddles
Of the dusky narrow galleries, delighting
In the soft spring of the resilient turf.
Still round and round the field they raced, unchecked
By tugging traces, at their heels no longer
The trundling tubes, and round and round and round,
With a soft thunder of hoofs, the sunshine flashing
On their sleek coats, through the bright April weather
They raced all day; and even when the night
Kindled clear stars above them in a sky
Strangely unsullied by the stack which now
No longer belched out blackness, still they raced,
Unwearied, as through their short, sturdy limbs
The rebel blood like wildfire ran, their lungs
Filled with the breath of freedom. On they sped
Through the sweet dewy darkness; and all night
The watchmen at the pithead heard the thudding
Of those careering and exultant hoofs
Still circling in a crazy chase; and dawn

Found them still streaming raggedly around,
Tailing into a lagging cantering,
And so to a stumbling trot: when gradually,
Dropping out one by one, they started cropping
The dew-dank tender grass, which no foul reek
From the long idle pit now smirched, and drinking
With quivering nostrils the rich living breath
Of sappy growing things, the cool rank green
Grateful to eyes, familiar from their colthood
Only with darkness and the dusty glimmer
Of lamplit galleries...
   Mayhap one day
Our masters, too, will go on strike, and we
Escape the dark and drudgery of the pit,
And race unreined around the fields of heaven!

Wilfrid Gibson, *Fuel* (1934)

The Mare Without a Name

The redoubted output of Wittonhoe Old Pit called for more galloways for the Busty Seam. One Saturday morning a goods train, with a consignment of ten, ran into the railway sidings. Marable, the horse-keeper underground, and two stable-men, were there to disembark them; and I – it was my third year's 'prenticeship to mining engineering – went, curious to see how they would take to a mole's life in the Busty Coal Seam. They came in cattle-trucks, roughly divided into head-stalls or pens and the last of the batch to sniff and baulk at the gangway was a little mare that set us staring with wonder. She was about the usual height of a good galloway, a matter of fourteen hands; but she seemed of another breed altogether. You would have thought she had Arab blood in her. She was so light on her feet, that she danced down the planks and seemed hardly to feel the ground; and she moved with a swaying to and fro of her deer's head in a way to make you think of open moors and flowing airs. The gleaming sun was delighted with her bay coat.

   The road from the siding to the pit-mouth lay along the colliery tramway and over a high bridge that crossed the river Brune. When she came to this bridge approach, walking last in the string, she suddenly stopped. Kit Pout, the stableman who held her leading-rope, could not, do what he would, persuade her to budge a step farther. The river there made a wide curve and the meadows on either side had not been, at that day, buried under huge heaps of pit-waste, and were April-green after the recent rains. The little mare threw her head up and down, snuffed the air with sensitive, dilating nostrils and pawed the ground, as if in a craze of ecstasy to have escaped the train after that wearisome, long journey. Then she got restive, danced sideways, and reared. Kit Pout could barely hold her and soon lost his temper. He cursed her with murderous oaths, and jerked her head down with a savage, sawing pull that almost broke her fine jaws. But she was too much for him. In a moment she had lashed out at the old fool and sent him spinning. She went away like the wind at that, down the high embankment, along the clumps of thorn and hazel at the meadowside, making light of every dike, leaping the hedges like a running stag.

The chase was not easy to take up; it meant a long detour to reach her vanishing point, where the colliery fields ended and the pastures of Low Finings Farm began. Kit Pout's cry of rage had brought back Marable, the horse-keeper. He had a feeling for a horse, and stared after the runaway with mixed dismay and delight.

'My hinnies!' he said, 'she's a goer, that one; she's a Northumberland Plater! Look at her!'

'She's brakt my shin!' said Kit Pout, 'wait till aa get hould on her.'

'Ye auld sump!' said Marable, 'ye're not fit to handle a little race-mear like her. Ye s'uld have treated her canny.'

'Aa'll treat her to summat,' said Kit Pout.

II

There was reckless hunting that day after the lost mare. Marable and I saddled two galloways and rode miles up the Brune, tracking her. We lost her hoofmarks at last in the river, five or six miles away; and no one had seen her or heard tell of her along the road or at the next village of Bruneford. But that evening, as I was locking up the viewer's office, a lad from the Finings Farm brought me a message from his master, Matthew Clarke, saying he would like to see me that evening.

Matthew was both horse-breeder and sheep-farmer. He bred four or five horses every season, and often gave me a mount, or asked me in to a farmer's tea and a game of cards or chequers. When I arrived, he led me to the stables; there was the lost mare, with sandy streaks on her forelegs and marks of dry blood still on her jaw where Kit Pout had given her that devil's wrench.

She had made her way at last to an upland field, far above High Finings, where two of Clarke's colts were running at grass. After some trouble — and Matthew had a way with him no wise beast could resist — he had got her down here. Then, at a loss to account for the ownership of the creature, it occurred to him that she might be part of the Black Horse Pit stud.

When he heard her story, first he laughed a grim laugh, then patted her cheek and her flank, and examined her.

'Man! T'd be a cruel shame to send her down yon shaft. She's no galloway, but a bit of real fine breed. I'd swop any galloway and forty pound for her if I saw her at Stagshawbank Fair.'

Well she understood – 'ears up-prick'd' – that Matthew understood her. She rubbed her deer's head confidently on his shoulder while he spoke.

'She's that starved with her railway journey,' he said, 'and her mouth's that sore, she cannot eat. I'll give her bran mash.'

We consulted what further we could do; whether we could possibly get Black Horse Pit to part with her. But there was no hope of it. Our chief viewer, or manager, was a strict man-of-habit. She had been sent to him for a galloway, to work in the Busty Seam, and a pit-galloway she had to be.

'She'll never stand it,' said Matthew, 'she won't take her feed down there, you can be sure of that. I give her a month!'

The following night they blindfolded her, and down she went.

III

Marable, the horse-keeper, knew his trade. He did all he could to humour her. The pick of the oats, the sweetest hay, the cleanest-drawn water, the airiest stall, were hers. And he spent hours grooming her silken coat.

'Now,' said he, when I went in on the second day to look at her, and brought her some coarse salt – on Matthew's suggestion – 'now if we could nobbut find a name for her, she do varra well.'

I suggested two or three. 'What do you say to Medina? She's like an Arab, and that's an Arab name.'

'She's no Dinah; Dinah is a darkie – a genooine nigger! This one is gotten gold thread in her mane.'

'Fatima, then?'

'She's not fat, not ivor like to be. Hold on, sir – I saw a name on a cream-coloured pony Boneyparty used to ride. We have his bi'graphy in the hoose, and I'll look it up. Charlie, mind me to hunt up that pony's name, and we'll christen her proper. I've fair lost me heart to this little harab.'

As I left the stable, a set of tubs was coming out-bye, drawn at a gallop by a strong galloway, 'Champion', the pick of the Black Horse Pit stables. I stood back to avoid the flying coal-dust and the splash of a black puddle between the rails.

The galloway was travelling for all he was worth, his eyeballs fixed and strained unnaturally, his neck thrust out quite straight from his shoulders, his breath snorting hot and hard. It was a terrific display of a strong creature putting out every ounce of exact force. I went away, very down in the mouth, thinking of the little 'harab'.

IV

Marable did all he could, as I said. It was of no use. She only ate pretend-mouthfuls of hay; and her sighs were such as I have never heard a horse utter before or since. And when they took her out and tried to harness her to a set of tubs, she became a fiend possessed, kicking right and left. Three times she was taken back, and three times given a respite.

Then came a desperate last attempt, when she fairly drove in the planks of one tube and terrified the reckless putters and drivers. The end of it was she burst her traces, and set off up the mainway at a terrific pace. She galloped on till she saw the lights of a set of tubs approaching, and turned off sharp into some old workings, breaking her way through the brattice that fenced off the return airway.

I am thankful that that last event was spared me. When she came to a low-roofed headway, where there was not room enough for her to travel, she forced her way in some-how, scrambling on her knees into the blind alleys. There, making fearful groans, she 'scraffled on' – Marable's word – to what seemed an impossible last place of retreat in the stythe and darkness. The men had come up with lights by that time. They had got near enough to see her on the ground, lashing with her hoofs and knocking out the pit-props like ninepins on either side.

This brought the end. The roof-stone, left without support, came down with a rush. The men ran back, and, as they ran, heard her scream – 'just like a seized woman.'

'Aa call it determined suicide, if ever there was one,' said Marable.

That night, the old working – already closed at its farther end – was, by the over-man's orders, walled up. There the Mare Without a Name rests, waiting the resurrection of the sun-lovers.

Ernest Rhys, *Black Horse Pit* (1925)

Trompette Goes Underground

The miners, men and women, had arrived at the pit bottom too soon and could not be taken up for half an hour, more especially since some complicated manoeuvres were going on for lowering a horse... The signal hammer had struck four blows, and the horse was being lowered. There was always excitement at such a time, for it sometimes hap-pened that the beast was seized by such terror that it was landed dead. When put into a net at the top it struggled fiercely; then, when it felt the ground no longer beneath it, it remained as if petrified and disappeared without a quiver of the skin, with enlarged and fixed eyes. This animal being too big to pass between the guides, it had been necessary, when hooking it beneath the cage, to bind back the head and attach it to the flanks. The descent lasted nearly three minutes, the engine being slowed as a precaution. Below, the excitement was increasing. What then? Was he going to be left on the road hanging in the blackness? At last he appeared in his stony immobility, his eye fixed and dilated with terror. It was a bay horse hardly three years of age, called Trompette.

'Attention!' cried Father Mouque, whose duty it was to receive it. 'Bring him here, don't undo him yet.'

Trompette was soon placed on the metal floor in a mass. Still he did not move: he seemed in a nightmare in this obscure infinite hole, the deep hall echoing with tumult. They were beginning to unfasten him when Bataille, who had just been unharnessed, approached and stretched out his neck to smell his companion who lay on the earth. The workmen jokingly enlarged the circle. Well! What pleasant odour did he find in him? But Bataille, deaf to mockery, became animated. He probably found in him the good odour of the open air, the forgotten odour of the sun on the grass. And he suddenly broke out into a sonorous neigh, full of musical gladness, in which there seemed to be the emotion of a sob. It was a greeting, the joy of those ancient things of which a gust had reached him, the melancholy of one more prisoner who would not ascend again until death.

'Ah! That animal Bataille!' shouted the workmen, amused at the antics of their favourite, 'he's talking with his mate.'

Trompette was unbound, but still did not move. He remained on his flank, as if he still felt the net straining him, garrotted by fear. At last they got him up with a lash of the whip, dazed and his limbs quivering. And Father Mouque led away the two beasts, fraternising together.

Emile Zola, *Germinal* (from the original edition translated by Havelock Ellis, 1894 and revised in 1933)

Trompette and Bataille

All the entrances to the Voreux had been closed, and the sixty soldiers, with grounded arms, were barring the only door left free, that leading to the receiving-room by a narrow staircase into which opened the captains' room and the shed. The men had been drawn up in two lines against the brick wall, so that they could not be attacked from behind.

At first the band of miners from the settlement kept at a distance. They were some thirty at most, and talked together in a violent and confused way.

Maheude, who had arrived first with dishevelled hair beneath a handkerchief knotted on in haste, and having Estella asleep in her arms, repeated in feverish tones:

'Don't let anyone in or anyone out! Shut them all in there!'

Maheu approved, and just then Father Mouque arrived from Requillart. They wanted to prevent him from passing. But he protested; he said that his horses ate their hay all the same, and cared precious little about a revolution. Besides, there was a horse dead, and they were waiting for him to draw it up. Étienne freed the old groom, and the soldiers allowed him to go to the shaft. A quarter of an hour later, as the band of strikers, which had gradually enlarged, was becoming threatening a large door opened on the ground floor and some men appeared drawing out the dead beast, a miserable mass of flesh still fastened in the rope-net; they left it in the midst of the puddles of melting snow. The surprise was so great that no one prevented the men from returning and barricading the door afresh. They all recognised the horse, with his head bent back and stiff against the plank. Whispers ran around:

'It's Trompette, isn't it? It's Trompette.'

It was, in fact, Trompette. Ever since his descent he had never become acclimatised. He remained melancholy, with no taste for his task, as though tortured by regret for the light. In vain Bataille, the doyen of the mine, would rub him with his ribs in his friendly way, softly biting his neck to impart to him a little of the resignation gained in his ten years beneath the earth. These caresses increased his melancholy, his skin quivered beneath the confidence of the comrade who had grown old in darkness; and both of them, whenever they met and snorted together, seemed to be grieving, the old one that he could no longer remember, the young one that he could never forget. At the stable they were neighbours at the manger, and lived with lowered heads, breathing in each other's nostrils, exchanging a constant dream of daylight, visions of green grass, of white roads and of infinite yellow light. Then, when Trompette, bathed in sweat, lay in agony in his litter, Bataille had smelled at him despairingly with short sniffs like sobs. He felt that he was growing cold, the mine was taking from him his last joy, that friend fallen from above, fresh with good odours, who recalled to him his youth in the open air. And he had broken his tether, neighing with fear, when he perceived that the other no longer stirred.

Mouque had indeed warned the head captain a week ago. But much they troubled about a sick horse at such a time as this! These gentlemen did not at all like moving the horses. Now, however, they had to make up their minds to take him out. The evening before the groom had spent an hour with two men tying up Trompette. They harnessed Bataille to bring him to the shaft. The old horse slowly pulled, dragging his dead comrade through so narrow a gallery that he could only shake himself at the risk of taking the skin off. And he tossed his head, listening to the grazing sound of the carcass as it went to the knacker's yard. At the pit-eye, when he was unharnessed, he followed with his melancholy eye the preparations for the ascent – the body pushed on to the crossbars over the sump, the net fastened beneath the cage. At last the porters rang meat; he lifted his neck to see it go up, at first softly, then at once lost in the darkness, flown up for ever to the top of that black hole. And he remained with neck stretched out, his vague beast's memory perhaps recalling the things of the earth. But it was all over; he would never see his comrade again, and he himself would thus be tied up in a pitiful bundle on the day when he would ascend up there. His legs began to tremble, the fresh air which came from the distant country choked him, and he seemed intoxicated when he went heavily back to the stable.

———————

Mouque appeared with Bataille, whom he was leading to work, and he had to hold him with both hands, for the sleepy old horse had suddenly reared up and, with a shrill laugh, was stretching his head towards the shaft.

'Well, philosopher, what troubles you? Ah! It's because it rains. Come along, that doesn't concern you.'

But the beast quivered all over his skin, and Mouque forcibly drew him to the haulage road.

Almost at the same moment as Mouque and Bataille were disappearing at the end of a gallery, there was a crackling in the air, followed by the prolonged noise of a fall. It was a piece of tubing which had got loose and was falling a hundred and eighty metres down, rebounding against the walls...

Father Mouque, who had brought back Bataille without hurrying, was still holding him by the bridle, both of them stupified, the man and the beast, in the face of this rapid flow of the inundation. The water was already rising to their thighs...

At the bottom of the shaft the abandoned wretches were yelling with terror. The water now came up to their hips. The noise of the torrent dazed them, the final falling in of the tubing sounded like the last crack of doom; and their bewilderment was completed by the neighing of the horses shut up in the stable, the terrible, unforgettable death-cry of an animal that is being slaughtered.

Mouque had let go of Bataille. The old horse was there, trembling, with its dilated eye fixed on this water which was constantly rising. The pit-eye was rapidly filling; the greenish flood slowly enlarged under the red gleam of the three lamps which were still burning under the roof. And suddenly, he felt this ice soaking his coat, and he set out in a furious gallop, and was engulfed and lost at the end of one of the haulage galleries.

Then there was a general rush, the men following the beast...

The flood was beating against their breasts, and they walked very slowly. As long as they had light they did not despair, and they blew out one of the lamps to economise the pil, meaning to empty it into the other lamp. They had reached the chimney passage, when a noise behind them made them turn. Was it some mates, then, who had also found the road barred and were returning? A roaring sound came from afar; they could not understand this tempest which approached them, spattering foam. And they cried out when they saw a gigantic whitish mass coming out of the shadow and trying to rejoin them between the narrow timbering in which it was being crushed.

It was Bataille. On leaving the pit-eye he had wildly galloped along the dark galleries. He seemed to know his road in this subterranean town which he had inhabited for eleven years and his eyes saw clearly in the depths of the eternal night in which he had lived. He galloped on and on, bending his head, drawing up his feet, passing through these narrow tubes in the earth, filled by his great body. Road succeeded to road, and the forked turnings were passed without any hesitation. Where was he going? Over there, perhaps, towards that vision of his youth, to the mill where he had been born on the bank of the Scarpe, to the confused recollection of the sun burning in the air like a great lamp. He desired to live, his beast's memory woke; the longing to breathe once more the air of the plains drove him straight onward to the discovery of that hole, the exit beneath the warm sun into light. Rebellion carried away his ancient resignation; the pit was murdering him after having blinded him. The water which pursued him was lashing home on the flanks and biting him on the crupper. But as he went deeper in, the galleries became narrower, the roofs lower and the walls protruded. He galloped on in spite of everything, grazing himself, leaving fragments of his limbs on the timber. From every side the mine seemed to be pressing on to him to take him and to stifle him.

Then Étienne and Catherine, as he came near them, perceived that he was strangling between the rocks. He had stumbled and broken his two front legs. With a last effort, he dragged himself a few metres, but his flanks could not pass; he remained hemmed in and garrotted by the earth. With his bleeding head stretched out, he still sought for some crack with his great troubled eyes. The water was rapidly covering him; he began to neigh with that terrible prolonged death-rattle with which the other horses had already died in the stable. It was a sight of fearful agony, this old beast fractured and motionless, struggling at this depth, far from the daylight. The flood was drowning his mane and his cry of distress never ceased. He uttered it more hoarsely, with his large open mouth stretched out. There was a last rumble, the hollow sound of a cask which is being filled; then deep silence fell.

Emile Zola, *Germinal* (from the original edition translated by Havelock Ellis, 1894 and revised in 1933)

Wee Danny

Wee Danny's deid, and buried in the bing,
A trig bit pownie aince upon a day,
When Cadger Jock, noo deid and buried tae,
Gied roon' the Raws wi' caller cod and ling.

Man, Danny never took tae doon alow,
A thrawn wee tyke, he'd tak' it in his heid,
And wouldna' move for a' your crust o' breid,
Nor though you marked his hide wi' mony a blow.

Na, Danny couldna weel forget the days
When winds blew fresh frae aff the Lomond hills,
And blackies woke the echoes wi' their trills,
And grass grew sweet and green amang the braes.

Eternal darkness cut him tae the he'rt,
And hard he fought for freedom. But the chains –
The self-same chains that cut us tae the banes –
Were ower secure, and nae yin took his pairt.

Na, nae yin took his pairt, and we're the men
Wha grouse sac muckle at oor present state;
We curse the tyrants, yet we vend oor hate
On the puir brute until he curbs wi' pain.

'Get oot the bloody coal!' is a' the cry,
And every mither's son's at breakin' strain
Tae sell his sowl that ither folk may gain
The world, and a' that rotten gold can buy.

But, Danny, ye hae broke your chains at last,
You'll feel nae mair the curse, not yet the pain
O' savage strength. A martyr you lie slain
Tae freedom's cause, a Christ o' different cast.

Joe Corrie, *The Image O' God and Other Poems* (1937)

The Pit Pony

They're using machinery down our pit
For ponies' jobs;
They doän't keep fit
For long, and oftentimes I find
After a bit they go almost blind,
It's better for them to be clear of this,
But some on us Pals will rarely miss
Ways of them;

They're so friendly-like
Seems like having another tyke
In the clammy darkness snuffling near,
Their nickerings most of us like to hear.
But after to-morrow motors will do
Jobs they did.

There's one named Sue,
Been here for years;
I've offered for her…
By gum! an' didn't it make a stir
When I told my missus.
'What's the good
Of summat that's allus needing food!'
So I went to market and bought some hay,
Enough to keep her for many a day,
For it weänt be long ere my missus, too,
Will larn to luve you pony, Sue,
She's blind as a bat, and needs a rest
Afore she sets out on her journey West.

Dorothy Una Ratcliffe, *Fairings – A Yorkshire Miscellany* (1928)

The Darkness of the Mine

Hermann Kätelhön

George Bissill

The Mine

I took the lamp and stepped into the cage;
For half a mile I plumbed the dreadful dark
To learn how miners earned a petty wage.
The light I carried was a feeble spark
That made the darkness felt and visible.
Far, far I toiled, from pit-shaft to the face,
A mile of heat and night, a road in hell,
To crouch with hewers in a three-foot place.

Deep, deep, I saw them sweat beneath the vale;
Above, their wretched homes that mocked the Sun
Stood gaunt upon the hill. Here was the tale
of wealth in poverty of life begun.
Here, in the fiery mine; her, housed in shame,
The miners worked and died for Britain's fame.

Leo Chiozza Money, *Sonnets of Life* (1932)

The Miner and His Lamp

What ails the lamp? It burns so dim;
Yes, yes, its cup is dry,
But I've no time to heed its whim
If oil it lacks – not I!

See, see, it pouts, like all who pout,
The more its mood we mark –
Well, well, if so then – out – flick out!
Than this I'll face the dark.

Referenced by William Maurice as Joseph Skipsey, but not identifiable

The Lamp Lighting Underground

When his eyes became a little more accustomed to the strange place, he saw ahead of him a long, gloomy tunnel, with dim lights all along the side of the archway, and wires, ropes, and wheels running overhead. In the middle of the road were hundreds and hundreds of trams, those on the left full of coal, which glittered under the lights; the trams on the right were empty. Shadowy figures of men and boys moved about the trams. The lights running with the road showed forms of men trudging heavily along the tunnel that stretched back into blackness. The forms grew vague and more shadowy as they neared the last of the lights burning dimly at the archway side. At this point the shades stopped awhile. One stretched out an arm to the flame; and when he withdrew it the hand held a tiny spark. Manifestly the shade had used the spark to light its pipe. But after that the spark glowed and swung near the ground. A man who had lighted his lamp and carried it in his hand, walking, would swing it in that fashion. Other forms went up to the light, and went through the same performance. Then the shades, six or seven in Indian file, moved inwards, each with a bedimmed spark swinging and twinkling at his side; and the dark forms, against the background of black space, were instantly swallowed up. But Maurice saw the half dozen sparks swinging to and fro for a little while longer. They gradually grew fainter. Then the farthest one vanished, followed by the second and third, until there was left in the dark distance only a single white speck of light, gleaming like a diamond set in ebony. Soon this solitary little light vanished also, and once more unbroken blackness filled the tunnel-like roadway ahead.

Jonah-the-Haulier's lamp was 'hitched' to his waist-belt. This served the double purpose of 'showing light' and leaving his hands free to work by that light. The darkness of the pit was all around him.

But with his small lamp swinging at his belt a circle of gold was about his middle. His head and body rose into the darkness above, and he looked like a tall demon who had pushed his way up through the halo of a saint.

Joseph Keating, *Maurice, A Romance of Light and Darkness* (1905)

Red Shean's Baptism of Darkness

They had given Red's lamp to a stone shifter who was in the dark, and he was put to opening a trapdoor to let tubs through, sitting crouched in the side with chilly darkness cloaked about him. Martin, his lamp completely shrouded under his vest, had crept close and set swinging a short chain hanging on a prop so that tissue paper, inserted in the last link, had swished against the prop eerily. Red's hair had crept as his mind reverted to the mealtime conversation about snakes and spirits that haunted the old workings of the mine. He didn't know that this was his baptism of darkness. He had made no outcry, but hunched his knees and shivered as he fought back fear.

The sticky, urinated clay squashed against the door, and stones rattled against the top. Despite himself, Red had leaped to his feet crying: 'What is tha'? Show a light!' – forgetting the lowness of the roof and thumping his head against a jagged stone. A thousand needles of pain darted through him, and he moaned as he fell to his knees. Martin had shown his light then, grinning as he said: 'Nay, Ginger, tha' cannot get to bank through the top. Tha' must to t' the shaft for that.' Red bellowed with rage at the trick. He chased Martin until the latter struck his lamp against a rail and disappeared in darkness, from which he mocked Red... Had he laid hands on Martin then he would have murdered him, he felt. But later the foreman had lectured him on the unwritten laws of the mine: he must never fight below ground, never bring matches into the mine or drink another man's water without permission; and he must learn to keep his head low and be able to stand the darkness without growing hysterical with fear...

Harry Carlisle, *Darkness at Noon* (1932)

When the Light Died out...

When the light died out...

There is nothing so awful as the darkness of a mine. When the lamp fails the mighty depths of the ocean overwhelm one. A million tropic nights is as nothing to it, for there is nothing to relieve the horrid monotony of the dense blanket of darkness. The moment the light is gone all sense of values is lost. The roof and the sides vanish into nothingness. When one is sitting in a place where there is an infinity of freedom of movement and the light goes out, that sense of freedom is lost. It becomes a pain to move. Nothing is tangible but that part of the mine that is in contact with the feet. All sense of distance to the nearest obstruction is gone. The roof and the sides vanish with the floor. It becomes painful to move the eyeballs. Every task that one must perform is loaded with fright. There are no real values in the darkness attendant upon the womb of the earth. The eyes see nothing. The minute particles of dust swimming about in the atmosphere – these particles of dust that are merely gas with which to feed explosions – take on gigantic shapes and assail the eyeballs. The eye searches for light, and rebels because there is no reward. When the position becomes tense the slightest movement sends a dull red light piercing through the eye.

Lamps have two methods of going out – violently, when the light is jerked; slowly, when the oil in the vessel is being consumed. In the case of these entombed men it died out gradually. How tenderly they nursed this light. All the time they had sat with the light drawn down so low that only a speck of blue remained on the tip of the wick. In reality it was an 'oil cap'. But how assuring it had been to the eye! A minute speck knocking a hole into the blanket of nothingness. It had given but little heat; yet, it had given a world of comfort. Through that point of light Joe Tarrant and Rutter had held contact with a sorrowing world.

'I wish I was bloody well dead!' said Jim.

Joe laughed a little, 'Y'll easily droon!' he told him.

The light flickered out.

Harold Heslop, *The Gate of a Strange Field* (1929)

A Thousand Feet Below...

Daily the miners of Easingden prodded and antagonized a lurking death.

When they went forth from their homes, their wives and children, they did not know if, in the designs of inscrutable fate, they would return alive or dead.

Down there a thousand feet below the earth's surface, in little gutted crevices, they stabbed at the coal face, where the tenebrous darkness was so close to you that you could almost feel it: in silence as deep and inpalpable as if all the world were dead: darkness that gripped you with the power of a nightmare coiled about the soul: where a slight quiver of the flame in your lamp made the heart beat faster, knowing the significance of that trembling light; with millions of tons of earth, rock, sand and stone congealed above you, whipped together in layers of infinite weight through the turmoil and terror of the earth's ages.

J. G. Sinclair, *Easingden* (1926)

Pit Lamps

Wagons rumbled in the darkness about him, loomed up into the light of his lamp, crept by, and were gone with an air of indescribable mystery about them... The darkness in front of him kept always a little ahead, and the darkness behind crept after him, pace for pace, and close on his heels. If he stopped for a moment to let one of the wagons creep by, the two darknesses stopped with him, starting the moment he started. If he swung his lamp forward the darkness in front jumped forward as though he had frightened it, and the darkness behind would leap on as though it were glad that the darkness in front had been frightened.

Walt lifted his lamp, which was flickering dully, and turned up the wick, wiping his oily fingers on his moleskins.

The flame leapt in its casing of glass and gauze and flickered over his thin face and sly eyes. 'Thee see,' he said, setting his lamp at his side again. The darkness hung round them like a curtain.

Frederick C. Boden, *Miner* (1932)

Glow-Worms on a Foggy Night

Here, at the coal face, it was very, very dark...

One would find one's way to the little group only by the sound of their voices, which echoed a long way off. If they happened to be silent, one would have to be right on top of them to detect them. From a distance of a few yards, all one could see ahead was inky blackness.

Now and again, curious, white, glittering butterflies would appear and disappear suddenly. They always seemed to move about in pairs. Soon enough one got to know they were the whites of human eyes...

The light of the pit-lamps was weak and watery... Resting on protruding pieces of coal and rock they resembled glow-worms on a foggy night.

J. C. Grant, *The Back to Backs* (1930)

Nystagmus

'Did tha hear? – Wilkerson, that putter fra Cumberland, has gone for a soldier.'

The men exclaimed their surprise. One of them said, turning to Wilson, 'Mind how he cursed the pit after he got nystagmus... eh, but I knew he was up to summat when I seed his face on the ramp after Martin's corpse rode today. It's a wonder if they take him in the Army wi' them weak blinkers.'

'He said he was in for another attack if he stayed on,' said the putter.

'He was puttin' for me when the nystagmus come on,' said Wilson. 'Down i' the wet pit. 'Tis not often a putter gets it, but he was that greedy for extra pay. I warned him when I seed him rubbin' his eyes every time he went t' hewin' a loose end… his lamp was that far away fra the face. I mind how he yelled how the face started turning like a wheel an' his eyeballs burnin', then he wanted me t'put out my leet. Three months he was on the Compensation. 'Twas poor pay for a lad after the tarts like he was.'

'Joined the yeomanry, he did,' said the putter. 'I shouldna' like that life.'

'Nay, it's a poor life for a man that likes to call his mind his own.'

Harry Carlisle, *Darkness at Noon* (1932)

He Lives in Eternal Light

Red wandered across the cemetery to the grave of Hughie Tylor. He clumsily rearranged a wreath that had blown from its tilted position against the headstone. Clasping his hands behind his back, he read the inscription for the hundredth time:

'… who perished of firedamp following an explosion in Blackstone Colliery.
HE LIVES IN ETERNAL LIGHT'

It was poor consolation, he thought of the epitaph, for a man who had spent the bulk of his life in half-darkness. His mind refused to grasp such a theological abstraction as 'eternal light' – he was concerned with the literal use of 'light' and knew nothing of eternity. And the thought occurred to him, as he twirled his hat slowly around with nervous fingers, that there were times when a man emerged from the darkness and encountered light so direct that it hurt his eyes.

Harry Carlisle, *Darkness at Noon* (1932)

The Flame Lay…

The flame, a miserable little semblance from the first, now lay a tiny purple pool upon the burner crown. The central pinnacle of amber had completely vanished, and with it, whatever radiance the 'safety' had to give.

Instead, a ghostly purple moon, predestined to only half a minute more of life, occupied the thick glass roundhouse of the lamp, useless in point of illumination – I could very dimly see the curve of my own fingers as they looped above the standards on the other side – yet distinctly valuable to me as the final outwork of radiance against the utter and enveloping darkness.

I swore a little – very softly yet half-humorously recognising both the futility of the spoken word and the pathetic remnant of that once-clean light.

I should have known considerably better. In the first place to set out upon a journey of this length, with the foreknowledge that I had had, of a rapidly expiring flash, and in the second place to have ignored the fact of Sunday night, a time of relative quietness and solitude; when the haulage systems were altogether out of action and only a few individual colliers, widely distributed, were occupied upon the faces? – Malediction!

No matter! There the tiny blue button of flame floated insecurely upon the surface of the burner. Screw as I might I could not give it increase. And then... Well – as I watched, the light just seemed to creep into itself; to roll up into nothingness, so silently, and with a movement so utterly secret and remote, as to suggest the winking out of some penultimate star.

It was now completely dark, and, so far as I could remember, somewhere about half-past eleven. Three courses were left open to me; the first, to push on to the right and make my way into the pit bottom where an adequate reserve supply of lamps was ordinarily kept; the second, to travel back again to where the Temperton party of colliers was working, and there to borrow a light of the three or four lamps that I knew they had; the third, to sit down where I was awaiting chance relief in the event of our itinerant Deputy or some other night wanderer – a very doubtful eventuality.

Without much hesitation therefore, I hit upon the second as the likelier course of action. After all, comparing distances, the Temperton working place was certainly nearer than the shaft itself, and since I had lately come that way, each gate and turning was still closely familiar, and even vividly placed within my memory, and so I slung my useless lamp upon my belt, advancing with an outstretched hand.

––––––––––

Utter darkness, within whose indefinable medium it was possible to pass a hand backwards and forwards an inch or two before one's eyes without the slightest visible hint of its locality. Atmosphere as soft as silk; warm, yet tempered by a steady current of the ventilating air. Roadway, one of a hurriedly driven lighter type, where tiny heaps of rubble and slippery stone made all going extremely unequal. The sleepers themselves contributed a permanent series of cunning little traps, wherein the slope soles of one's clogs were apt to slide, not far enough to mean disaster, but making progress additionally difficult, and raising the temper in the very moment when it should have been particularly level and controlled.

As I moved forward, fluttering apprehensive fingers upon the shale and timber, I could still remember the Temperton working place, and the approach into the faces from the southern side. The tortuous route thereto, leapt out and glowed within my mind rather as the trading lines stand out upon a commercial chart. I was perfectly certain of the number of turnings that I should be compelled to negotiate – there were four in all, and then –

Steady! Steady!...

My hand scraped suddenly as my foot turned on a piece of stone. I lurched violently forward without the slightest knowledge of where I was to fall. But by a desperate effort of will (yet more by luck than anything else, I suppose) I was brought up standing against the opposite wall of the 'gate' in which I stood, pawing at the timber of the roof, but mainly conscious of the devilish tingling that occupied my left hand.

'Steady lad, steady!' I found myself saying softly. 'This... simply... will... not... do' 'Be quiet, will you' – this to the safety lamp whose pull I could feel upon my belt, for there had been a slight metallic crash as the base of it struck solid.

Where had I stumbled?

Surely only a yard or two removed from the starting-point. A yard or two? In my growing exasperation and embarrassment I could not be altogether sure even of this, and the demon of doubt, having set my fortifications crumbling, pounded in merrily until I found myself questioning the four turnings that I had already established as the accredited direction.

I stood for a little while completely still. It was extremely possible that I might be able to hear the miners busy with their wedges and blades; but no such sound came to my ears; only the distant sighing of the air currents as they travelled through the passages and past the dusty brattice curtains.

Of one thing, at any rate, I began to feel perfectly sure, I had certainly not turned round. My face was still set to the proper direction.

So – en avant!

There was nothing more for it. Cautiously though, no rattling of nerves... and all would be well.

Eureka! The wall stopped suddenly. My out-stretched palm encountered empty air, waved wildly for a moment, and took the corner at last, very cautiously, into the first turn to the left. Here a teeny, almost imperceptible soughing of wind spoke of the presence of brattice cloth.

Good again! – but not so good. Oh! I found it possible to remember the place well enough; that was not the rub. It was just a 'no road' aperture. Did I not recall the fencing placed across a week or two ago? Ah, there it was! My fingers found the two wooden bars that had been nailed diagonally across with the legend 'No Road' in chalk scrawled upon them, and the dusty tarpaulin cloth that was nailed up beyond, bagging against the timber. Come comfort that, when I could not remember whether this avenue was counted as an active road or not.

'Forward' I said pettishly, 'there can be no doubt at all that this is number one.'

What the devil is the use of closing one's eyes?

The little popping curves and dots and streaking lines are all as indecipherable as a Persian Screed. And what is the good of opening upon precisely the same sort of vision, the same elusive twirls, the same blind dead aspect?

What's the use of walking at all in the heart of this blasted, velvet atmosphere? You might as well be walking in the catacombs in blasted Rome, with the damned lion and bloody Androcles, and Paul or who the hell Apostle it was who ever went to Rome...

'Temperton! Temperton! Ho-ee! Ho-ee! Ho-ee!'

The timber again! The blasted timber waits for you – it cracks and chuckles, and launches out-crack! Ah, would you, you devil?

'The temple bells are ringing

The young green corn is springing:'

Where the hell I've got to I can't say!

Roger Dataller, *A Pitman's Notebook* (1925)

Harry Hicken

George Bissill

Accidents and Disasters

Theophile Steinlen

The Disaster

Against the sunset's rose
Purple the pit-head glows –
The mound of slate and slack
That all day long gloomed black:

And the gaunt shaft-wheel seems
Hub to a wheel of dreams,
With flaming spokes that whirl
In a celestial swirl

Of hues beneath whose fire,
With patience naught can tire,
Quiet, with close-shawled head,
Each woman 'waits her dead.

Wilfrid Gibson, *Collected Poems* (1926)

John Fellows Gets Hurt

'Abner... Abner...'
   'What the hell's up with you?' he said roughly.
   'Your father, Abner...' she sobbed. 'It's your father'
   'What's that? What's he done?'
   'It's an accident at the pit. Father sent up Elsie with the message.'
   'You mean he's dead?' said Abner, suddenly sobered.
   'No... not dead... I don't think so. It's an accident. Some kind of accident. Elsie was that moithered she couldn't say proper. So I left her there and ran off for you. I couldn't take him in myself. I couldn't think of nowt but running for you.'
   'Well, if he bain't dead what the hell's the matter?' said Abner practically.
   They left the works together. Alice, still out of breath, could scarcely keep pace with Abner's long strides, but now her nervous sobbing had ceased and she even smiled. At the corner of Hackett's Cottages they met the procession from the colliery. For some obscure reason Alice's father had lost the key of the store in which the stretchers were kept, and so they carried John Fellows home on a door. In his progress from the pit they had fallen in with a stream of children suddenly disgorged from the Ragged Schools, and a train of these had swollen the cortege, curious to find out who, or what, lay under the

brown blanket. All the women of Hackett's Cottages gathered at the gateway of Number Eleven to receive him, many of them carrying babies and offering haphazard advice in the intervals of giving them refreshment. The doorway of the house was too small to admit the improvised stretcher, so they laid it down at the side of the garden.

'Be careful of my bloody tomatters,' John Fellows growled. It was the first sign of life he had given. Abner and two others lifted him from the door and carried him through the kitchen and up the twisting stairs. The boards creaked under their weight as though they were on the point of splintering. It was his right thigh that had been broken; and once, on the journey upstairs, they jolted him so much that he unclenched his teeth and roared like a bull. The crowd in the roadway shuddered. This was their first considerable sensation.

They laid him on the bed. Alice, now very pale and composed, followed them upstairs with a cup of tea.

'God! If I'm come to tea drinking it's a gonner,' said John Fellows. 'Send out for a spot of brandy!'

A small boy was sent running to the Lyttleton Arms. Elsie had already gone for the doctor. The news had spread quickly in various forms, and all Halesby heard with sensation that John Fellows had had his skull smashed in Mawne pit. The brandy came. He wouldn't have it spoiled with water and swallowed it neat, but even the brandy could not alter the ashen pallor of his face beneath its coating of coal dust.

John Fellows was a hard case and could bear pain or any other human calamity with fortitude. He lay on his back, gritting his teeth and squirting the floor with tobacco-juice. Whenever he spoke it was with a curious dry humour that seldom appeared in his ordinary conversation. He never complained of his own sufferings, though he cursed the criminal economy of the Mawne management in the matter of pit-props. 'They might as well use match-sticks as this Norway stuff. They've put a stopper on my football!' he said. 'But I'll see that they pay for it. I will, and no fear!'

Indeed they owed him something. The collapse of coal that had buried him had taken place in a remote gallery on one of the lower levels of the mine; and though Mr. Willis, proud of his electric lighting and American coal-cutting machinery, was in the habit of describing Mawne as a drawing-room pit, the arrangements for salvage were by no means elegant. John Fellows had lain for three hours beneath a ton or more of coal; and though the weight of it saved him from the pain of movement, acting as a kind of ponderous splint to the broken limb, the suspense of waiting till he was dug out would have broken the nerve of a more sensitive man. From this purgatory he had been hauled to one of the trolley-lines that traverse the galleries of the pit: his only moment of relative smoothness between the scene of the accident and his home being his upward journey in the hoisting cage.

They waited anxiously for the doctor. The boy made three more journeys to the Lyttleton Arms for brandy. 'It's the only thing that keeps the life in me,' John Fellows said.

In a couple of hours Dr. Moorhouse arrived. 'Sorry to see you like this, Fellows,' he said.

'You'd be sorrier if you was me!' Fellows grunted.

With the help of Alice they split up his trouser leg, and the doctor manipulated the thigh until he felt the crepitus of the broken bone. The he disturbed the patient no longer. 'It's a three months' job,' he said. 'You can't have it seen to properly here. You want X-rays. You'll have to go into hospital.'

'Hospital...!' John Fellows cried.

Then, at last, he became fluent. The brandy had stimulated his imagination even if it had dulled the pain, and he launched into an uncompromising statement of the opinions with which poor people regard the institutions that are erected for their care. He made it plain that he, at any rate, wasn't going to die in any hospital, or be pulled about by students, and not a spot to drink.

'I don't want you to die in any hospital,' the doctor said. He was painfully used to this kind of outburst. It was always a long and bitter controversy, and it always ended, as he knew well, in submission. While John Fellows was fuming he fixed him up on a temporary splint and then went home to telephone for the ambulance. At the foot of the stairs his eyes fell on the patient face of Mrs. Mosely, who had driven up on the cart of a friendly baker as soon as she heard the news.

'You here again!' he cried. 'Upon my word a lunatic asylum's the place for you. Take your leg out of my sight. I never want to see it again. I wash my hands of you!' He went off grumbling and Mrs. Mosely climbed the stairs.

It pleased John Fellows to see her. Indeed, from the moment of her arrival, he would not let anyone else touch him. In the old days Alice would have been jealous; but hardship and difficulty had so changed her nature that she even concerned herself with Mrs. Mosely's comfort. The old woman moved about the room like a soothing influence, and when, an hour later, the ambulance arrived, she insisted on accompanying her old friend to the infirmary at North Bromwich. John Fellows went off cheerfully, with a quartern of brandy in his coat pocket. He was even bright enough to joke with Mr. Higgins, who now arrived on the scene, having just discovered the key of the stretcher-store in his hip pocket.

John Fellow's removal to hospital made no great difference to anyone but Alice. To her the relief was enormous, for it not only saved her the trouble of irregular meals, allowing her to devote her days to her baby, but freed her nights from, at the best, uncertainty, and, at the worst, terror. Now, when Abner had said goodnight to her she need no longer sit with her nerves on edge, waiting for Fellows to come home, wondering what would be the humour of his entrance. Instead of this she now sat over the fire for half an hour of luxurious drowsiness, then picked up the baby and went off placidly to bed.

Francis Brett Young, *The Black Diamond* (1921)

Rescue: Sir George Tressady Lends a Hand

England knows these scenes so well!

When Tressady, out of breath with running, reached the top of the bank, he threw a hurried look in front of him. His feeling was that he had seen everything before – the wintry dawn, the crowds of pale men and weeping women ranged on either hand, the police keeping the ground round the shafts clear for the mine officials – even the set white face of his manager, who, with Macgregor the fireman and two hewers, had just emerged from the cage that was waiting at the mouth of the downcast shaft.

As soon as Madan saw Tressady rounding the corner of the engine-house he hurried towards his employer.

'Have you been down yet?' Tressady cried to him.

'Just come up, Sir. We got about fifty yards – air fairly good – then we found falls along the main intake. We got over three or four, till the damp rose on us too bad – we had a rough bit getting back. I thought you'd be here by now. Macgregor thinks from the direction in which things were lying that the blast had come from Holford's Heading or thereabouts.'

And the manager hastily opened a map of the colliery he was carrying in his hand against the wall of the engine-house, and pointed to the spot.

'How many men there?'

'About thirty two in the workings round about – as near as I can reckon it.'

'Any sign of the rest? How many went down?'

'Eighty six. A cageful of men and lads – just them from the shaft-bottom – got up immediately after the explosion. Since then, not a sound from anyone! The uptake shaft is chockfull of damp. Mitchell, in the fanroom had to run for it at first, it was coming up so fast.'

'Good God!' said George under his breath; and the two men eyed each other painfully.

'Have you sent for the inspector?' said Tressady, after a moment.

'He ought to be here in five minutes now, Sir.'

'Got some baulks together?'

'The men are piling them by the shaft at this moment.'

'Fan uninjured?'

'Yes, Sir – and speed increased.'

Followed by Madan, Tressady walked up to the shaft, and himself questioned Macgregor and the two hewers.

Then he beckoned to Madan, and the two walked in close converse towards the lamphouse, discussing a plan of action. As they passed slowly along the bank the eyes of the miserable, terror-stricken throng to either side followed every movement. But there was not a sound from anyone.

Once Tressady looked up and caught the faces of some men near him — dark faces, charged with a meaning that seemed instantly to stiffen his own nerve for what he had to do.

———————

As they shot down into the darkness George was conscious of a strange exhilaration. Working on the indications given him by the first exploring party, his mind was alive with conjectures as to the cause of the accident, and with plans for dealing with the various obstacles that might occur. Never during these weeks of struggle and noise and objurgation had he felt so fit, so strenuous. At the bottom of the shaft he had even to remind himself, with a shudder, of the dead men who must be waiting for them in these black depths.

For some little distance from the shaft nothing was to be seen that spoke of an explosion. Some lamps in the porch of the shaft and along the main roadway were burning as usual, and the 'journey' of trucks, from which the 'hookers-on' and engine-men had escaped at the first sign of danger, was standing laden in the entrance of the mine. The door of the under-manager's cabin, near the base of the shaft, was open. Madan looked into the little den, where the lamp was still burning on the wall, and groaned. The young fellow who was generally to be found there was a great friend of his, and they attended the same chapel together. A little farther on an open cupboard was noticed with a wisp of spun yarn hanging out from it — inflammable stuff, quite untouched. But about thirty yards farther they came upon the first signs of mischief. A heavy fall of roof had to be scrambled over, and beyond it afterdamp was clearly perceptible.

Here there was an exclamation from Bewick, who was to the front, and the first victim showed out of the dark in the pale glow-worm light of the lamps turned upon him. A man lay on his side, close against the wall, with an unlocked lamp in his hands, which were badly burnt. But no other part of him was burnt, and it was clear that he had died of afterdamp in trying to escape. He had evidently come from one of the nearer workplaces, and fallen within a few yards of safety. The inspector pounced upon the lamp at once, while the doctors knelt by the body. But in itself the lamp told little. If it were the illegal unlocking of a lamp that caused the disaster, neither this lamp nor this man could be at fault; for he had died clearly on the verge of the explosion area, and from the after effects of the calamity. But the inspector, who had barely looked at the dead man, turned the lamp round in his hands, dissatisfied.

'Bad pattern! Bad pattern! If I had my way I'd fine every manager whose lamps could be unlocked,' he said to himself, but quite audibly.

'The fireman may have unlocked it, sir, to re-light his own or someone else's,' said Madan stiffly, put at once on his defence.

'Oh! I know you're within your legal right, Mr. Madan,' said the inspector briskly. 'I haven't the making of the laws.'

And he sat down on the floor, taking the lamp to pieces, and bending his shrewd black-eyed face over it, all the time that the doctors were examining its owner. He was, perhaps, one of the most humane men in his profession, but a long experience had led him to the conclusion that in these emergencies the fragments of a lamp, or a 'tamping', or a 'shot' matter more to the community than dead men.

Meanwhile George crouched beside the doctors, watching them.

The owner of the lamp was a strong, fair-haired young man, without a mark on him except for the burning of the hands, the eyes quietly shut, the face at peace. One of the colliers in the search party had burst out crying when he saw him. The lad was his nephew, and had been a favourite in the pit, partly because of his prowess as a football-player. But the young life had gone out irrevocably. The doctor shook his head as he lifted himself, and they left him there, in order not to waste any chance of getting out the living first.

Twenty yards further on three more bodies were found, two oldish men and a boy, very little, burnt. They also had been killed in escaping, dragged down by the inexorable afterdamp.

A little beyond this group a fall of mingled stone and coal from the roof blocked the way so heavily that the hewers and timbermen had to be set to work to open out and shore up before a passage could be made. Meanwhile the air in the haulage road was clearing fast, and George could sit on a lump of stone and watch the dim light playing on the figures of the men at work. The blows struck echoed from floor to roof; the work of the bare arms and back, as they swayed and jerked, woke a clamour in the mine. Were there any ears still to listen for them beyond that mass? He could scarcely keep a limb quiet, as he sat looking on, for impatience and excitement. Bewick meanwhile was wielding a pick with the rest, and George envied him the bodily skill and strength that, in spite of his irregular way of life, were still left to him.

To restore the ventilation-current was their first object, and the foremost pick had no sooner gained the roadway on the other side than a strong movement of the air was perceptible. Madan's face cleared. The ventilation circuit between the downcast and upcast shafts must be already in some sort re-established. Let them only get a few more 'stop-pings' and brattices put temporarily to rights, and the fan, working at its increased speed, would soon drive the renewal air-currents forward again, and make it possible to get all over the mine. The hole made was quickly enlarged, and the rescuers scrambled through.

But still fall after fall on the farther side delayed their progress, and the work of repairing the blown-out stoppings by such wood brattice as could be got at, was long and tedious. The rescuers toiled and sweated, pausing every now and then to draw upon the food and drink sent up from behind; and the hours flew unheeded. At last, upon the farther side of one of the worst of these falls – a loose mingled mass of rock and coal – they came on indications that showed them they had reached the centre and heart of the disaster. A door leading on the right to one of the side-roads of the pit known as Holford's Heading was blown outwards, and some trucks from the heading had been dashed across the main intake, and piled up in a huddled and broken mass against the farther wall. Just inside that door lay victim after victim, mostly on their faces, poor fellows, as they had come running out from their stalls at the noise of the explosion, only to meet the fiery blast that killed them. Two or three had been flung violently against the side of the heading, and were left torn, with still bleeding wounds, as well as charred and blackened by the flame. Of sixteen men and boys that lay in this place of death, no one had survived to hear the stifled words – half groans, half sobs, of the comrades who had found them.

'But, thank God, no torture, no thought,' said George to himself as he went from face to face; 'an instant – a flash – then nothingness.'

Many of the men were well known to him. He had seen them last hanging about the village street, pale with famine – the hatred in their eyes pursuing him.

He knelt down an instant beside an elderly man who he could remember since he was quite a boy – a weak-eyed, sallow fellow, much given to preaching – much given, too, it was said, to beating his wife and children, as the waves of excitement took him. Anyway, a fellow who could feel, whose nerves stung and tormented him, even in the courses of ordinary life. He lay with his eyes half open, the face terribly scorched, the hands clenched, as though he still fought with the death that had overcome him.

George covered the man's face with a handkerchief as the doctor left the body. 'He suffered,' he said under his breath. The doctor heard him and nodded sadly.

Hark! What was that? A cry – a faint cry!

'They're some of them alive in the end workings,' cried Madan, with a sob of joy. 'Come on, my lads! Come on!'

And the party – all but Mr. Dixon – leaving the dead, pushed on through the foul atmosphere, over heaps of fallen stone and coal, in quest of the living.

'Leave me a man,' said Mr. Dixon, detaining the manager a moment. 'I'll stay here. You have enough with you. If I judge right, it all began here.'

A collier stayed with him unwillingly, panting all the time under the emotion of the rescue the man had imagined but was not to see.

For while the inspector measured and sketched, far up the heading, in some disused working off a side-dip of roadway, Bewick was the first to come upon twenty five men, eighteen of whom were conscious and uninjured. Two of them had strength enough, as they heard the footsteps and shouts approaching, to stagger out into the heading to meet their rescuers. One, a long thin lad, came forward with leaps and gambols, in spite of his weakness, and fell almost at Tressady's feet. As he recognised the tall man standing above him, his bloodless mouth twitched into a broad grin.

'I say, give us a chance. Take me out – won't you?'

It was Mary Batchelor's grandson. In retribution for the assault on Letty the lad had been sentenced to three weeks' imprisonment, and George had not seen him since. He stopped now, and poured some brandy down the boy's throat. 'We'll get you out directly,' he said, 'as soon as we have looked for the others.'

'There's some on 'em not worth takin' out,' said the boy, clinging to George's leg. 'They're dead. Take me out first.' Then, with another grin, as George disengaged himself, 'some of 'em's prayin'.'

Indeed, the first sight of that little group was a strange and touching one. About a dozen men sat huddled round one of their number, a Wesleyan class-leader, who had been praying with them and reciting passages from St. John. All of them, young or old, were dazed and bent from the effects of afterdamp, and scarcely one of them had the strength to rise till they were helped to their feet. Nevertheless, the cry which had been heard by their rescuers had not been a cry for help, but the voices of the little prayer-meeting raised feebly through the darkness in the Old Hundredth.

A little distance from the prayer-meeting, the sceptics of the party leant against the wall or lay along the floor, unheeding; while seven men were unconscious, and possibly dying. Two or three young fellows meanwhile, who had been least touched by the after-damp, had 'amused themselves' as they said, by riding up and down the neighbouring level on the 'jummer' or coal-truck of one of them.

'Weren't you afraid?' Tressady asked one of these, turning a curious look at him, while the doctors were examining the worst cases, and rough men were sobbing and shaking each other's hands.

'Noa,' said the young hewer, his face, like something cut out in yellowish wax, returning the light from Tressady's lamp. 'Noa, theer was cumpany. Old Moses, there-ee saved us.'

Old Moses was the leader of the prayer-meeting. He was a fireman besides, who had been for twenty six years in the mine. At the time of the explosion, it appeared, he had been in a working close to that door on the heading where death had done so ghastly and complete a work. But the flame in its caprice had passed him by, and he and another man had been able to struggle through the afterdamp back along the heading, just in time to stem the rush of men and boys from the workings at the farther end. These men were at the moment in a madness of terror, and ready even to plunge into the white death-mist advancing to meet them, obeying only the instinct of the trapped animal to 'get out'. But Moses was able to control them, to draw them back by degrees along the heading, till in the distant workings where they were found, the air was more tolerable, and they could wait for rescue.

George was the first to help the old fireman to his feet. But instead of listening to any praises of his own conduct, he was no sooner clinging to Tressady's arm than he called to Madan:

'Mr. Madan, Sir!'

'Aye, Moses.'

'Have ye heard aught of them in the West Heading yet?'

'No, Moses; we must get these fellows out first. We'll go there next.'

'I left thirty men and boys there this morning at half past six. It was fair thronged up with them.' The old man's voice shook.

Meanwhile Madan and the doctors were busy with the transport of the seven unconscious men, some of whom were already dying. Each of them had to be carried on his
back by two men, and as soon as the sick procession was organised it was seen that only
three of the search party were left free – Tressady, Bewick and the Scotch fireman,
Macgregor.

Up the level and along the heading, past the point where Dixon was still at work, over
the minor falls that everywhere attested the range of the explosion, and through the
pools of water that here and there gathered the drippings of the mine, the seven men
were tenderly dragged or carried, till at last the party regained the main intake or roadway.

'You will have your hands full with these poor fellows. Macgregor and I – Mr.
Bewick, if he likes – will push on to the West Heading.'

Madan looked uneasy.

'You'd better go up, Sir George,' he said in a low voice, 'and let me go on. You don't
know the signs of the roof as I do. Eight or nine hours after an explosion is the worst
time for falls. Send down another shift, sir, as quick as you can.'

'Why should you risk more than I?' said George quietly. 'Stop! What time is it?' He
looked at his watch. Five o'clock – nearly nine hours since they descended! He might
have guessed it at three, if he had been asked. Time in the midst of such an experience
contracts to a pin's point. But the sight of the watch stirred a pang in him.

'Send word at once to Lady Tressady,' he said in Madan's ear, drawing the manager to
one side. 'Tell her I have gone on a little farther, and may be another hour or two in
getting back. If she is down at the bank, beg her from me to go home. Tell her the
chances are that we may find the other men as safe as these.'

Madan acquiesced reluctantly. George then plundered him of some dry biscuits – of
some keys, moreover, that might be useful in opening one or two locked doors further
up the workings.

'Macgregor, you'll come?'

'Ay, Sir George.'

'You, Mr. Bewick?'

'Of course,' said Bewick, carelessly, throwing back his handsome head.

Some of the rescued men turned and looked hard at their agent and leader with their
sunken eyes. Others took no notice. His prestige had been lost in defeat; and George had
noticed that they avoided speech with him. No doubt this rescue party had presented itself
to the agent as an opening he dare not neglect.

'Come on then,' said George; and the three men turned back towards the interior of
the pit.

Old Moses, from whose clutch George had just freed himself, stopped short and
looked after them. Then he raised a hoarse voice:

'Be you going to the West Heading, Sir George?'

'Yes,' George flung back over his shoulder, already far away.

'The Lord go with yer, Sir George!'

No answer. The old man, breathing hard, caught hold of one of his stronger comrades and tottered on towards the shaft. Two or three of his fellows gathered round him. 'Ay,' said one of them, out of Madan's hearing, "ee's been a-squeezing of us through the ground, 'ee 'ave, but 'ee's a plucky lot, is the boss.'

'They do say as Bewick slanged 'im fine at the station yesterday,' said another, hoarsely. 'Called 'im the devil untied, one man told me.'

The first speaker, still haggard and bowed from the poison in his blood, made no reply, and the movement of old Moses' lips, as he staggered forward, helped on by the two others, his head hanging on his breast, showed that he was praying.

Meanwhile George and his two companions pushed cautiously on, Macgregor trying the roof with his lamp from time to time for signs of firedamp. Two seams of coal were worked in the mine, one of which was 'fiery'. No naked lights, therefore, were allowed and all 'shots' or charges for loosening the coal were electrically fired.

As they made their way, now walking, now scrambling, they spoke sometimes of the possible cause of the disaster: whereof Dixon, as they passed him, had bluntly declined to say a word till his task was done. George, by a kind of contradiction – his mind alive all the time with feverish images of death and mutilation – fell into a strain of caustic remark as to the obstinate disobedience of carelessness of a certain type of miner – disobedience which, in his own experience even, had already led to a score of fatal accidents. Bewick, irritated apparently by his tone, took up a provoking line of reply. Suppose a miner, set to choose between the risk of bringing the coal-roof down on his head for lack of proper light to work by, and the risk of 'being blown to hell' by the opening of his lamp, did a mad thing sometimes, who were other people that they should blame him? His large ox-like eyes, clear in the light of his lamp, turned a scornful defiance on his companion. 'Try it yourself, my fine gentlemen' – that was what the expression of them meant.

'He doesn't only risk his own life,' said George, shortly. 'That's the answer – I say, Macgregor, isn't this the door to the Meadow's Pit? If anything cut us off from the shaft, and supposing we couldn't get round yet by the return, we might have to try it, mightn't we?'

Macgregor assented and George, as he passed, stepped up to the heavy wooden door, and tried one of the keys he held, that he might be sure of opening it in case of need.

The door had been unopened for long, and he shook it backwards and forwards to make the key bite.

Meanwhile Macgregor had lingered a little behind, while Bewick had walked on. Suddenly, above the rattle of the door a cracking noise was heard. A voice of agony rang through the roadway.

'Run, Sir George! Run!'

A rattle like thunder roared through the mine. It was heard at the pithead, and the people crowded there ran hither and thither in dismay, thinking it was another explosion.

Hours passed. At last in George's numbed brain there was a faint stir of consciousness. He opened his eyes slowly.

Oh, horror! Oh, cruelty! To come back from merciful nothingness and peace of this burning anguish, not to be borne, of body and mind. 'I had died,' he thought, 'it was done with.' And a wild impotent rage, as against some brutality done him, surged through him.

A little later he made a first slight movement, which was answered at once by another movement on the part of a man sitting near him. The man bent over him in the darkness and felt for his pulse.

'Bewick!' The whisper was just perceptible.

'Yes, Sir George.'

'What has happened? Where is Macgregor? Give me some brandy – there, in my inner pocket.'

'No. I have it. Can you swallow it? I have tried several times before, but your mouth was set – it ran down my fingers.'

'Give it me.'

Their fingers met, George feeling for the flask. As he moved his arm a groan of anguish broke from him.

'Drink it – if you possibly can.'

George put all the power of his being into the effort to swallow a few drops. Still the anguish! 'Oh God, my back! And the legs – paralysed!'

The words were only spoken in the brain, but it seemed to him that he cried them aloud. For a moment or two the mind swam again; then the brandy began to sting.

He slid down a hand slowly, defying the pain it caused him, to feel his right leg. The trouser round the thigh hung in ribbons, but the fragments lying on the flesh were caked and hard; and beneath him was a pool. His reason worked with difficulty, but clearly. 'Some bad injury to the thigh,' he thought. 'Much bleeding – probably the bleeding had dulled the worst pain. The back and shoulders burnt –.'

Then, in the same hesitating, difficult way he managed to lift his hand to his head, which ached intolerably. The right temple and the hair upon it were also caked and wet.

He let his hand drop, 'How long have I –?' he thought. For already his revived consciousness could hardly maintain itself; something from the black tunnels of the mine seemed to be perpetually pressing out upon it, threatening to drown it like a flood.

'Bewick!' – he felt again with his hand – 'where's Macgregor?'

A sob broke from the darkness beside him.

'Crushed in an instant. I heard one cry. Why not we, too?'

'It was such a bad fall?'

'The whole mine seemed to come down.' George felt the shudder of the huge frame. 'I escaped; you must have caught some of it. Macgregor was right underneath it. But there was an explosion besides.'

'Macgregor's lamp? Broken?' whispered George, after a pause.

'Possibly. It couldn't have been much, or we should have been killed instantly. I was only stunned – a bit scorched, too – not badly. You're the lucky one. I shall die by inches.'

'Cheer up!' said George, faintly. 'I can't last – but they'll find you.'

'What chance for either of us' said Bewick, groaning. 'The return must be blocked, too, or they'd have got round to us by now.'

'How long – ?'

'God knows! To judge by the time I've been sitting since I got you here – it's might long ago.'

'Since you got me here?' repeated George, with feeble interrogation.

'When I came to I was lying with my face in a dampish sort of hollow, and I suppose the afterdamp had lifted a bit, for I could raise my head. I felt you close by. Then I dragged myself on a bit, till I felt some brattice. I got past that, found a dip where the air was better, came back for you, and dragged you here. I thought you were dead at first; then I felt your heart. And since we got here I've found an air-pipe up here along the wall, and broken it.'

George was silent. But the better atmosphere was affecting him somewhat, and consciousness was becoming clearer. Only, what seemed to him a loud noise disturbed him – tortured the wound in his head. Then, gradually, as he bent his mind upon it, he made out what it was – a slow drip or trickle of water from the face of the wall. The contrast between his imagination and the reality supplied him with a kind of measure of the silence that enwrapped them – silence that seemed in itself a living thing, charged with the brooding vengeance of the earth upon the creatures that had been delving at her heart.

'Bewick! That water – maddens me.' He moved his head miserably. 'Could you get some? The brandy flask has a cup.'

'There is a little pool by the brattice. I put my cap in as we got there, and dashed it over you. I'll go again.'

George heard the long limbs drag themselves painfully along. Then he lost count again of time, and all impressions on the ear, till he was roused by the water at his lips and a hand dashing some on his brow.

He drank greedily.

'Thanks! Put it by me – there, that's safe. Now, Bewick, I'm dying, leave me. You can't do anything – and you – you might try for it. There are one or two ways that might be worth trying. Take these keys. I could explain –.'

But the little thread of life wavered terribly as he spoke. Bewick had to put his ear to the scorched lips.

'No,' he said gloomily. 'I don't leave a man while there's any life in him. Besides, there's no chance – I don't know the mine.'

Suddenly, as though answering to the other's despair, a throb of such agony rose in George it seemed to rive body and soul asunder. His poor Letty! His child that was to be! His own energy of life that he had been so conscious of at the very moment of descending to this hideous death – all gone, all done! His little moment of being torn from him by the inexorable force that restores nothing and explains nothing.

A picture flashed into his mind, an etching that he had seen in Paris in a shop window – had seen and pondered over. 'Entombed' was written underneath it, and it showed a solitary miner, on whom the awful trap has fallen, lifting his arms to his face in a last cry against the universe that has brought him into being, that has given him nerve and brain – for this!

Wherever he turned his eyes in the blackness he saw it – the lifted arms, the bare torso of the man, writhing under the agony of realisation – the tools, symbols of a life's toil, lying as they had dropped for ever from the hands that should work no more. It had sent a shudder through him, even amid the gaiety of a Paris street.

Then this first image was swept away by a second. It seemed to him that he was on the pit bank again. It was night, but the crowd was still there, and big fires lighted for warmth threw a glow upon the faces. There were stars, and a pale light of snow on the hills. He looked into the engine-house. There she was – his poor Letty! Oh God! He tried to get through to her, to speak to her. Impossible!

A sound disturbed his dream.

His ear and brain struggled with it – trying to give it a name. A man's long, painful breaths – half sobs, Bewick no doubt, thinking of the woman he loved – of the poor emaciated soul George had seen him tending in the cottage garden on that April day.

He put out his hand and touched his companion.

'Don't despair,' he whispered, 'you will see her again. How strange – we two – were enemies – but this is the end. Tell me about her.'

'I took her from a ruffian who had nearly murdered her and the child,' said the hoarse voice after a pause. 'She was happy – in spite of the drink, in spite of everything – she would have been happy till she died. To think of her alone is too cruel. If people turned their backs on her, I made up.'

'You will see her again,' George repeated, but hardly knowing what the words were he said.

When next he spoke it was with an added strength that astonished his companion.

'Bewick, promise me something. Take a message from me to my wife. Come nearer.'

Then, as he felt his companion's breath on his cheek, he roused himself to speak plainly:

'Tell her – my – love – was all hers – that I thanked her with my whole heart and soul for her love – that it was very hard to leave her – and our child. Write the words for her, Bewick. Tell her it was impossible for me to write, but I dictated this.' He paused for a long time, then resumed. 'And tell her, too — my last wish was — that she should ask Lord and Lady Maxwell — can you hear plainly?' — he repeated the names 'to be her friends and guardians. And bid her ask them — from me — not to forsake her. Have you understood? Will you repeat it?'

Bewick, in the mood of one humouring the whim of the dying, repeated what had been said to him word by word, his own sensuous nature swept the while by the terrors of a death which seemed but one little step farther from himself than from Tressady. Yet he did his best to understand, and recollect; and to the message so printed on his shrinking brain a woman's misery owed its only comfort in the days that followed.

'Thank you,' said Tressady, painfully listening for the last word. 'Give me your hand. Good-bye. You and I — the world's a queer place — I wish I'd turned you back at the pit's mouth. I wanted to show I bore no malice. Well — at least I know —'

The words broke off incoherently. Bewick caught the word 'suffering' and some phrase about 'the men', then Tressady's head slipped back against the wall, and he spoke no more.

Mrs. Humphrey Ward, *Sir George Tressady* (1896)

The Destruction of the Voreaux Mine

For an hour the Voreux remained thus, broken into, as though bombarded by an army of barbarians. There was no more crying out; the enlarged circle of spectators merely looked on. Beneath the piled-up beams of the sifting shed, fractured tipping-cradles could be made out with broken and twisted hoppers. But the rubbish had especially accumulated at the receiving-room, where there had been a rain of bricks, and large portions of wall and masses of plaster had fallen in. The iron scaffold which bore the pulleys had bent, half buried in the pit; a cage was still suspended, a torn cable-end was hanging; then there was a hash of trams, metal plates and ladders. By some chance the lamp cabin remained standing, exhibiting on the left its bright rows of little lamps. And at the end of its disembowelled chamber, the engine could be seen seated squarely on its massive foundation of masonry; its copper was shining and its huge steel limbs seemed to possess indestructible muscles. The enormous crank, bent in the air, looked like the powerful knee of some giant quietly reposing in his strength. After this hour of respite M. Hennebeau's hope began to rise. The movement of the soil must have come to an end, and there would be some chance of saving the engine and the remainder of the buildings. But he wished not to shout and they shouted, with swollen breasts, and arms in the air, before the immense hole which had been hollowed out. This crater was, as of an extinct volcano, fifteen metres deep, extended from the road to the canal for a space of at least forty metres. The whole square of the mine had followed the buildings, the gigantic platforms, the footbridges with their rails, a complete train of trams, three wagons; without counting the wood supply, a forest of cut timber, gulped down like a straw. At the bottom it was only possible to distinguish a confused mass of beams, bricks, iron, plaster, frightful remains, piled up, entangled, soiled in the fury of the catastrophe. And the hole became larger, cracks started from the edges, reaching afar, across the fields. A fissure ascended as far as Rasseneur's bar, and his front wall had cracked. Would the settlement itself pass into it? How far ought they to flee to reach shelter at the end of this abominable day, beneath this leaden cloud which also seemed about to crush the earth?

A cry of pain escaped Négrel. M. Hennebeau, who had drawn back, was in tears. The disaster was not complete; one bank of the canal gave way, and the canal emptied itself like one bubbling sheet through one of the cracks. It disappeared there, falling like a cataract down a deep valley. The mine drank down this river; the galleries would now be submerged for years. Soon the crater was filled and a lake of muddy water occupied the place where once stood the Voreux, like one of those lakes beneath which sleep accursed towns. There was a terrified silence, and nothing now could be heard but the fall of this water rumbling in the bowels of the earth.

Then on the shaken pit-bank Souvarine rose up. He had recognised Maheude and Zacharie sobbing before this downfall. They would not yet allow anyone to approach, considering another half hour's patience desirable. This waiting became unbearable; the hope increased the anguish, and all hearts were beating quickly. A dark cloud, growing large at the horizon, hastened the twilight, a sinister dayfall over this wreck of earth's tempest. Since seven o'clock they had been there without moving or eating.

And suddenly, as the engineers were cautiously advancing, a supreme convulsion of the soil put them to flight. Subterranean detonations broke out; a whole monstrous artillery was cannonading in the gulf. At the surface, the last buildings were tipped over and crushed. At first a sort of whirlwind carried away the rubbish from the sifting-shed and the receiving-room. Next, the boiler buildings burst and disappeared. Then it was the low square tower, where the pumping-engine was groaning, which fell on its face like a man mown down by a bullet. And then a terrible thing was seen; the engine, dislocated from its massive foundation, with broken limbs was struggling against death. It moved, it straightened its crank, its giant's knee, as though to rise; but, crushed and swallowed up; it was dying. The chimney alone, thirty metres high, still remained standing, though shaken, like a mast in the tempest. It was thought that it would be crushed to fragments and fly to powder, when suddenly it sank in one block, drunk down by the earth, melted like a colossal candle; and nothing was left, not even the point of the lightening conductor. It was done for. The evil beast crouching in this hole, gorged with human flesh, was no longer breathing with its thick long respiration. The Voreaux had been swallowed whole by the abyss.

The crowd rushed away yelling. The women hid their eyes as they ran. Terror drove the men along like a pile of dry leaves, the weight to which was so heavy on the heads of the wretches who were in agony beneath. And he threw down his last cigarette; he went away, without looking back, into the now dark night. Afar his shadow diminished and mingled with the darkness. He was going over there, to the unknown. He was going tranquilly to extermination, wherever there may be dynamite to blow up towns and men. He will be there, without doubt, when the middle class in agony shall hear the pavement of the streets bursting up beneath their feet.

Emile Zola, *Germinal* (from the edition translated by Havelock Ellis, 1894 and revised in 1933)

Entombed

The hours succeeded one another, all equally black; but they were not able to measure their exact duration, becoming ever more vague in their calculation of time. Their tortures, which might have been expected to lengthen the minutes, rapidly bore them away. They thought that they had only been shut up for two days and a night, when in reality the third day had already come to an end. All hope of help had gone; no one knew they were there, no one could come down to them. And hunger would finish them off if the inundation spared them. For one last time it occurred to them to beat the call, but the stone was lying beneath the water. Besides, who would hear them?

Catherine was leaning her aching head against the seam, when she sat up with a start. 'Listen!' she said.

At first Étienne thought she was speaking of the low noise of the ever-rising water. He lied in order to quiet her.

'It's me you hear; I'm moving my legs.'

'No, no; not that! Over there, listen!'

And she placed her ear to the coal. He understood, and did likewise. They waited for some seconds, with stifled breath. Then, very far away and very weak, they heard three blows at long intervals. But they still doubted; their ears were ringing; perhaps it was the cracking of the soil. And they knew not what to strike with in answer.

'You have the sabots. Take them off and strike with the heels.'

She struck, beating the miner's call; and they listened and again distinguished the three blows far off. Twenty times over they did it, and twenty times the blows replied. They wept and embraced each other, at the risk of losing their balance. At last the mates were there, they were coming. An overflowing joy and love carried away the torments of expectation and the rage of their vain appeals, as though their rescuers had only to split the rock with a finger to deliver them.

'Eh!' she cried merrily; 'wasn't it lucky that I leant my head?'

'Oh, you've got an ear!' he said in his turn, 'now, I heard nothing.'

From that moment they relieved each other, one of them always listening, ready to answer at the least signal. They soon caught the sounds of the pick; the work of approaching them was beginning, a gallery was being opened. But their joy sank. In vain they laughed to deceive each other; despair was gradually seizing them. At first they entered into long explanations; evidently they were being approached from Requillart. The gallery descended in the bed; perhaps several were being opened, for there were always three men hewing. Then they talked less, and were at last silent when they came to calculate the enormous mass which separated them from their mates. They continued their reflections in silence, counting the days and days that a workman would take to penetrate such a block. They would never be reached soon enough; they would have time to die twenty times over. And no longer venturing to exchange a word in this redoubled anguish, they gloomily replied to the appeals by a roll of the sabots, without hope, only retaining the mechanical need to tell the others that they were still alive.

Thus passed a day, two days. They had been at the bottom six days. The water had stopped at their knees, neither rising nor falling, and their legs seemed to be melting away in this icy bath. They could certainly keep them out for an hour or so, but their position then became so uncomfortable that they were twisted by horrible cramps, and were obliged to let their feet fall in again. Every ten minutes they hoisted themselves back by a jerk on the slippery rock. The fractures of the coal struck into their spines, and they felt at the back of their necks a fixed intense pain, through having to keep constantly bent in order to avoid striking their heads. And their suffocation increased; the air, driven back by the water, was compressed into a sort of bell, in which they were shut up. Their voices were muffled, and seemed to come from afar. Their ears began to buzz, they heard the peals of a furious tocsin, the tramp of a flock beneath a storm of hail, going on unceasingly.

At first Catherine suffered horribly from hunger. She pressed her poor shrivelled hands against her breasts, her breathing was deep and hollow, a continuous tearing moan, as though tongs were tearing her stomach.

Étienne, choked by the same torture, was feeling feverishly round him in the darkness, when his fingers came upon a half-rotten piece of timber, which his nails could crumble. He gave a handful of it to the putter, who swallowed it greedily. For two days they lived on this worm-eaten wood, devouring it all, in despair when it was finished, grazing their hands in the effort to crush the other planks which were still solid with resisting fibres. Their tortures increased, and they were enraged that they could not chew the cloth of their clothes. A leather girdle, which he wore round the waist relieved them a little. He bit small pieces from it with his teeth, and she chewed them, and endeavoured to swallow them. This occupied their jaws, and gave them the illusion of eating. Then, when the girdle was finished, they went back to their clothes, sucking them for hours.

But soon these violent crises subsided; hunger became only a low deep ache with the slow progressive languor of their strength. No doubt they would have succumbed if they had not had as much water as they desired. They merely bent down and drank from the hollow of the hand, and that very frequently, parched by a thirst which all this water could not quench.

After that there was nothing more. Étienne was seated on the ground, always in the same corner, and Catherine was lying motionless on his knees. Hours and hours passed by. For a long time he thought she was sleeping; then he touched her. She was very cold; she was dead.

He did not move her, however, for fear of arousing her. The idea that he was the first who had possessed her as a woman, and that she might be pregnant, filled him with tenderness. Other ideas, the desire to go away with her, joy at what they would both do later on, came to him at moments, but so vaguely that it seemed only as though his forehead had been touched by a breath of sleep. He grew weaker, he only had strength to make a little gesture, a slow movement of the hand, to assure himself that she was certainly there, like a sleeping child in her frozen stiffness. Everything was being annihilated; the night itself had disappeared, and he was nowhere, out of space, out of time. Something was certainly striking beside his head, violent blows were approaching him; but he had been too lazy to reply, benumbed by immense fatigue; and now he knew nothing, he only dreamed that she was walking before him, and that he heard the slight clank of her sabots. Two days passed; she had not stirred; he touched her with his mechanical gesture, reassured to find her so quiet.

Étienne felt a shock. Voices were sounding, rocks were rolling to his feet. When he perceived a lamp he wept. His blinking eyes followed the light, he was never tired of looking at it, enraptured by this reddish point which scarcely stained the darkness. But

George Sampson

some mates carried him away, and he allowed them to introduce some spoonfuls of soup between his clenched teeth. It was only in the Requillart gallery that he recognised some-one standing before him, the engineer, Négrel; and these two men, who felt contempt for each other – the rebellious workman and the sceptical master – threw themselves on each other's necks, and sobbed loudly in the deep upheaval of all the humanity within them. It was an immense sadness, the misery of generations, the extremity of grief to which life can fall.

Emile Zola, *Germinal* (from the edition translated by Havelock Ellis, 1894 and revised in 1933)

Hermann Kätelhön

The Hartley Calamity

The Hartley men are noble, and
  Ye'll hear a tale of woe;
I'll tell the doom of the Hartley men –
  The year of sixty-two.

'Twas on a Thursday morning, on
  The first month of the year,
When there befell the thing that well
  May rend the heart to hear.

Ere chanticleer with music rare
  Awakes the old homestead,
The Hartely men are up and off
  To earn their daily bread.

On, on they toil; with heat they broil,
  And streams of sweat still glue
The stour into their skins, till they
  Are black as the coal they hew.

Now to and fro, the putters go
  The waggons to and fro,
And clang on clang of wheel and hoof
  Ring in the mine below.

The din and strife of human life
  Awake in 'wall' and 'board',
When lo! a shock is felt which makes
  Each human heart-beat heard.

Each bosom thuds, as each his duds
  He snatches and away,
And to the distant shaft he flees
  With all the speed he may.

Each, all, they fell-by two-by three
  They seek the shaft, to seek

An answer in each other's face,
   To what they may not speak.

'Are we entombed?' they seem to ask,
   For the shaft is closed, and no
Escape have they to God's bright day
   From out the night below.

So stand in pain the Hartley men,
   And o'er them speed'ly comes
The memory of home and all
   That links us to our homes.

Despair at length renews their strength
   And they the shaft must clear,
And soon the sound of mall and pick,
   Half drowns the voice of fear.

And hark! to the blow of the mall below
   Do sounds above reply?
Hurra, hurra, for the Hartley men
   For now their rescue's nigh.

Their rescue nigh? The sounds of joy
   And hope have ceased, and ere
A breath is drawn a rumble's heard
   Re-drives them to despair.

Together, now behold them bow;
   Their burden'd souls unload
In cries that never rise in vain
   Unto the living God.

Whilst yet they kneel, again they feel
   Their strength renew'd – again
The swing and the ring of the mall attests
   The might of the Hartley men.

And hark, to the blow of the mall below
   Do sounds above reply?

Hurra, hurra, for the Hartley men
  For now their rescue's nigh.

But lo! you light, erewhile so bright
  No longer lights the scene;
A cloud of mist you light have kiss'd
  And shorn it of its sheen.

A cloud of mist you light have kiss'd,
  See! how along it steals,
Till one by one the lights are smote,
  And deep the gloom prevails.

'O father, till the shaft is rid,
  Close, close beside me keep;
My eye-lids are together glued,
  And I – and I – must sleep.'

'Sleep, darling, sleep, and I will keep
  Close by – Heigh-ho! – To keep
Himself awake the father strives –
  But he – he too – must sleep,

'O, brother, till the shaft is rid
  Close, close beside me keep
My eye-lids are together glued
  And I – and I – must sleep.'

'Sleep, brother, sleep, and I will keep
  Close by – Heigh-ho! – To keep
Himself awake the brother strives –
  But he – he too – must sleep.

'O, mother dear! wert, wert thou near
  Whilst I sleep!' – and the orphan slept;
And all night long by the black pit-heap
  The mother's dumb watch kept.

And fathers, and mothers, and sisters and brothers –
  The lover and the new-made bride –

A vigil kept for those who slept,
　From eve to morning tide.

But they slept – still sleep – in silence dread,
　Two hundred old and young,
To awake when heaven and earth have sped
　And the last dread trumpet sung!

Joseph Skipsey, *Poems.* (1952)

The poem refers to a disaster that occurred on January 6th 1862 when the shaft of the Hartley mine was blocked by a fallen beam and two hundred and four colliers were entombed (Lloyd, 1952)

Bringing Out the Dead

Out of the reeking shaft the great cage came
Bearing the broken bodies of the dead,
A clanging, creeking, grinding iron frame
That swayed and thudded on the black pit-head.

Officials scurried to and fro, afraid,
Rugs and stretchers waited, cars were prepared,
First-aid for men beyond all reach of aid,
Such are for those who neither knew nor cared.

Even the little pit-sparrows were hushed,
Those poor, lost things that haunt an old pit-top,
Even they sensed something and sat crushed
As the great cage came slowly to a stop.

They craned their necks and shook their ragged wings.
Watching the cage lift up again and fall,
They could not understand, those little things,
The cruel, brutal heartbreak of it all.

Frederick C. Boden, *Out of the Coalfields* (1929)

A Pit Funeral

For two days and nights before the funeral of Geordie and Willie it snowed continuously, and lay — an unprecedented event in the living history of Hagger. So thick was the fall, in fact, that it was quite impossible to use a cart and a troop of pit-ponies to take the coffins in the usual way to the graveyard. Instead, the horse breaker's sledge was brought into action, though few people recognised it as such. It made no noise at all as it glided over the snow, whereas, when it was serving its proper purpose and dashing up and down the street with a wild pit-pony attached, people knew it at once by the hellish clatter.

Funerals were very popular in Hagger. Youngsters were brought up to attend them, being taken there first in the arms of their mothers and then dragged there by the hand and shoved forward to look into the hole among a crowd of hysterical women. 'Look at the last of him, hinnie,' they would blubber to the bairns; and the latter would peer over the perilous brink, dropping pieces of coal on the lid as a sort of parting gift — and a very appropriate one too. As everybody in the village seemed to be related and as there were so many deaths at the pit, the Haggerites were always going to funerals. Every one of them had to have a funeral outfit; for there was no sharing of bowlers and black coats as for occasional funerals in the work outside. Every man considered it his duty to be present at every funeral, and the same applied to the women and children.

The funeral of Geordie and Willie was a really great event. Within living memory there had never been two such remarkable deaths of two such remarkable characters. People were used to disasters at the pit and strings of coffins afterwards, but here was something out of the ordinary, something really fresh to think and gossip about, a relief to the monotony of death down below. Of course, there were always plenty of suicides. But it was always girls and women who committed suicide, and in any case they were secret sorts of affairs which it was thought proper to hush up and forget about as soon as possible. And the old dregs in the back kitchens often went to sleep over a blazing fire and doddered into it, or clumsily let their aprons get alight, taking a kettle off. But they were only old dregs, unknown, half-buried, spinning out their lives in pampered senility, and no one cared very much when their charred bones were bundled out of sight. What was the fiery end of an old hag compared with that of Willie on the heaps?

A couple of dozen stalwart pit-lads dragged the coffins along the street. They were followed by a long procession of mourners. It was not a silent procession by any means. People coughed and snivelled, clapped their hands and stamped their feet in the biting cold. At odd intervals there were bands, or bits of bands. Here and there somebody played an evangelical tune on a concertina; a man who had lost his band blared away on a trumpet; little groups started singing different hymns with crazy emotion; religious maniacs yelled their warnings, waving their placards from side to side, as if they were mortal drunk; Salvation Army lasses banged their tambourines and screamed, their bodies swaying with a croon-like rhythm as they danced from toe to toe; somebody slipped and fell, cursing, and there followed a second of silence more profound than a bird-roost at sunset; and up and down the flanks of this long procession scampered a horde of repulsive mongrels yelping like the damned.

Next to the coffins came the relatives. Ailie never knew the Shieldykes had so many relatives until now; and how anxious they were to make known their kinship, and to take a conspicuous place in the front of the procession! Nor had she realised until now how many very dear friends Geordie and Willie had had, most of who she had hardly seen before. They also wanted to occupy prominent positions. Certainly she had never heard either Geordie or Willie mention these relatives and friends, but she understood their despicable motives and turned a deaf ear to their impertinent introductions. Of course, the ministers were there – Chapel, Church, Catholic – strutting along in front of everyone, like drill-sergeants instructing a raw mob how they should dress, walk, distort their features, sigh and generally conduct themselves at funerals.

Tradesmen came in force, for advertisement; but deep annoyance at having lost two valuable customers was plainly written on each face. The publicans gave the procession its one big splash of richness, both as regards attire and complexion; but they too were cursing the fact that they had lost, in Willie, a client of immeasurable worth. The stewards and office-bearers of the Chapel were very much in evidence, of course. They claimed the two Shieldykes body and soul now that they were dead. The Salvation Army followed in a very large body, for it was at such emotional events as funerals and disasters that they made so many captures. Next came representatives or members of the various organisations to which the two men belonged: such so-called benevolent institutions as the Most Noble and Venerable Order of the Nag's Head, complete with regalia, the Band of Hope, the Cadets of Sobriety and the Rechabites. These last three claiming them as former members and generously overlooking the failings of manhood, in the interest of publicity; Bolam's Bank, a local savings business which paid out once a year amid wild enthusiasm followed by a night of appalling drunkenness; the Hagger Black Watch and the Wesleyan Sunday School Football Clubs; the Haggar Prize Bank, with a child in front carrying a huge silver cup; innumerable societies connected with the pit, to which the deceased had subscribed faithfully for years so that one or two of their fellow-workers could give up work and become gentlemen of leisure in the Parliament down south; a miscellaneous collection of clubs – Leek, Onion, Celery, Canary, Pigeon, Whippet, Quoit, Bowling, Pitch-and-Toss, Domino, Card, Christmas, Slate and so on. Every one of these organisations had its huge, square banner – a hideous, gaudy, pictorial representation of its activities or functions held aloft on two poles, with two men in front and two behind grasping the tasselled ropes. And whenever a gust of wind swept down the street, the standard-bearers reeled and floundered from pavement to pavement as if drunk beyond the dreams of a drunkard.

Hundreds of women and children flocked along, a ragged unseemly mob, jabbering, weeping, screaming in the filthy ecstasy of emotional curiosity. With their black shawls flying in the wind, they resembled a flock of vultures crowding towards a rotten carcass. After them came probably the most sincere and respectable group of mourners – those steady life-long friends, those plain, unostentatious pitmen, whose banner could never be discerned because it fluttered in their hearts.

Halfway up the street, the colliery manager with some of his staff joined the procession. He wore a top hat and frock coat, and looked terribly out of place – an alien in manner and dress who had just drifted into the village. He had the appearance of a total stranger and knew it, for his face had that nervous puzzled expression of a newcomer in a bewilderingly-different society. That expression gave way in time to one of fearful agitation, and he looked for all the world like a French aristocrat being led by the mob to the scaffold.

There were many other mourners not in the procession. Grinning bairns, with the knowledge of men of the world, were strung on dilapidated palings and ruined walls, chewing stalks; and out from the shadows of sheds and closets, rotten unnameable sinners peered with eyes like kestrels', dishing up in their minds again the filthy deeds of the past. Gliding and sliding from cover to cover, these self-banished creatures resembled a screen of scouts covering a convoy which had in its care a body precious to them even in death. And there were many girls and women who were absent and yet vividly present in thought. Many of the girls who screened the coal at the pit, sorting and filling sacks, cared little for their work when the sounds of the procession reached them, for they could think of nothing but Willie's beautiful body and his stupendously original wiles. Some of them, too, could not help thinking how fat their own bellies and bosoms were growing. All over the village, in fact, lasses peppered with artificial pearls or bespatted with coaly slime were standing in silent sorrow and wondering, not without a throb of pleasure, why they did not fall, or, fallen and childless, how great was their luck.

The two bodies were buried in a hole that looked terribly black in contrast with the surrounding snow. Not that the snow was virgin white; it looked as if someone had gone round everywhere with a huge castor and sprinkled the surface with black pepper. And here and there, especially on the heaps, there were ugly black rents, as if the white decomposed skin of the earth had burst, revealing the hard black blood which men valued so greatly nowadays and which had once been the green blood of fierce, surging, primitive life. And the rents also released that typical pit-village stench which the snow had collected and kept beneath its surface – a mixture of gas, garbage, smoke-fumes and offal.

The Chapel minister was in great glee at the honour that had come his way. As he ranted, he kept glancing at his two great competitors, gloating over their silence and scoffing at them with his eyes. He talked of nothing but blood. Blood alone would wash away people's sins and make them white as snow. They could only reach salvation through the blood of the Lamb. Blood, blood, blood – the air became stinking and clammy with it, and the listeners wallowed in murderous, blood-thirsty emotions. He hissed out his bloody metaphors, almost disembowelling himself in order to illustrate his arguments. Then everybody sang a hymn with great enthusiasm, leaving Geordie and Willie 'safe in the arms of Jesus'. Immediately afterwards came the flop of earth on the coffins, and, in a short while, the slithery slap of the spades on the long, narrow mound. The mob swarmed round to lay their wreaths or to read the tickets on the wreaths, fighting and cursing in the process. The women were particularly keen to read the little cards. They wanted to know all about each wreath, who had given it, and the most important point of all, why. If the name was a Christian name, and particularly a female one, they gloated over it like a cloud of bluebottles, taking it away in their memories so that they could feast their depraved imaginations upon it for weeks and months to come. People waved their black-hemmed handkerchiefs to one another whenever they discovered something especially suspicious, so that they could all gather together and nudge one another and exchange their nasty knowing glances.

Suddenly a band began to play, then another; not funeral dirges but lively exhilarating tunes. Even the Salvation Army forgot itself to the extent of indulging in a frivolous jaunty air. And as soon as the people heard the bands begin, they ran away after them like a great crowd of children. The funeral was forgotten. People were singing very different songs now and laughing uproariously. Even before they had left the graveyard, the men began to snowball one another. Someone was hit in the face and let out a terrible word which set everybody smiling. After all, people could not take funerals very seriously in Hagger: there were so many of them, life was relatively cheap and they were so used to them. To forget them was undoubtedly the wisest thing to do. And to keep their wits they had to forget a great many things, besides funerals, in Hagger.

The ministers and those leech-like principal mourners did not disperse at once. They hung around for an invitation to the usual funeral feast. And being a thoroughbred Haggerite, Ailie had made all arrangements for this disgusting orgy – it always ended that way even if it began on tea and cake. Then they followed her out of the graveyard, boisterous, insinuating, like a mob of sycophants.

That night, very late, a weird black form could be seen every now and then clambering over the wall at the far end of the graveyard. As the form slid down from the top of the wall, the blackness seemed to unfold and reveal momentarily a cloud lining of white. Then it moved quickly to the grave, stopped, returned again to the wall and disappeared. Another form would come and go, sometimes two, even three. They did not speak. They did not appear to see one another. The night concealed their identity. They were secure in the night. That was why they came in the night, perhaps.

They were the girls who frequented the heaps, soberly dressed tonight, save for what the wall revealed – the dainty extravagant underwear – as they scrambled over it. They did not mind showing their long lovely white limbs tonight in the graveyard, because Willie was there. Of course it was because of him that they had come. Somehow they felt they could not let his burial pass without showing their respect for him. He had been their king and they had been his concubines. He wasn't Solomon, he didn't appear in the Book of Books, and yet the relationship was the same and sanctified only in a less lyrical degree, for Willie did not write songs. They brought little tokens with them to lay on the grave – curious evergreens with the Bottles, with their usual commercial foresight, and brought from the city, bunches of rank blossoms that resembled weeds, and in many cases artificial flowers and fruits stripped from some Sunday hat. Secretly, silently, swiftly, they laid their wreaths on the mound of earth and shrank away into the night. Of the vast procession that had gone before, they alone had known the utter depths of humility and love. They alone could measure and recall whatever acts of compassion Willie may have done in the dark ungodly drama of his life.

J. C. Grant, *The Back to Backs* (1930)

After the Funeral

The really important business of a funeral comes after the burial of the corpse. The actual ceremony of burial has something exciting about it. It is a popular event, like going to a wedding or a christening. Something is definitely accomplished, in accordance with custom and the law: the body is placed in a box, taken to a hole and buried there. After the feast, the funeral as such is over and done with: people turn to the future, especially the next of kin, and the corpse is only dragged out again in connection with its bearing on the future. The dead are dead, but the living must live; and how to live is the problem that immediately confronts them as soon as the blinds are raised and the windows opened to purge the house of the scent of death.

Ailie was faced with tremendous difficulties, obvious to everyone. The two wage-earners of the household had gone, and with them, all her income. She should have to look around for a job to keep herself and Tom. To begin with, however, she had to investigate the affairs of the husband and his father, left, as they were, as if death had never crossed their minds. Fortunately, there were certain sums payable by certain benevolent assurance institutions on the death of each of them. That about covered the cost of the funeral, including the feast. Then certain savings clubs had to shell out reluctantly. But Geordie had saved quite a tidy sum which he was in the habit of accumulating in such receptacles as baking powder and cocoa tins, scribbling the amounts on the lids and stowing them away in an old black chest. Of course, he had never made a will. Death, even where death was a continual occurrence and terribly imminent, was a thing to be blotted out of the mind altogether in Hagger, and old stagers like Geordie had been brought up to disregard it completely. Life otherwise would have been quite impossible. So, for some time ahead, she and Tom felt comparatively secure, but she realised, nevertheless, that sooner or later their little capital would come to an end and that work must be found.

It was almost exciting going through the belongings of Geordie and Willie. They had collected so many queer things, especially Willie, that she blushed often enough when she laid them bare to her prying eyes. Several of Willie's pockets contained filthy relics of his lustfulness, and Geordie had collected an extraordinary number of rupture belts in the hope, no doubt, of obtaining the relief promised by advertisements. There were letters too, which she read with sorrow or disgust; screaming epistles from girls with unborn children or pathetic notes from Jane to Geordie in the early days of their compulsory courtship. Everything was cruelly revealed. She felt sorry for the dead, even in their secret dirtiness. Faint signs of unexpected ambitions in fields beyond the craft of the pit; of intentions to deal generously and kindly with those for whom they appeared to have nothing but hatred and contempt, even glimmerings of a yearning after the beauty of religion. She saw these and treasured them, treasured them far more than the long watch-chain which Geordie had promised her when he died and which lay now on the table like a heap of battered coins. Every link on that chain had a medal fastened to it; medals for football, bowling, whippets, leeks and all the numerous activities of his life from beginning to end. It was a record of his simple success, and how proud he was of it. Whenever he wore it across his great belly, his stature seemed to increase and his carriage become almost arrogant. He loved to hear the medals tinkling one against the other. And nothing pleased him better than to watch the eyes of people, as they spoke to him, gazing with awe at the pit of his stomach.

She had one or two humiliating duties to perform. On several nights following the funeral, women with their features hidden in shawls would come to her with long tales of woe or threats of blackmail. Sometimes they were accompanied by a child in arms or a great clumsy lad whose features were unmistakable. Willie had always supplied them with money because of – well – then they would nod significantly at the bundle in their arms or the lad alongside. Ailie understood. She sympathised with them. But her settlement was a final one: she had made that perfectly clear. There was no such thing as blackmail in Hagger; everybody knew everybody else's business. She gave them some of Geordie's savings and some of Willie's clothes, and they came to her no more.

J. C. Grant, *The Back to Backs* (1930)

Masters and Men

Theophile Steinlen

George Bissill

One of Our Directors

'"Tis neither as you think, nor as you think, nor as you think.' Hiero-nimo's words in the play kept running in my head, as I thought about it. The hour was that sluggish one in the afternoon which does not favour illusion, the scene – Black Horse Pit offices. I had gone back there, after a long morning's surveying underground, in a dead stupid mood, not at all inclined for plotting the survey – a tiresome task. But, as I went past the window, fumbling in my pocket for the latch-key, something unusual inside it attracted me. A patch or disc of coppery-red, above a greyish figure, was distinctly to be seen through the window, though I did not expect any visitor. By some Friar's Goose recast, I concluded the mysterious intruder to be the 'Marquis of Plaws', as we called the latest addition to our Black Horse Directors. What could have brought him there, and how had he got into the office? He had never been near the place before, and I had left the office locked up on going to lunch.

Imagine my bewilderment, then, on entering the door to find the office empty. The only living thing was the fire in the grate, and even that was smouldering. Before falling to upon my survey, I looked round again for any patch of red and grey to explain the delusion. There was absolutely nothing to account for it; and the 'Marquis' soon slipped out of my mind.

For about an hour I worked away steadily. Then a heavy step made me look up. A big, read-headed man went past the window, and entered the door which I had left open, and without ceremony made his way in. It was the 'Marquis of Plaws'.

'Um, ah!' he said. 'You are not the man I wanted to see!' The voice was well-bred but meagre for so burly a man, and it had a guttural roughening of some words so that 'not' sounded almost like 'nghot'.

The title of 'Marquis' was only a sobriquet. Mr. Headley of Plaws was his real name; but however he came by it, the nickname suited him extravagantly. It was not derisive; it pointed to something in his manner, born of the old standing of his family, and the immense new wealth he had brought to it. When 'the Marquis' was spoken of, we felt sure of something piquant; for he attracted rumours as a sunflower attracts small flies. His big, handsome red head seized on people's fancy much as the curl of Disraeli, or the nose of Cyrano de Bergerac, had done. And indeed there is an uncanny attraction about the colour red, which suggests blood, fire and roses, and affects alike the bull in the pasture and the servant-girl lured by a red-coat.

'Mr. Fish?' I stammered; 'he is not here, my lo–' In my confusion I was going to say my lord Marquis.

'Mr. Headley of Plaws,' he corrected, with a not displeased smile, marching in and sitting down in the chair where I had seen his phantom red head an hour before. He wore a grey coat and buff riding breeches: I noticed that his legs were rather spindle-shanked for so big a man. He was riding by and thought he would like to have 'a look at the pit!' as he explained.

Sitting there, he took an inquisitive interest in the survey on the table, and the adjacent pens and blotting-paper. He picked up a pencil I had been using – a J-pencil to which I was fondly attached, with which I wrote rhymes on the sly – and put it in his pocket.

Thereupon he got up, and said, looking at his watch, 'I've barely half an hour – there is just time to show me over the place.'

He did not want to go below ground. To the pit-head accordingly I escorted him, and there the heap-keeper, Hollover, had the pleasure of reminding the 'Marquis' that he had been ostler's boy at the Plaws racing-stables thirty years ago.

The 'Marquis' did not stay long, but he was inquisitive, and had a curious way of testing things with the horn handle of his riding-stock. He left me with a sharp impression of the alert brain housed under his close-cropped red hair and bowler hat.

Ernest Rhys, *The Black Horse Pit* (1925)

Morel and the Manager

Authority was hateful to him, therefore he could only abuse the pit-managers. He would say, in the Palmerston:

'Th' gaffer come down to our stall this morning, an' 'e says, "You know, Walter this 'ere'll not do. What about those props?" An' I says to him, "Why what art talkin' about? What d'st mean about th' props? It'll never do this 'ere," he says, "You'll be havin' th' roof in, one o' these days." An' I says, "Tha'd better stan' on a bit o' clunch then, an' hold it up wi' thy 'ead." So 'e wor that mad, 'e cussed an' 'e swore an' t'other chaps they did laugh!'

Morel was a good mimic. He imitated the manager's fat, squeaky voice, with its attempt at good English.

'I shan't have it, Walter. Who knows more about it, me or you?'

'So I says, "I've niver fun out how much tha' knows, Alfred, it'll 'appen carry thee ter bed an' back."'

So Morel would go on to the amusement of his boon companions, and some of this would be true. The pit-manager was not an educated man. He had been a boy along with Morel, so that, while the two disliked each other, they more or less took each other for granted.

But Alfred Charlesworth did not forgive the butty these public-house sayings.

Consequently, although Morel was a good miner, sometimes earning as much as five pounds a week when he married, he came gradually to have worse and worse stalls, where the coal was thin, and hard to get, and unprofitable.

D. H. Lawrence, *Sons and Lovers* (1913)

The Manager

Mr. Robbins was one of the last of the 'old guard' of managers, rough as the rough life in which he had been born and bred. A pitman who had sometimes shared in the hectic sports; had taken to mining science, got his 'ticket' and his colliery. A pitman first, and a mining engineer a long way behind. He knew the pit and its people from A to Z, for he was the fibre of both.

He lived in a good sized house standing by itself on the fell, keeping a little reserve, and a certain 'distance' between him and the men.

But he knew everybody, their family records, their personal characteristics – and on the quiet he had an occasional drink with some of the older men.

Jack Lawson, *Under the Wheels* (1934)

It's Fine Tae Keep in Wi' The Gaffer

For many a year ha'e worked doon alow,
But never in bits that are wet or are low,
For I mak' it my business wherever I go,
Aye tae keep in wi' the gaffer.
  Oh! It's fine tae keep in wi' the gaffer.

I wasna' lang started till plain I could see
That some had it easy as easy as could be,
So I thocht tae mysel' that the best thing for me
Was tae try and keep in wi' the gaffer.
  Oh! It's fine tae keep in wi' the gaffer.

My boss at the time was a Mason, ye ken,
So I went tae the bank for my seven pounds ten,
And bravely I bearded the goat in its den,
A' tae keep in wi' the gaffer.
  Oh! It's fine tae keep in wi' the gaffer.
The next ane tae come was a musical hand,
He stood in the middle and waggled the wand,
So I learned the cornet and played in his band,
A' tae keep in wi' the gaffer.
  Oh! It's fine tae keep in wi' the gaffer.
The next was a cratur o' different stamp,
A high heid cadet in the Salvation camp,

So I got him tae 'save' me, and I carried the lamp,
A' tae keep in wi' the gaffer.
  Oh! It's fine tae keep in wi' the gaffer.

The next was a punter – a horse-racin' man,
So I bocht the *Noon Record* and followed his plan;
And I finished it up wi' my shirt in the pawn,
A 'tae keep in wi' the gaffer.
  Oh! It's fine tae keep in wi' the gaffer.

Tae the lad wi' ambition I gi'e this advice,
Nae maitter who say, tae the gaffer be nice,
Jist work tae his orders and never think twice,
For it pays to keep in wi' the gaffer.

Joe Corrie, *The Image O' God and Other Poems* (1937)

Stacks Gate

The car was rising towards Stacks Gate. The rain was holding off, and in the air came a queer pellucid gleam of May. The country rolled away in long undulations, south towards the Peak, east towards Mansfield and Nottingham. Connie was travelling south.

As she rose on to the high country, she could see on her left, on a height above the rolling land the shadowy, powerful bulk of Warsop Castle, dark grey with below it the reddish plastering of miner's dwellings, newish, and below those the plumes of dark smoke and white steam from the great colliery which put so many thousand pounds per annum into the pockets of the Duke and other share holders. The powerful old castle was a ruin, yet still it hung its bulk on the low skyline, over the black plumes and the white that waved on the damp air below.

A turn, and they ran on to the high level to Stacks Gate. Stacks Gate, as seen from the high road, was just a huge and gorgeous new hotel, The Coningsby Arms, standing red and white and gilt in barbarous isolation off the road. But if you looked, you saw on the left rows of handsome 'modern' dwellings, set down like a game of dominoes, with spaces and gardens, a queer game of dominoes that some weird 'master' were playing on the surprised earth. And beyond these blocks of dwellings, at the back, rose all the astonishing and frightening overhead erections of a really modern mine, chemical works and long galleries, enormous and of shapes not before known to man. The head-stocks and pit-bank of the mine itself were insignificant among the huge new installations. And in front of this, the game of dominoes stood forever in a sort of surprise, waiting to be played.

This was Stacks Gate, new on the face of the earth, since the war. But as a matter of fact, though even Connie did not know it, downhill half a mile below the 'hotel' was old Stacks Gate, with a little old colliery and blackish old brick dwellings, and a chapel or two and a shop or two and a little pub or two.

But that didn't count any more. The vast plumes of smoke and vapour rose from the new works up above, and this was now Stacks Gate: no chapels, no pubs, even no shops. Only the great 'works', which are the modern Olympia with temples to all the gods; then the model dwellings; then the hotel. The hotel in actuality was nothing but a miners' pub, though it looked first-classy.

Even since Connie's arrival at Wragby this new place had arisen on the face of the earth, and the model dwellings had filled with riff-raff drifting in from anywhere, to poach Clifford's rabbits among other occupations.

D. H. Lawrence, *Lady Chatterley's Lover* (1929) Paris Edition

Jan Toorop

Shipley

Connie called for a moment at Shipley. The park gates, at the back, opened just near the level crossing of the Colliery railway; the Shipley colliery itself stood just beyond the trees. The gates stood open, because through the park was a right of way that the colliers used. They hung around the park. The car passed the ornamental ponds, in which the colliers threw their newspapers, and took the private drive to the house. It stood above, aside, a very pleasant stucco building from the middle of the eighteenth century. It had a beautiful alley of yew trees, that had approached an older house, and the hall stood serenely spread out, winking its Georgian panes as if cheerfully.

Behind there were really beautiful gardens.

Connie liked the interior much better than Wragby. It was much lighter, more alive, shapen and elegant. The rooms were panelled with creamy-painted panelling, the ceilings were touched with gilt, and everything was kept in exquisite order, all the appointments were perfect, regardless of expense. Even the corridors managed to be ample and lovely, softly curved and full of life.

But Leslie Winter was alone. He had adored his house. But his park was bordered by three of his own collieries. He had been a generous man in his ideas. He had almost welcomed the colliers in his park. Had the miners not made him rich! So, when he saw the gangs of unshapely men lounging by his ornamental waters — not on the private part of the park, no, he drew the line there — he would say: 'The miners are perhaps not so ornamental as deer, but they are far more profitable.'

But that was in the golden — monetarily — latter half of Queen Victoria's reign. Miners were then 'good working men'. Winter had made this speech, half apologetic, to his guest, the then Prince of Wales. And the Prince had replied in his rather gutteral English: 'You are quite right. If there were coal under Sandringham I would open a mine on the lawns, and think it first rate landscape gardening. Oh I am quite willing to exchange roe deer for colliers, at the price. Your men are good men too, I hear.'

However, the Prince had been a King, and the King had died, and now there was another King, whose chief function seemed to be to open soup kitchens.

And the good working men were somehow hemming Shipley in. New mining villages crowded on the park, and the Squire felt somehow that the population was alien. He used to feel, in a good natured, but quite grand way, lord of his own domain and of his own colliers. Now by a subtle pervasion of the new sprit, he had somehow been pushed out. It was he who did not belong any more. There was no mistaking it. The mines — the industry — had a will of its own, and this will was against the gentleman owner. All the colliers took part in the will, and it was hard to live up against it. It either shoved you out of the place, or out of life altogether. Squire Winter, a soldier, had stood it out. But he no longer cared to walk in the park after dinner. He almost hid, indoors. Once he had walked, bare headed, and in his patent leather shoes and purple silk socks, with Connie down to the gate, talking to her in his well bred rather haw-haw fashion. But when it came to passing the little gangs of colliers who stood and stared without either salute or anything else, Connie felt how the lean, well-bred old man winced — winced as an elegant antelope in a cage winces from the vulgar stare. The colliers were not personally hostile: not at all. But their spirit was cold and shoving him out.

And deep down there was a profound grudge. They 'worked for him'. And in their ugliness they resented his elegant, well-groomed, well-bred existence.

'Who's he?' It was the difference they resented.

And somewhere, in his secret English heart, being a good deal of a soldier, he believed they were right to resent the difference. He felt himself a little in the wrong, for having all the advantages.

Nevertheless he represented a system and he would not be shoved out.

Except by death. Which came on him soon after Connie's call, suddenly. And he remembered Clifford handsomely in his Will.

The heirs at once gave out the order for the demolishing of Shipley. It cost too much to keep up. No-one would live there. So it was broken up. The avenue of yews was cut down. The park was denuded of its timber, and divided into lots. It was near enough to Uthwaite. In the strange, bald desert of this still-one-more-no-man's-land, new little streets of semi-detacheds were run up, 'very desirable!' The Shipley Hall Estate!

D. H. Lawrence, *Lady Chatterley's Lover* (1929) Paris Edition

Fride Miller

The Inquiry

A head emerged for a moment, with a touch of blue tunic and a glint of metal: then a voice rapped through the half open door, and hearing his name, he passed into the larger room.

At last. For over an hour he had been kicking his heels in the 'snug' that opened off the bar of the 'Jolly Pitman'. Not that he had been requested to lounge alone. Others were waiting to deliver evidence at the inquest now proceeding in the best room of the tavern. Two colliers with the bony shaven polls of their kind had kept him company, peppering the conversation with cheerful irony. 'Goo on,' tendered Phipps, the elder of these, his pale lips delivered for a moment from the stem of his pipe, ''tis nobbut formal-li-tee –' The other collier extended jaunty finger tips as he passed. 'It'll soon be ower for thee – cheer up!'

He conceded a faint smile (really he was rather pleased that they had been with him), but his heart throbbed painfully as he entered the inquiry. A swift glance captured everything. There sat manager Birchells on the other side of the big table – who could deny the Birchell's moustache? – and Copeland, the under-manager, stocky and vibrant with energy beside him. The rather sleepy figure with the black watered eyeglass ribbon dangling would be the Coroner. And –

'James Edward Bagnold?'

It was the Company's solicitor speaking, and the witness made the admission remotely, doubtful, it would appear, of the validity of his own existence. Funny! One's name intoned like that. And where was Perrin? Ah, spacious in the roomy chair, hands in pockets, and a silver watch chain only slightly spanning his aldermanic front, sat the Union representative. 'Must keep my eyes on Perrin,' he concluded, 'Perrin the Union man. Never did care for Perrin. And he's bound to have his questions.'

Meanwhile, still a little abstractedly he was conceding the other particulars. The deceased roadlayer, Worfolk, had been discovered asphyxiated in the workings over which he, witness, was deputy in charge. Yes, one admitted all that. And the crisp voice of the Company's solicitor hurried from point to point of the preliminaries. 'This man's friendly', thought the deputy. 'Perrin now?' Undoubtedly, Perrin would need watching –

'Do you recognise the ventilation door marked 'X' upon the plan?' The solicitor's white finger ran over the map of the colliery workings, switching along the ribbed outline of the familiar galleries, and finally halting at a point in the north-east district – 'There?'

'Yes, Sir.' That door! He swallowed hard, hoping that Perrin hadn't noticed. Perrin would read anything into evidence. You knew Perrin's style, sweeping, rhetorical. 'The air current is the life blood of the miner. The air current is the life line of the workings.' Perrin always speechified.

'You are aware that the door in question was propped open with a fragment of stone, and left open?'

'I have been told so, Sir.'

'And that such a door remaining open would short circuit the air supply from the place where the unfortunate man happened to be working, leaving him with little or no air at all to carry on with?'

'Yes, Sir.'

'We may take it that whoever propped and left open the door in question would in all probability be held responsible for the atmosphere in which the deceased met his end?'

'I suppose so, Sir.'

'Now I want you to consider the next question very carefully. It is most important to the bearing of this case. What kind of workman was the deceased?'

'Oh, pretty fair, Sir.' What else could one say? Worfolk was pretty fair. You couldn't find a better roadlayer in the colliery.

'No, no. I don't mean quite that. In character now. Would you consider the deceased man at all given to negligent habits? Is it possible that he himself left the door open in the course of his activities?'

'It is quite possible.'

'Would the deceased use the door in carrying supplies?'

'He would need various things at his work, Sir.'

'Tell us what he would need?'

'Oh, timber, hammers, nails —'

'Fairly heavy material?'

'Yes, Sir, pretty heavy.'

'I suggest that the deceased in carrying supplies propped the door open himself and omitted to close it?'

'It is quite probable.'

'Extremely probable?' The pursuing voice admitted no compromise.

'Yes, Sir.' Out it came. Well, what harm could there be in that? Praise or censure, it was all one now to poor Wolfolk. The solicitor, however, still rubbed his cheeks with faint dubiety. Was this the end? The solicitor sat down. And slowly Perrin arose —

Perrin straightened his waistcoat, cleared his throat and turned his fresh, fleshy face with the twinking grey eyes in the direction of the witness. He had the big, vain mouth of an orator.

'You are the district deputy?' Perrin glanced demurely downwards at the table littered with papers.

'Yes.' No 'Sir' for Perrin.

'Tell us what you were doing when the tragedy occurred.'

'Surveying the roadways.'

'You were fully occupied with this job?'

'It's a one man's job' – hotly. Just the sort of question Perrin would ask.

'Don't answer at length,' said the sleepy man with the watered ribbon, mildly. 'Yes or no will do.' And Perrin smiled faintly at the farthermost corner of the building.

'What had you been doing for the previous hour?'

What was Perrin getting at? How much did he really know? Better tell the truth at any rate. 'I was dragging a tarpaulin from the slant in 52's airway for one thing.'

Perrin slid a fat finger over the map and gave a significant snort. 'Ah, and so on your journey you would take the doorway in question?'

'Yes, at that particular time I did.'

'Were you alone?'

'Yes.'

'You did not fail to close the door behind you?'

'I did not.'

'It would be criminal if you did not. You recognise that?'

'Yes.'

'Now then –' Perrin hitched his thumbs in his waistcoat armholes. 'Shall we make absolutely certain? Did you prop the door open as you passed through with your burden?

'I did.'

'With what did you wedge the door?'

'I don't remember.'

'Think now – a piece of wood, a piece of stone?'

'A piece of stone I think.'

'And you displaced the stone when you had passed through with the cloth?'

'I did.'

Perrin smiled faintly. 'This is rather curious. You can't recall with what you propped the door open, yet you remember perfectly well that you closed it?'

'I do remember.'

'Definitely?'

'Definitely.'

'What time would you make that?'

'About ten minutes past ten.'

'And they found poor Worfolk gassed at eleven?'

'I believe so.'

'What did you do after the job related?'

'I went to the north side of the district.'

'And you remained there?'

'Yes.'

'So that you and the deceased, it appears, had the door marked 'X' upon the plan between you?'

'What do you mean?'

'I suggest that there is no real evidence to suppose that Worfolk met his death through his own negligence, and quite enough to suppose that he might have met it at the hands of another.' And Perrin stared intently at the witness. Then he shrugged his shoulders. 'I have no more questions to ask.'

So that was what he thought? What could one say? 'You can assume what you like – I tell you I did close the door!' Remotely, Perrin was muttering, 'No usefulness in asking further questions...'

Ought one to step down now? A mute appeal to the body of the court evoked a slight response. Someone uttered thanks faintly, and the witness realised he was at liberty to depart.

He regained the 'snug' and dropped into a seat beside the colliers who were still waiting. 'By gum! but thou art lookin' sallow,' observed the elder. 'Am I?' he commented simply, 'I think I'll take a breath of air. I – don't think I'm feeling well.'

He left them and entered the quiet street. The newly-gilded clock on the parish church said twelve. In half an hour – perhaps much less – that flagrant insinuation started by Perrin, and extended by Perrin's friends – would be circulating around the colliery area. 'Jim Bagnold, he –.'

He slipped down an alley into Summer Lane. 'How do, Jimmy?' a voice came from the shadow. 'How do,' he answered. He did not know who had spoken nor did he pause to ascertain. A hundred yards beyond the houses where the first green pastures climbed a ridge to the skyline, he perched on the nearest available railings. Of course, he had opened and propped the door, and of course he had closed it again. Stage by stage he endeavoured to reconstruct the course of that momentous morning. He had no witnesses to advance, worse luck, to prove how, single-handed, he had dragged the tarpaulin from point to point. It would appear that you could be a cursed sight too independent at times. He saw himself approaching the door – there was a broken roof bar just in front of it – and scouting around for a wedge of some sort, wood or stone? But why particularly wood or stone? Why not a piece of coal? Why not?

He set his teeth upon his thumb as his memory rekindled with the suggestion it was all bearing in like some point in a negative newly developed. He had hovered over a litter of both stone and coal fragments, and finally selected, because of its roughish surface, a wedge of coal. He remembered now, and would in all probability have recalled as much before, had he not been so distracted and confused by Perrin's cross examination. The wedge that they had found had been a stone one. 'I must go back and tell them,' he muttered, slipping from the fence, and setting off at a jog trot down the road in the direction of the 'Jolly Pitmen'.

When he burst into the 'snug' it was empty. The two colliers had vanished. No matter. His business being in the best room, he had half opened the door when the brawny arm of a policeman fell across his chest. 'Go slow mister – no hurry – wait you a minute…'

'But it was coal – coal,' he vociferated, 'I know now –.'

'That's quite all right,' said the policeman disposedly. 'You'll be able to talk as much as ever you like in a minute or two. They're breakin' up now.'

'I must say what I have to say!'

But even as he spoke the room began to empty of its occupants. They streamed into the corridor and swarmed into the 'snug' as he lingered helplessly watching the exit. As Phipps the collier and his mate emerged, 'It was a piece of coal,' he muttered tremulously, 'I forgot at the time.' He saw them gaze upon him with steady, contemptuous eyes, and he followed a step or two, almost plucking at their sleeves. Then they hurried out. 'A piece of coal,' he repeated, 'coal –' but of the others nobody seemed to be listening…

J. C. Grant, *The Back to Backs* (1930)

A. G. Meek

Coil Barrers

Aw'm missin t' sahnd ot owd barrers,
O't clatter'd o'er t'door stooan wi' coil,
Push'd and shuv'ed bi't shooil childer,
Neer heedin they bump'd ivvery hoil.

For year uppa year ther've fetched it,
Throo coil places, offen, and cheeap,
Fer t'poor couldn't affooard a gret deeal,
Wi' nivver a full sized coil heeap.

But nah at coils offen soo scarce,
An't poor as to do wi' aht foire,
Them waggins and barrers is quiet,
For t'price as gone hoigher and hoigher.

Fooak kale it at coil-shop wi' bags,
And wait I wots nah call'd a Q,
But wat ivver a kew may mean,
Aw daw'nt think they're gerrin their due.

Its same wi me warking at 't hearth,
Awm one o't last own uns i't trade.
An cowk's that awkard to get,
For sum weeks aw've not made a blade.

Aw can't stan waiting much longer,
Aw wish ther'd ger on wi' ther wark,
For loike me theers thahsands grooapin,
Wi trubble, an loss, an i't dark.

Awm wantin to lissen t'clatter,
Just same as aw used to affoor,
Ah! lissen to t'sahnd o't 'owd barrers.
Wi coil in, an passin ahr door.

Think on us hinnies, if you please,
An' it war but to show your pity;

For a' the toils and tears it gi'es
To warm the shins o' Lunnon City.

The fiery 'blast' cuts short wor lives,
And steep wor hyems in deep distress;
Myeks widows o' wor canny wives,
And a' wor bairns leaves faitherless.

And wait'ry 'wyest', main dreadful still,
Alive oft barries huz belaw;
Oh dear! It myeks wor blood run chill,
May we sic mis'ry nivver knaw.

To be cut off frae kith and kin,
The leet o'day te see ne mair,
And left, frae help and hope shut in,
To pine and parish in despair.

If ye could on'y tyek a view,
And see the sweet frae off us poorin' –
The daily dangers we gan through,
The daily hardships we're endurin'!

Ye wad send doon, aw ha'e ne doubt,
Some chaps on what they call a 'mission',
Te try if they could ferret out
Somethin' to beeter wor condition.

Quoted from Richard Fynes, *The Miners of Northumberland and Durham* (1873)

Strikes and Lay-offs

Jean Louis Forain

George Bissill

Two Sides to a Question

'Then I tell you plainly I shall stand no more interference from the Miner's Union. It brought the men out two years ago over that business of the checkweighman. It brought the men out last spring through some stupid misunderstanding about the coal-cutter; it stopped them again for a week in October about heaven only knows what. The men are all right if they are left alone, and I am quite capable of managing my works without the advice of the Union. If it were any serious question of injustice I would not complain, but this petty interference in every new arrangement at the pits simply paralyses trade. It is ruining the country, and it's a damned tyranny!'

Sir James poked the fire fiercely to relieve his outraged feelings.

Christopher listened gravely and nodded his head.

'Of course there is some truth in that,' he said. 'The Union makes a lot of mistakes. But it does good work; keeps the men from underselling each other, and settles any number of disputes. And you know, Sir, it hasn't steadied to work just yet. New power is always abused. And there's no denying whatever injustice the masters suffer now is not a tithe of the injustice the workers have suffered in the past.'

'What? We are to pay for the sins of the fathers, eh?' Sir James chuckled. 'Well, there is some consolation in the thought that future generations will gather a plentiful harvest of weeds from the sowings of the present British workman. Listen to me, Mr. Dent,' he broke out again angrily, 'my father began life at the pit brow, but he gave his son a university education, and left me almost all I possess today. He had good luck, of course, I don't deny it; but the money didn't fall into his hands, I can tell you; he had to work for it with his nose to the grindstone. No weekends at Blackpool for him; no races, football matches and institute billiard-rooms; no schools and technical colleges and other 'learning-made-easy' fads. My father earned and saved his wealth. Until he was fifty he worked ten hours every day, Saturday included, and his sole relaxations were a fortnight's holiday a year and an occasional quiet evening rubber of whist with his cronies at home. And now I, his son, am expected to spend his money in providing clubs, libraries, orphanages, old age pensions, and heaven only knows what besides, in order that those idle rascals down yonder may spend every penny they earn on their backs and their stomachs. I do it – because I'm a fool. I build them schools and bribe them to attend – and precious little good do they learn there. I pay fair wages, and I keep their houses in repair. But one thing I will have – I will be master of my own men, and if I have any more impertinent interference from the Union, I swear I'll shut down every pit, and let the Union keep them.'

Christopher listened to this tirade with interest. When Sir James ceased speaking he put down his glass and stood up.

'I think you are a little hard on the men, Sir James,' he argued. 'All mine-owners don't take the same personal interest in their employees that you do, and an organisation like the Union can't differentiate – it must treat all alike. Besides, the men are not all the feckless lot you think. Some are short-sighted and perhaps ignorant, but there are a splendid lot of decent fellows among them. They only want to see justice done.'

'Not they,' interrupted Sir James scornfully. 'They only want their mouths filled. The case with most of us, I suppose,' he added with a good-humoured laugh. He was a little ashamed of this outburst to his guest. 'And that reminds me,' he continued, 'you will stay to dinner, won't you Mr. Dent? My daughter will want to thank you for your help.'

The Lodge meeting was but sparsely attended. The subject of the dispute was an application by the men, in one district of the mines, for an increase in their wages in consideration of the extra long distance the coal had to be brought from the face (where it was severed from the seam), to what may be termed the highway of the mine. The work of bringing the coal over this distance is called 'the drawing' and the men who do this work are called 'drawers'.

A small increase of wages had been offered, and the men, with the exception of a small minority, were disposed to agree with the manager's proposals. Matters would scarcely have gone as far as the convening of a Lodge meeting, had it not been for the insistence of the checkweighman at White Rose Pit, where the dispute had arisen, one Paul Chambers by name.

Chambers was a man full of ignorance and ambition, and oppressed with a bitter sense of the injustice of a world in which one man spends his days driving £1000 Panhards about the country, and dining off every delicacy out of season, and another man has to work ten hours a day to earn a living wage. He had attended evening schools and technical colleges and done his utmost to educate himself up to his ambitions, but he was pathetically conscious of the limit of his accomplishment, and was perpetually haunted by a suspicion that every educated man was bent on getting the better of him, if he suffered himself for an instant to relax his watch upon them. He was ever perceiving tyrannical designs behind each new regulation at the pits, and encouraged the men to oppose every proposal emanating from the employers.

Tonight Kit Dent's finger was on the pulse of the meeting. He knew that the majority of the men were opposed to extreme measures, and only wanted a lead to induce them to accept a peaceful solution to the difficulty. He lost no time in giving them this lead.

'Well – what's the trouble?' he asked, when he took his place at the end of the long room where the meeting was held. 'Best settle it if we can. Work is good and wages are up at present. We don't want a strike if we can help it, and as far as I've worked it out, Mr. Stevens' offer isn't far out.'

He proceeded to lay the plain figures before the meeting, and argued strongly in favour of a settlement. His words were few and to the point. A blunt, silent man as a rule, he had not attained his position by power of eloquence. But he had worked beside these men for twelve years; he had made the Union a power, and championed the cause when he thought they were in the right with unflinching determination. And if they knew little else about him they had learned one thing – they knew that he was dead straight. They trusted him; and when a man has earned that opinion amongst miners he has little need to waste his breath in doctoring the truth. The men listened to his arguments and nodded agreement. Not a tithe of them really followed his statements, but wages were good, and they were not seeking trouble. The explanation seemed satisfactory, and the agreement with the manager's proposals was on the point of acceptance.

Beth Ellis, *Blind Mouths* (1922)

The Strike

She soon learned the stark details. The owners wished to reduce the wages by a shilling a day. The men, earning scarcely enough to live, had rebelled and a strike was called by the tiny ineffective union that then existed. Two years ago, in 1872, hours had been reduced to a maximum of nine per day, and in this year to eight hours per day, but, as if in revenge for these shorter hours, the owners made persistent attacks upon the small wages. For the first time since she came into the area, Mrs. Rudd found herself confronted with disaster.

'But can't y' – wunna the Bosses discuss it?' she asked the group of men. 'Canna y' come to some agreement with 'em?'

'The owners refuse to discuss terms until the men have accepted the shilling-a-day drop,' said Cotterling, a clear-skinned, young-old man with a healthy look, shaggy eyebrows and a stiff frame. A man who had been holding miners' meetings on the Common every Sunday for some time. His pale blue eyes held laughter that would only vanish when indignation came, and his moustached lips hummed ever a little tune. 'It's come at last, and it's a case of now or never. This time we must organise the men; they are helpless at present. It makes me feel like crying, almost, to see them unorganised before such a threat as this! But we must get to work. There's no time like this to appeal to them... Jake, I'm dependin' on you!'

'An' I'm dependin' on you too, Cotterlin',' said Jake with fervour in his soft, stammering voice. 'At tonight's meetin' we must meck things 'um! You're comin' ain't y', Zay?'

'Ah, course I am,' said Zay seriously. 'But if I'd got my way I'd put a bomb down every shaft, an' see 'ow the swine like that!'

Cobble and Cotterling exchanged fleeting glances at the foolish remark.

'But we couldna' manage on a shillin' drop!' broke in Mrs. Rudd's deep, hoarse voice, 'I couldna pay the rent and buy food wi' the money, then even if Zay worked every day in the wik!'

'It's what I've alwis said to you, missis,' said Jake. 'If only we could get 'em organised we could meet a challenge like this. They talk about usin' force, but isna' this force, this drivin' a man back to serfdom? Y' want to read 'istory! Well I'm a Christian man, but sometimes I feel inclined to get up an' swear when I read about it!'

Cotterling had been humming a little tune, a little absent-minded opera-air, for he loved music, and his trombone, his 'insterment' was as a wife to him; to see him practising with his band was to see a happy man. 'I wisht we 'adna bought them uniforms for our band, that's all,' he said now, 'we shall be wantin' the money, I'm thinkin'.'

When they had gone: 'An' I've just gone an' bought that new Russian tail boa!' said Mrs. Rudd irritably.

'Wheer's young George?' he asked.

She told him of Nikkum's terror. 'There's a mon bin killed at the Valley,' he said. 'I reckon ae got too near, wheer ae 'adna oughter ha' bin... God, missus, I 'ope this blasted strike isna' a long 'un! It's a good job yow got that pig.'

'Yes,' she said absently, 'but it took the last bit in the bank... Oh, Zay, I 'ope it isna' a long strike!'

'We'll ha' to wait, missus, an' see what comes on it... Get us a bit o' snap will y'.'

II

For the first few weeks of the strike the small union paid out strike-pay to its members, but at the end of the first week the majority, non-union men, found themselves faced with starvation. Zay ordered the instant killing of the pig, and the killing was one of the events of the strike that George remembered best. The two sides of bacon were hung upon the wall in place of Queen Victoria and her Consort, and Zay would look at them and rub his hands and declare to visitors; 'Them am the two best pictures I've ever sin, my lad!' George remembered Mr. Cotterling and other men speaking at great meetings of miners on the Common, and when the multitude of ragged, starving and desperate miners knelt on the silk-grass to pray to the unseen God for succour even Stunk could not jeer. Pit ponies were brought up the mines, and a strange, uneasy silence fell upon the world, a silence that unnerved Mrs. Rudd, beneath whose life ran always the murmur of pit-engines. And George remembered, too, the marching away of Cotterling's band, in the new black uniforms to tour South Staffordshire in search of funds, remembered Cotterling and Little Burton the conductor, and Dicky Thomas the cornet player and Fatty Hackwood at the drum and Elliman with the euphonium and Cobble with the second cornet and the rest of them, remembered how they went playing up the street 'Come Lasses and Lads' at the beginning of their weary odyssey, and how Zay marched with them and how he himself wept to go, and was only appeased when Aunt Carrie, whose one shoulder stood much higher than the other, promised to take him to stay at the big house near Canford where she had been housekeeper for seventeen years. And so opened a wonderful memory for George, his chief memory during the strike, and a memory that he carried, like the grey-blue wound beside his chin, to the day of his death. His best suit was put upon him and he was bidden to behave himself, and then he and Aunt Carrie set off to walk down the strange road to Canford.

When they had walked a distance that seemed to George's strange eyes about three miles they passed under two railway bridges, and turning to the left along the Canford Road, reached the tree-hung entrance gateway to a big house.

'Here we are, then!' said Aunt Carrie, the little deformed woman whose shadowed face and folded lips bore the marks of her loveless, responsible years. And George had hardly time to gasp at the size of the house when she opened the gate, and he was tip-toeing beside her along a curving, rather neglected drive, with evergreens bushing out over the path. And soon they arrived at a big side-door with a polished brass door-knob and knocker and Aunt Carrie, becoming suddenly businesslike, unlocked the door and bade him come in.

He found himself at the side of a big hall, from which ascended a wide flight of stairs that turned by a stained-glass window to the upper rooms. A suit of old armour stood threateningly beside him, and soft rugs were on the polished floor. 'They' were away, Aunt Carrie told him and he wondered what 'they' were like who lived in such a beautiful place. But he mustn't stand there staring, said Aunt Carrie, but must come along in 'here' and have something to eat, for she was sure he wanted it.

And in that wonderful house George stayed for more than five weeks. At first he was homesick, but a visit home, where he found most of the pig's carcass gone, eased his pain, and he settled down to enjoy the house. Cook and the maids were willing to chat with him, since there was little work to be done while 'they' were away, and since, too, he was Miss Rudd's nevvy. He had the free run of the house while his boots were clean, and of the garden when they were not. On his first morning, he sped about here and there, discovering his kingdom, like a tranced thing. The stained-glass window chiefly held him indoors, and he would sit silent on the carpeted stair and gaze at it until one of the maids ventured to caution Miss Rudd that he looked as if he wanted to smash it. But she was wrong: he wanted to look and stare merely. But some magic means the glass bore a brilliant picture of a knight and a fair lady, and he pondered upon them and their comeliness and the brilliant mosaic in which they stood until his eyes grew dizzy. But then there was the garden with a wide lawn and great friendly trees, and a fountain that sometimes played, and a short terrace of stone, and a garden behind the house with a long greenhouse filled with growing tomato plants. He would wander about from this favourite place to that, lying on the lawn, surreptitiously climbing a tree, standing before trim flower beds with vacant eyes, or sitting in his favourite place upon the stairs.

To live in such a house partook of the nature of a dream, and a dream it remained to the end of his life. Everything was clean, everything orderly, everything coloured. When his Aunt discovered him sitting on the rugs in a dark corner of the hall and asked him what he doing there for lawk's sake, he grew restless, and said that he was looking. 'Wouldn't you like to have a big house like this?' she asked him inquisitively.

He nodded his head, and licked his dry lips, as if, thirsty he had been offered a drink.

'Well, you're a rum-un for a Rudd!' she said, contemplating him with a puzzled expression. And then she remembered something that Zay had said about him being 'soft' about flowers and things, and moved by some impulse she bent and took him in her arms, that had never held her own child. 'What is it, the colours an' things?' she whispered.

He wriggled uncomfortably, and then turned and recognised a friend in the lined grey eyes of his aunt. 'Yes', he mumbled.

'Do you like pretty things?'

He nodded his head hardly at ease.

'Well, I'll give you somethin' nice, what the fairies made,' she said, and took him to her room, where she reached out a tiny brass cylinder, and when George put his eye to the end and turned it round and round, brilliant colour-patters formed and reformed against the light. 'There, 'ow d'y like that?' she asked. And he kissed her, and became thereafter her favourite. Feeling some need in her for love he rubbed his fat cheeks against the dusty leather of her pain-lined face, and squeezed her in his chubby arms.

And that night one of the maids remarked with a snigger to the cook that 'Ur' – meaning Miss Rudd – was gettin' younger every day and had been seen in secret singing to herself in a cracked voice and waving her shrunken paw in accompaniment.

III

It was the sixteenth week of the strike. Many families had gone to the workhouse, their furniture sold, and most had debts that would cripple them for many years.

They were terrible days. Shopkeepers forced up their prices to cruel rates, and after many meetings Cotterling was in despair. The men seemed apathetic, too passive and drilled by ignorance and the polite impositions of a happier class even to smash windows for food for starving children. They listened to Cotterlin's and Stanley's and Cobble's demands for a strong union and seemed to take heart, but nothing came of it, and day after day the dribble blacklegs returning to work continued.

At No. 3, when Zay marched back with the Black Uniforms he found the new couch, two chairs, a chest of drawers, and the People's harmonium, that cost four good guineas, all sold and the pig gone – for Mrs. Rudd could not refuse starving children – and his first job, on reaching home, was to sell a pair of pictures they had brought from Crawford – the two oleographs of Italian scenes, a transaction that brought vividly to their minds the day he would have sold them on the Uxbridge corner for beer. Once Mrs. Rudd appealed to Zay to go back to the country, and he stared in surprise, for a fiercer partisan in the fight did not exist. But debts held them back from that way of escape. She continued to make stew with scraps of pork and distributed it to queues of half-starved children, and ever afterwards she remembered the little pale faces: they impressed her so that she was satisfied to remain, to cease to desire Crawford, to remain and help in the bitter work of salvation.

The Rudds owed nearly twenty pounds, and in furniture they had been reduced to two beds, the kitchen table, two chairs and very little besides.

When Zay took the kitchen table, that table her mother and grandmother had used, the table that had ridden on the handcart, like an old friend from Crawford to Hendiford on that June morning eight years ago, the forced spirit that had upheld Mrs. Rudd seemed to collapse.

'No, teck it, teck it!' she said, as Zay would have brought it back. 'It's got to be, I reckon. I canna 'ave y' goin' after rabbits agen or we shall be wuss off than before... But, oh Zay, Zay, it 'urts me, it does, teckin' that table! God knows what's gonna 'eppen to we!'

'We'll get it back, my wench, soon's the strike's over,' he said. He looked thin and starved, she saw. 'An' all them other things. They'm at the same shop.'

'Lord knows when that'll be, Zay,' she said dispiritedly. 'What wi' the money we owe... An' I'm sure Mrs. Jervis's children are almost starvin'... They dunna get anythin' besides what I give 'em... You'd better teck it.'

But when he had gone, leaving a great empty space in the middle of the floor, she sobbed bitterly. Then she rose to give the baby his food and for some time sat silent, the child gurgling and crowing peacefully in her arms, her face dark and passionate. Her full cheeks were lined, her brown eyes, in which hidden anxiety always reigned, looked sullen and brooding and her pale lips seemed to have lost their country look of firm repose: they pressed together viciously. She had the air of one driven to the wall, striving still to preserve her spirit but in mortal terror of the future: she looked a stricken Andromeda as she nursed her child in the bare fireless room. Thank God George was safe. But suddenly there were steps in the passage and Zay came blundering in with the table on his back and shouting. Her eyes grew wide in terror and one hand went up to her open mouth. Zay was singing Jack's Farewell and capering about like a mad thing.

'It's over, over!' he cried, setting down the table with such force that ever afterwards it wobbled. 'We goo back tomorrer! Jake's just told me! By God, it's the best bit of news I've 'eerd for a long time! 'Ere's y' table missus! By God, we'll be getting' all them other things back in a month or two –!'

'Over?' she said, her head trembling violently, her body motionless. ''Ow? Over? The Bosses ha' bin beat?'

He looked at her foolishly. 'Oh dam the shillin'!' he said with bravado. 'No, we're gooin, back tomorrer, but the bob's off. The swine ha' won, o' course, but they alwis do!'

She sat very still. 'So you'm beat, are y'? You'm gooin' back beat?... Beat!... Oh, my God, if only they'd 'ad a bit more spunk an' stuck out!... Gooin' back beat!... Oh, the dam cowards, the dam cowards!' And, unnerved and weak after self-starvation, she leaned forward over the child, weeping bitterly.

Bruce Beddow, *A Man Of The Midlands* (1928)

The Case for the Miners

Something goes wrong with my synthetic brain
When I defend the Strikers and explain
My reasons for not blackguarding the Miners.
'*What do you know?*' exclaim my fellow-diners
(Peeling their plovers eggs or lifting glasses
Of mellowed *Château Rentier* from the table),
'*What do you know about the working classes?*'

I strive to hold my own; but I'm unable
To state the case succinctly. Indistinctly
I mumble about World-Emancipation,
Standards of Living, Nationalisation
Of Industry; until they get me tangled
In superficial details; goad me on
To unconvincing vagueness.
When we've wrangled
From soup to savoury, my temper's gone.

'*Why should a miner earn six pounds a week?*
Leisure! They'd only spend it in a bar!
Standard of Life! You'll never teach them Greek,
Or made them more contented than they are!'
That's how my port-flushed friends discuss the Strike.
And that's the reason why I shout and splutter.
And that's the reason why I'd almost like
To see them hawking matches in the gutter.

Siegfried Sassoon, *Satirical Poems* (1926)

Unemployed

Jim crossed the road to speak to the manager as he left the pit. But Mr. Purdy met so many like him, almost every day between pit and home, that they were like impersonal things. To all alike he chanted:

'I'm setting nobody on.'

This was the salute Jim received, but he continued to walk by the manager's side.

'Sorry lad, but I can do nothing for you,' replied that gentleman, without looking at him.

'D'ye not ken me, Captain.'

Captain! That brought him up with a jerk. He looked at Jim, but shook his head, saying:

'You have the best of me, lad.'

'Corporal Rigby. 8th Durham Light Infantry.'

The ex-captain gripped the ex-corporal's hands.

'Man, I'm glad to meet you.'

Jim told him how things stood; but the state of things was written plainly, and the man was troubled as he looked at him.

'We thought we would live happy ever after when we left Ypres behind, Rigby, but –.'

'Aye. I always had a good suit and rations – when Jerry didn't interfere,' laughed Jim.

'Man, I'm sorry I cannot start you. There's a seam of men working their notices. I am sorry.' Then after a pause, 'In those days I always thought there was nothing in the world I wouldn't do for men like you, little thinking I would be lucky to have a job myself.'

Jim thanked him, saying he understood, and turned away. As he went the manager told him to come back again some time when things were more settled, but both knew that was only to emphasise sympathy.

So that was the end of his high hopes. And he had been so sure. Long ago his craft as a pitman had ceased to count, for there were masses as good and younger than he in the same position. But in this case hope had almost become certainty, only to stamp out the remaining spark of hope. He had changed; everything had changed; he was a stranger among his own. He was done...

––––––––––

Then he went, a scarecrow of a man, lacking hope, but erect. He went, pride squaring his shoulders, and the consciousness of his new-found friends' respect giving strength to his spirit. Out to the moors he went once more with a keen wind blowing round him. Mile after mile along narrow, little-trodden footpaths, numb of body, kept going by a little pride, a little respect. Life was objectless; it was like going from nowhere to nowhere.

Then there broke upon him the fury of a storm which will long be remembered throughout Britain. Men had thought the last bitter days were the climax of winter, but they had only been the slow-gathering ground of elemental forces, which would remind men of their frailty. Cars, buses, telegraph systems were left like broken toys by that snowstorm.

The wind whirled the large snowflakes, blinding Jim Rigby. Momentary relief from the wind only showed him circled by a white world moving in upon him. He walked almost blindly, relying more upon experience and his moor-wandering instinct than knowledge of the way. By and by the path was obliterated. Body tested by wind, wet and cold, hand over eyes to shield them from the snow which now smashed against his face, he struggled on, doubtful of direction.

Then, far off to the left, he heard the hooting of the horn of some car or omnibus, and he turned in that direction. Falling in hollows, tripping over furze and heather, he made straight for the point from which the sound had come. Thus he came to the road, and it seemed to him that his journey was ended when he found his feet upon it. There were yet long, roundabout miles to travel, but to be free from that lost, trackless world from which he had been saved by chance, seemed almost the end of his journey. It was dark when he arrived at his lodgings, sodden and exhausted. There was a pulp-like mass in his pocket which had been sandwiches. Mrs. Dunn pulled out a pair of ancient, patched trousers and an old shirt belonging to Jack. As he sat before the fire dry and warm, Jack Dunn asked:

'Did ye manage? Get work?'

'No.'

'Ah knew. They're all alike. A grateful country will nivir forget ye.'

'Eh, it wasn't his fault. Ah was sorry for him.'

'Sorry, mm! Hell of a lot they care.'

And Mrs. Dunn said:

'Things'll nivir be reet again.'

Jack Lawson, *Under The Wheels* (1934)

George Bissill

Emlyn Discusses the 'Dole'

Emlyn, the miner, and I were sitting on a wall outside the village. We were smoking and talking about marriage, women, music, coal and greyhounds. Then we discussed the 'dole'.

'It's bad,' said Emlyn, 'but what can you do? It's State charity but when the citizens of a State are thrown out of work through no fault of their own you cannot let them starve. It's bad because it makes a certain kind of man lazy. It encourages him to expect something for nothing. It's a common thing to hear a man on the 'dole', who has a chance of work, thinking of his wages not as £2 a week, but as a few shillings more than he would get for doing nothing! And when wages are so low, can you blame him? Aren't we all lazy at times?'

'I've been on the 'dole' and I hated it,' he said. 'I'm not the only one.'

'Pride,' I said. 'I've seen pride behind white curtains in a bare room.'

'Pride?' said Emlyn, taking his pipe out of his mouth and looking over the valley. 'You're right. There's good and bad in all walks of life, but the best type of Welsh miner is proud. I could tell you... goodness, I could tell you...'

When a Welshman says this you know that he will tell you, so I kept quiet and waited.

'There's a lot of very good work going on in the valley,' said Emlyn, 'in the way of feeding school-children and giving them shoes and things, but only if the father is out of work. Some of the worst cases of hardship I've known have been in homes where the father was trying to keep six children on £2.5s. a week and was too proud to accept help from anyone...'

'There was Bill So-and-So. We worked together in Number Two Pit. When you're on a shift you fall out for twenty minutes and eat bread and butter, or bread and cheese, which the wife puts in your food tin. Well, Bill and I used to fall out together and get away from the coal face into the stall, or heading, you see. And we'd sit on each side of the road with our feet on the tram rails and our lamps on the floor. And then we'd open our food tins and eat our food. Now, you've been down a mine. You know that when two fellows are sitting with their lamps on the floor the light only reaches to their knees. I could see Bill's knees. That was all...

'One day we were sitting like this talking when Bill didn't answer. Then I saw his light go over, and he fell in the middle of the tram rails. He'd fainted. So I lifted him and carried him to the pit bottom to send him home, but before I did this I gathered up his food tin. There wasn't a crumb in it! There hadn't been a crumb in it for days! He'd been sitting there in the dark pretending to eat, pretending to me – his pal –. Now that's pride, if you like! You may think it's silly, but it's pride, isn't it?'

Emlyn knocked out his pipe on the wall and looked at me for confirmation.

'Yes; but that's surely not the end of the story,' I said. 'A man getting money, no matter how little, doesn't starve himself like that unless...'

'Oh, doesn't he,' said Emlyn. 'When you're on the starvation line you must keep up appearances.'

'Yes, but there was something more behind it.'

'There was. Bill has five children. The week he fainted in the pit was the week they had to have new shoes. Now I'm the only one who knows that. His wife told me. But do you think I'd even let him know I know? Not blinking likely!'

We got up and walked back over the still countrified road to the mining village.

'If you write about that,' said Emlyn, 'you'll wrap it all up and put in different names; and you'll have a lot of letters saying you made it up! There is a feeling that the miner is a fellow who starves his family to keep greyhounds. Well, you know enough about South Wales now to see that it doesn't happen here. Mind you, I could introduce you to bad fellows – we aren't all angels – but just because we work underground and come up looking like niggers some people think we're half savages.'

'If you had a wish, Emlyn, what would it be?'

'Let's see, now. I'd like five quid a week and a pit with the coal boiling out. I'd also like to stand for Parliament. Perhaps I will some day when the good times come round.'

H. V. Morton, *In Search of Wales* (1932)

Coal Owners and a Strike

Deep in the coal-pits of Lancashire, Yorkshire, Derbyshire, Worcestershire and North Wales, far away in those black underground cities of darkness, where the narrow streets are so low that man had to stoop, where he has to be a lamp to his own feet, where he has to go almost naked because of the heat, and have the breath of life pumped down to him because of gas and where his companion four-footed little colliers, the ponies, become cramped, dwarfed and blind. Far, far away in those thickly populated and sub-terranean cities under the cities and dales of England and Wales, where man, with a daring that is of the brute, a trust that is of the angel, and a power that is, verily, even of God, scoops the primeval forests out of their beds to give fire to the hearths, steam to the works and light to the nights on the surface cities of the earth. Deep and far away in the dark, in the damp, in the dense air of alley-like cuttings and dungeon-like corners, there moved to and fro, from man to man, through quiet passages and ways, along busy truck-lines and up echoing shafts, the growls of protest, the murmurs of revolt, the ironical hums of defiance and half-cynical songs of cool-headed courage.

Old ditties were revived. Britton Lloyd set 'Cheer, boys, cheer!' going the round of

Camel Hump Pit; it passed up the shaft and overland to No.1 and No.2, and into the homes and streets of Beckerton. Old weavers wondered if the days of the cotton famine were turning back in time, and a very old Chartist, with his long full grey hair, passed through dreamy resurrections of social strife as he leaned his head upon his hand and dandled his great-grandchild on his knee to the tune.

Outside of the pits there was what the newspapers called an impending coal crisis. The proprietors having under-contracted each other on the right and left, now began to think of a common ground of action.

They met. They met much as European monarchs sometimes meet, with a smile of peace masking the grin of war. The situation was grotesque. Each man had his own very pronounced private opinion of the other. 'He was a Judas; he a Peter; and he – oh, a very devil of a deceiver in the way of the back-door tricks of the trade.' But it was most essential that, for further highly critical business purposes, these same gentlemen should appear to the British and foreign public as a highly respectable, honest-minded, earnestly-endeavouring, but most grievously-injured, body as a whole; and as they were about to appeal for business justice as if it were alms to save them from falling headlong down the mine-shafts of bankruptcy and the vacant coal-cuttings of ruin, these gentlemen smothered their pronounced private opinions of each other. Judas shook hands with Peter, the cock of conscience crowed within in vain, the devil shook hands with them all, and warm with the Satanic salutation, they, with their tongues in their cheeks, resolved mock-righteously to demand – a reduction of wage.

Then those honest-minded gentlemen put on their gloves of decorum, their silk hats of propriety, buttoned up the still small crow of the now mere cockerel of a conscience deep beneath their frock-coats and tried to appear to the public eye as if they had been to a religious service, where they had become convinced of the Truth, the whole Truth, and nothing but the Truth, so help their –

Not long after that the colliers came up from the pits to read what had been posted up at the pit-mouth as solemnly as if it were a call to united prayer on the complex question of profit and loss. But it was a half-hypocritical notice that on and after a certain date in the balmy and beautiful July a reduction of twenty-five per cent on the current rate of wages would be made.

Although the men were vaguely aware of possible war, the definite words of that definite notice passed from the pit-banks to the pit-houses, and through village and town, and over hill and down dale, in various parts of England, with something of the terror of the date fixed for the execution of a father, a son or a friend.

It was telegraphed north, south, east and west; it was cabled to America, Australia and New Zealand; and the hearts of far-off colliers' kith and kin there answered with hopeful, anxious beats. Mothers, wives and sisters at home trembled. Mothers in Wales prayed that the masters would withdraw the shadow from over their sons in Yorkshire and Lancashire mines. Anxious, crude, ill-spelt letters passed to and fro, giving cheer and hoping for the best.

Many of the men laughed at the notices as if at an artificial ghost. It was only a piece of nonsense to play the bogy. Twenty five per cent off? More like twenty five per cent on! They would see who were masters at that.

Man responded to man; pit to pit; district to district; county to county and Wales to England. To submit would be wrong. To fight would be right. They knew the mean, self-ish motives – the absolutely immoral motives – at work behind that notice. To submit would be like compounding a financial felony, and committing themselves to the week-ly prospect – sometimes to the weekly certainty – of a wage that would leave their chil-dren without sufficient food and the grocer without pay – one inhuman, the other dis-honest and both wrong.

Then the final hour – lingered – and passed, and out the men came from the mines like wasps from their nests, and with something of the wasp's moodiness – many of them with something of the wasp's sting.

Possibly not one collier in all the thousands brought out his tools with a really light heart, but all at least brought them out with a light conscience.

W. E. Tirebuck, *Miss Grace of All Souls* (1895)

Julius Turnof

Why Not Emigrate?

'Theer isn't work enow these days
For all, an' chaps like me
Are told to seek for jobs in lands
Ower t'sea:
Happen when I wur younger
It wudden't have been so strange,
But when a man is sixty odd
It's hard to change.

'To me this world is Yorkshire,
Tho' other lands are rare
To a Dalesman, furrin countries
Aren't his affair:
An' t'thowt of leavin' Litton,
'At I'll love while t'day I die,
Takes t' heart out of everything –
Emigrate? Not I.'

Referenced by William Maurice as Dorothy Una Ratcliffe, *Tomorrow* (1934),
but unidetifiable

Hermann Kätelhön

Fears and Superstitions

Hermann Kätelhön

George Bissill

Coal

There is a saying in the coalfields that God made the world but the Devil made coal, and, with an ingenuity truly fiendish, he made it black, like himself and hid it in the earth, to drive men mad in seeking it. Coal either makes or maims a man. There are no half-measures. It's one thing or the other; all black or all white, a gold watch or a wooden leg, say the miners in their homely idiom.

And to those against whom the coal holds a grudge it is the wooden leg – always.

Alice Eustace, *Smoke Haze* (1930)

Earrings

He wore gold earrings. Now, Maurice had seen some of the miners wear earrings, and he knew that these men wore them because their sight suffered in dark pits; and there was a tradition that earrings, in some subtle way, preserved the sight.

Joseph Keating, *Maurice, A Romance Of Light and Darkness* (1905)

Divination by Black Pudding

There was French blood in Geordie Robertson's wife, Mary, and it may perhaps have been owing to her origin that she was so eager for revenge when she found herself deceived by her husband.

She had begun to suspect him of infidelity even before a neighbour had given her a hint that he had a 'fancy' wife away in Bridgeton, for her husband brought home less and less with his 'pack' after his weekly tramp was over, and when she asked for explanations he 'called' her with most abusive violence.

For her further satisfaction she determined to make trial, now that the pig was to be killed, of the ancient method of divination practised by the pit-wives, of which the following is the ritual.

When the animal has been slaughtered and the blood duly made into puddings, these puddings are 'set away' to boil by the inquirer of the oracle. Then, just before they are taken out of the 'pot', the officiating priestess must say aloud that she 'gives them' to him who is suspected of infidelity. Should the puddings emerge whole, gossip is dumb-founded; should they come forth broken, the man is proved to have a 'fancy' wife.

Mary, indeed, found she could scarcely control her impatience when the fatal day came, and, the pig duly slaughtered, she 'gave' the puddings to her husband Geordie.

She waited another minute to give the spell the lawful grace, then with a trembling hand plucked forth the puddings.

'Ah – ah!' she gasped, tremulous but triumphant, 'then it is so; he has a fancy wife', and her quick brain fell to pondering a plan for discovery and revenge.

Howard Pease, *Tales Of Northumbria* (1899)

Hollover's White Bottle

You would not have suspected Hollover of being a man with an infallible cure for all human ailments. There is a tradition of the lean apothecary with famine in his cheeks and need starving in his eyes. But Hollover was portly, six foot one in his boots and in every way enormous. He looked healthy, but his personal habits were gross, and he did not love fresh air. As there was lots of it on the Black Horse heapstead, where he was heap-keeper, he had a small triangular cabin boarded off at one corner, with a stove in it. And on cold days he shut himself up, with the stove red-hot, and in the intervals of active duty fell asleep over his time-sheet. But if the handle of the door so much as clicked, he was alert, loud-voiced and hugely effective, all in a moment.

A narrow shelf ran along the wooden wall up the cabin's back, and on this stood a queer array of objects; two old safety-lamps, a lump of soft clay for mounding into can-dle-holders, a bunch of kevels and, conspicuous by its milk-white colour, a great quart glass bottle nearly full of some thick, viscous liquid.

This was Hollover's 'White Bottle'.

In its magic powers and strange efficacy Black Horse Pit believed to a man – all save the pit-doctor, Dr. Smith, who made a grimace as if he were chewing bitter aloes when it was mentioned. It always was mentioned, for the recognised thing to do when a man was brought out of the pit disabled by a runaway tub or fall of stone, was to set him down at Hollover's cabin door. Hollover brought out the white bottle, and gave the damaged man a delicate douche on the joint affected, or, if it was a cut or wound, on a dirty rag fetched out of his rag-bag, which he applied secundum artem.

'It's enough to poison any man he puts it on,' said the doctor; 'rotten eggs, turps, lamp-oil, I shouldn't wonder; and a beastly, dirty, clarty clout to make it worse.'

But what is science against faith? If the management had suppressed Hollover's white bottle there would have been a strike. Hollover himself might, you would think, have been given another berth but he was a Wittonhoe institution. He had come there with Mr. Fish, the coal-viewer, and that gentleman, while he had a sense of Hollover's concomitant small vices, found him a useful go-between, trustable ally, and gave him his head.

Ernest Rhys, *The Black Horse Pit* (1925)

The Black Man

When he spoke of Mouquette, in order to embarrass her, she told some horrible stories in a quiet voice, with much amusement.

Ah! She did some fine things! And as he asked if she herself had no lovers, she replied jokingly that she did not wish to vex her mother, but that it must happen some day. Her shoulders were bent. She shivered a little from the coldness of her garments soaked in sweat, with a gentle resigned air, ready to submit to things and men.

'People can find lovers when they all live together, can't they?'

'Sure enough.'

'And then it doesn't hurt anyone.'

'One doesn't tell the priest.'

'Oh! The priest! I don't care for him!'

'But there is the Black Man!'

'What? Black man?'

'The old miner who comes back into the pit and wrings naughty girl's necks.'

He looked at her, afraid that she was making fun of him.

'You believe in those stupid things? Then you don't know anything.'

———

It was no longer the meadows, the odour of the grass, the song of larks, the great yellow sun; it was the fallen, inundated mine, the stinking gloom, the melancholy dripping of this cellar where they had been groaning for so many days. Her perverted senses now increased the horror of it; her childish superstitions came back to her; she saw the Blackman, the old dead miner who returns to the pit to twist naughty girl's necks.

'Listen! Did you hear?'

'No, nothing. I heard nothing.'

'Yes, the Man – you know? Look! He is there. The earth has let all the blood out of the vein to revenge itself for being cut into; and he is there – you can see him – look! Blacker than night. Oh, I'm so afraid, I'm so afraid.'

Emile Zola, *Germinal* (from the original edition translated by Havelock Ellis, 1894 and revised in 1933)

The Pie Wife

'The county death rate is above the average this quarter,' said Old Burley, a toothless veteran who had miraculously escaped death in numerous explosions and falls of stone. He removed his pipe and contemplated its cotton-wrapped stem as he continued with a slight chuckle that might have been interpreted as irony: 'The bloody Pie-Wife has been cutting up summat awful lately in this district.'

Red wondered if the old man really believed that superstition. The Pie-Wife was an imaginary being supposed to hover unseen in the intricate workings of the mine, causing death and disaster, playing jokes on the men, snatching lights from lamps or favouring hewers by loosening the coal for them. Every unusual incident was attributed to her, generally in a joking way by younger men, sometimes seriously by ancients – much as they might refer to an 'Act of God'.

Harry Carlisle, *Darkness At Noon* (1932)

Pearl Binder

Recreations

George Bissill

George Bissill

The Cock Fight

A section of Easingden citizens sought soul-satisfaction in game-cock fights. It was criminal, of course, to encourage the cocks to fulfil the cardinal purpose of their creation; precaution had to be practised to conceal the place where the combats were held.

Those who witnessed the cock-fights saw something of the soul of the Master-Artist. The passions that were stirred were strong and pellucid; and had persisted since the beginning of time. It was clear that God had rejoiced in creating the game-cocks. They were beautiful, proud, uncompromising. The splendid symmetry of line of their legs and breasts; the unyielding thrust of their haughty heads as they strutted in the ring, during the first moments of battle; these were sights to stir unashamed tears in the heart.

But these crimson encounters were not for the conventional. Though it happened that in the company of spectators a priest and his churchwarden surreptitiously enjoyed themselves; feasting on the precious spectacle of the raging cocks with an ardour and an attention, that the sacrament several hours later would fail to arouse. Routine is death!

None appeared to enjoy the encounter more than the priest and his churchwarden. So that it is impossible to say what scarlet passions throb beneath the dark clerical costume. It is certain, however, that the Creator of 'Wilhelm Meister', and his ardent disciple in Cheyne Row, were both wrong in asserting that clothes bespeak the man. The clerical patrons of the cock-fights gave the decisive lie to the whole Clothes-Philosophy.

The sportsmen emerged in all possible secrecy from their homes in the Rows in Easingden, while the darkness still enveloped normal, sleeping inhabitants. They moved like shadows, converging to a point pre-arranged among themselves; and once clear of the houses their talk became animated. There were four miles to walk to the moors; where the contests took place.

The birds were hooded and carried under the arms of their owners. More and more the men merged themselves in the approaching fight. And although their talk was not without good humour, latent antagonism worked in the souls of the supporters of each party. The game-cocks were more real to them than birds only. They were emblems of pride, of valour. In what manner they acquitted themselves would they bring triumph or defeat, honour or dishonour, to their owners and backers. And there were the bets.

Before they were thrown into the ring their owners finally stroked them; and even talked to them encouragingly. When these motions of affection had ceased, the birds were thrown into the ring simultaneously. For a second or two they sprouted their heads, churred and strutted majestically. They were instantly and proudly defiant. They masked their purpose. Their eyes glistened maliciously. Their quivering bodies thrilled to the miracle of their creation. In a further second or two there would be a lightning thrust of spur and wing; but as yet the birds were watchful; giving no sign.

———————

The fight was ended. Although both protagonists were done to death, one was clearly the victor; for he rose for a second from the earth, where his enemy lay prone, as if to take farewell of the scene of his triumph in a befitting manner. The vanquished bird was already dead; and in a second's space the victor too had fallen. He, like his enemy, had paid the final price of life: to draw a few breaths, and create a spectacle for others, in a sombre mystery.

———————

Later in the day the details of the fight were narrated in the Portland Arms; and any whose memory failed to do justice to the leading episodes in the progress of the fight were assisted by other spectators present. There were differences of opinion upon the respective merits of the birds; but all in all, the fight was always a bloody good one. This opinion was repeated over and over again. Its repetition unified the spectators in a spiritual bond: as Church-worshippers are unified when they simultaneously turn their faces to the East in order to repeat their Belief.

J. G. Sinclair, *Easingden* (1926)

George Bissill

A Long Main

'Bob Stevison fought Smithson's cocks for him, an' grandfeythor fought his own, kneelin' doon on the cock-pit floor wiv his coat off so as to handle them the better.'

'The first two or three battles grandfeythor wins easy, Stevison using his warst cocks at the first, d'ye se, oot o' craft mevvies to get longer odds i' the bettin', so that at one time grandfeythor was five battles to two to the good; a bit later it was eight all, an' the excitement was immense, bets flyin' aboot like snowflakes at Christmas.'

'Then Stevison oots wiv a beauty – a perfect picture it was ov a fighter; eyes like a furnace at night, liftin' his legs like a Derby winner, wings an' tail clipped short – glossy wi' health an' shinin' like mahogany.'

Howard Pease, *Tales of Northumbria* (1899)

Whippets

Red toyed with the broken peak of his cap and stared at a group of men passing.

One of them had a beautifully groomed whippet on a leash. It trotted nervously, a-quiver with suppressed energy. He compared its lithe grace with his own lumbering body and the stiffness of the older men at his side. He remembered puzzling over a remark made by Judd in the pub one night, to the effect that it was natural that miners should worship these speedy, graceful animals. Then one day, as he was watching dogs flash over the turf at a mad, free speed, he felt suddenly released from the cramping lowness of the mine and experienced the soaring sensation that he felt when he closed his eyes in the cage as it rushed madly up (not down) the shaft.

––––––––––

Throughout this scene Red moved idly, his face sullen and his manner distrait. Only when the first race started and the mechanical rabbits fled down the course, pursued by grey and dun streaks of beautifully running dogs, did he show interest. Here was flight such as he could never attain. The miners yelled hoarsely during the fleeting duration of the race, then the winners cheered and slapped one another on the back and the losers nodded dolefully. Race after race was run, with excitement mounting until it became a frenzy. Bottles passed from lip to lip, men staggered quickly from the starting-post to the far end of the course, jostling each other roughly but with good temper. Money changed hands rapidly. At the end of each race the names of winners and placements were announced on a chalked blackboard. Firefly, Bonny Lass, Black-Eyed Susan, Prince Charley, Cock O' The North, Ben Bolt, Thief O' Time, Flash, Starlight, Maggie O'Rourke – were some of the names greeted with cheers. Winners went to pat the dogs as they were being blanketed and put back in their boxes. Dog fanciers hovered around making offers to owners.

Harry Carlisle, *Darkness At Noon* (1932)

The Band Marches Past the Window

So he sat one Sunday when outside all the world was astir with life. In his suit of Sunday black – which, with kindly insistence, he had obtained – he sat before the open window, looking tall in his emaciation, his clothes hanging in drab folds about the body that had been so sturdy, while his glance crept over the heads of the crowd outside, the packed bedroom windows of the houses opposite, the purple and brown roofs, and the fringe of yellowing trees over in the church-yard seen through a gap in the houses, that also showed a strip of umber common. And as he sat there, the thin white hair and bare top of his head shining in the weak sunshine, his old blue eyes, tense with past pain, looked beyond the noisy hurry of the world outside, and ranged the spectral years of the past.

It was Hospital Sunday, and below on Church Hill the crowd shuffled uncomfortably in its Sunday clothes, keeping up an incessant buzz of talk as they awaited the procession of workmen's societies, boy scouts, mine officials, bandsmen and banners.

Playing the Old March.

And then, far away, like an echo across the years, came the sound of a brass band playing the old march. His pale blue eyes, slightly filmed with nystagmus, opened wide and his grizzled chin dropped slightly. It was 'Under the Double Eagle' they were playing...

He caught his breath like a whisper. Lord! 'Under the Double Eagle'! Hearing its martial strains a long-past day came to life again, a day of youth and freedom and health, and the crude joys of the golden times. How many times he had played that march! 'Ta-ra-ra pom pom pom! Ta-ra-ra pom pom pom! Ta-ra-ra pom, ta-ra-ra pom, ta-ra-ra pom pom pom!...' Lord, those were the happiest days of his life, when the world had been a wonderful fresh garden, before it had grown into a gigantic cockpit of industrial trouble. An incredulous smile came to his lips. Fancy that, now!...

That march!... He saw again the old room a little higher up the hill, where the band had met, and little Burton, the conductor – a martinet if you like! – standing by the mantelpiece and beating time like a clever cock-sparrow – beating it as well drunk as sober! 'Better drunk!' said Little Burton; and Dicky Thomas, the wonderful cornet-player, of whom great things were predicted, but who never achieved fame; and... Lord, what a lot of heroes!... The smile left his lips as he considered them in their black uniforms braided on the chest and arms, and their little shiny-peaked hats with the gold-braid button on the crown. And he had worn that uniform too, and the shiny-peaked hat... they were somewhere in the house now. Hark!

There they went again, 'Ta-ra-ra pom pom. Ta-ra-ra pom pom pom pom pom!' Lord, he knew every bar and all the difficult bits, for Little Burton had kept their noses to the copy. The happiest days of his life! To sit in the room with them, to see Little Burton raise his silver-mounted baton, to glance weightily over the music, to see the baton descend, and hear the full blare of the opening... sweet, sweet!... to be carried along upborne upon the rhythmic waves of sound, inserting one's own notes with the gravity and precision of a god, playing one's own little solo part in the critical silence, red face above the trombone assuring the world of an impeccable rendering, while the heart beneath the braided black uniform flustered in the crisis, then the full entry of the band again, the swelling rush to the climax, nearer and nearer, until the windows rattled again and all the world was a roaring Niagara of brazen sound, and then the staccato notes at the end, like a champion's reiterated defiance, and the startled silence, followed by heavy breathing and a rustling of legs and a murmured criticism to the euphonium player that it 'wasna so bad, teckin' it all round...'

'Ta-ra-ra pom pom pom!'

'Here they are!'

First came a great green banner, borne on his own level, and at a glance he saw it belonged to the Canford Chase Provident Society, of which he was the chief founder and three times chairman and present treasurer...

Hark! He stiffened slightly. Ah, he knew them! They were coming, the Black Uniforms...!

How they played! He forgot that strangers were in the ranks, that of the original band not one was left beside himself. It was his band, the band he had founded, and Little Burton was conducting, and Fatty Hackwood beating the drum so musicianly, and surely that was Dicky Thomas on the cornet? The Black Uniforms! They were here...!

'Ta-ra-ra pom pom pom!'

Bruce Beddow, *Man of the Midlands* (1928)

Fleet-As-Wind

'Then aal the shoutin' begins agen, an' the whole field start yellin', "Lancashire Lad's got the lead; he wins by a street; three to one on the faawn! The bitch is done!" I turned fair muzzy, an' grippin' the marrer, I says, "It's aal up, marrer, the bitch's shoulder's given, I doot", an' sits me doon on the dyke sick as a cat. But just then I hears Red Tom (who was clingin' tiv a tree, ti see better, close beside the dyke) sayin', in a puzzled sort o' way, tiv his marrer. "Smash, marrer, but that's a funny one; Wor Lanky's changed his colour!" And the next cam' a yell frae the crowd fit ti wake the dead, "Black leads, black leads, the bitch wins! She has it aal tiv hersel'! Ten to one on the bitch!" An' lookin' up again, sure enough I see the canny aad lass right i' the middle o' the next field gallopin' close on ti puss, 'Wor Lanky' nowheres ti be seen.

'Even then I cud scarce b'lieve my eyes, but the judge he comes ridin' back, an' shouts, "Black" an' up the flag-steward holds the white flag, an' I knaa'd it wes aal right.

'"Marrer," I says, "she's won; shake hands, for she's a jool." An' the marrer an' me shakes hands like madmen.'

Howard Pease, *The Mark O' The Deil And Other Northumbrian Tales* (1894)

A Violin-Maker in the North

Out from the noisome pit, from black caverns below the ground,
Blinded, and grimed with the coal, and worn with their weary round,
When gloaming lies on our land, and the peaceful sky is grey,
The miners homeward wend, for done is the task of the day.
High on the brow of the hill, where fields gleam yellow with corn,
A dozen red roofs are scattered round one tall shaft forlorn;
And there the poor folk dwell, and there the women must work,
Whilst the men go down to the pit from earliest dawn till mirk,
And children play in the road, or wander barefoot and free,
And gather the scarlet poppies, or count the ships on the sea.

There – a few years gone – a collier dwelt and toiled,
Like the rest, weary and poor, with cinders and earth besoiled;
But, though his hands were hard, his fingers were deft of touch,
And the coal that begrimed his brow had not darkened his thoughts o'ermuch.
Every eve – as soon as the welcome bell of release

Heralded rest and air, and some bless'd hours of peace —
He to his home would hie, as an arrow travels straight,
And seek his accustomed place by the narrow garden gate.
The northern twilight lingered and lasted that he might sit
And whittle a piece of wood, and curiously fashion it,
Till night, in gentle reproach, cast her veil across the land:
'Thou hast laboured, friend, all day. Come, stay the work of they hand!'
But he laughed as he trimmed his lamp, and cried: 'What is day to me?
The blue sky is not for miners — this shall my moontide be.
Victory lies before me, for they who work must win,
And I'll find the secret at last of the voice of the violin!'

Within a cupboard of oak, where none too close might spy,
Was the copy he sought to copy — a gem he prized o'er high.
Oft did he pause in work, to touch the treasure awhile,
To hold it lovingly close, and gaze on its form, and smile,
Till the shining pine grew alive, and the head and neck stretched out,
And answered with quivering gleam his almost jubilant shout:
'Ay, thou'rt kin to a Strad, thou wert moulded in self-same line,
The colour, the body, the purfling, the height and the breadth are thine;
Thou hast lain by the mighty dead; some luminous glance from him
Has flashed on thy golden varnish with flame that shall ne'er grow dim!
Should I call thee counterfeit? Thy speechless glory seems
Like the face of that mystic master who visits me oft in dreams
Whether I wake or sleep, whether I'm lying here
In my bothie upon the hill, where there's neither friend nor cheer,
Or when, in the womb of the earth, dark-prisoned, down underneath,
I stay the beat of my hammer to hear mine own gasping breath,
And he comes and bides awhile, and with patience he teaches me,
For his brow and his eyes tell much, though never a word says he.'

The miner's work went forth: in distant cities sold,
The thing that his thought had fashioned was prized and bartered for gold.
Men gazed thereon and said: 'It is well and bravely made;'
So strangers drew forth the music which he in a shrine had laid.
And I mind me one summer eve when a fiddle he brought to show
To her who pens these lines, and to whom he murmured low:
'Tis the best that I have achieved — see, I have brought it to you;
Now I can sleep at peace — 'tis the best I shall ever do.
Nay, it has ne'er yet uttered — in my hand it lies dumb and still;

Yet who shall say that it sings not? I gaze and I gaze my fill,
Whilst out of his heart I have wrought, through the quiet strings arise
Great waves of rhythmic measure – an ocean of melodies;
For the moan of the sea is there – I caged it with mine own hand –
And the cry of the soughing wind that sweeps o'er stricken land,
Or, methinks, the laugh of a child, or a girl's last-uttered sigh,
As she lays her hand in her sweetheart's and turns on her bed to die.
Forgive my foolish words – some things can I ne'er speak right,
But down in the mines they are clear, all clear though in darkest night.
For deep in the pathless seams, on those cramping blackened floors,
We seem nearer to God and music than in this sunshine of yours.'

Lady Caroline Lindsay, *The King's Last Vigil And Other Poems* (1894)

Singing

I was passing a village hall in a mining valley on a Sunday. I heard a male voice choir trying to lift the roof from the place. The sound was so good that I opened the door and
went in. Of course I could stay and listen, they said, with that instant politeness which
greets the stranger in every mining town and village in South Wales.

About thirty young men in blue serge suits were grouped round an ancient but hero-
ic piano. The pianist knew all the dead notes! The conductor stood facing his choir,
waving a baton and stamping his feet with the abandon of all Welsh conductors. And
the choir sang like angels in blue serge…

They were miners in their Sunday clothes. Some of them had done a week's work in
a pit; others were unemployed. Every one had put on a dark suit, a collar, and because it
was Sunday, a dark and sombre tie.

Now, it is not often that the casual visitor to South Wales sees thirty miners together
with clean faces. He sees thousands tramping home like niggers. The faces of these men
would have astonished those who think of the miner as a brutalized and dis-affected
person. They were fine, sensitive faces; keen, intelligent and distinguished above all, I
thought, for that look of religious fanaticism which you meet in Italian art and – in
South Wales!

I would have said, had I been ignorant of their calling, that they were theological students.

All over South Wales are male voice choirs recruited from the pits. English people, if
they ever consider the question, think that this passion for singing has something to do
with the Eisteddfod or that it has a purely financial aspect. This is not so. Most of these

choirs cannot afford to sing at the Eisteddfod, and few of them make much money. They sing for the joy of singing.

The old saying, that when you get two Englishmen together you get a club, Scotsmen a Caledonian Society, and two Irishmen a riot, might be extended to Wales. When you get two Welshmen together you get a choral society.

But why?

Because the Welsh express themselves more readily in song than in any other way. It is a national gift. They use their voices as a ladder to heaven. They are transfiguring in song.

'The history of this choir is interesting,' I was told during a pause in the singing.

'When the strike was on years ago — you remember the Tonypandy riots — a number of miners went over the hill to keep out of trouble. And, of course, they began to sing! When we feel sad in Wales we sing.

'Well, they liked their singing so much that they decided to become a choir! The members have changed with the years but the choir originated over on the hill-side there while the brickbats and the bottles were flying about below in the valley...

'And now,' asked the conductor, 'would you like us to sing something in Welsh?'

'I would!'

The choir grouped itself. This is characteristic of Welsh choirs. The members like to face one another, and seem to be singing to one another. And they sang something ineffably sad in Welsh.

At least three members looked ready for martyrdom. When the song was over the expression changed, and the singers came to earth with a smile.

'Something in English? Right!'

They sang a good old part-song, but there was nothing English in their rendering of it. There was no roystering village green in it, with jolly drinkers at an inn. They sang it religiously! And I realised that singing in Wales is a spiritual interlude, something like prayer.

H. V. Morton, *In Search of Wales* (1932)

A G Meek

Pitman's Songs

Hermann Kätelhön

George Bissill

A Miner's Morning Song

Awake, brother miner! the stars have grown dim,
'Tis time to be stirring the sleep-strengthened limb;
The lark is saluting the regions of love,
And soon will the sun flash the grey mists above:
Prepare thee to sink, though the fancy should soar;
We must to the dark scenes of labour once more.

Come! rise, brother rise! and from grumbling refrain;
He who murmurs in idleness, murmurs in vain;
A sweet slumber hangs on thy little one's brows,
A love-hallowed prayer's in the heart of thy spouse;
She pleads where thou knowest she had pled well before,
That angels may guard thee to safety once more.

Arise! brother miner! 'Twas only a dream,
That hum of green woodlands, that stroll by the stream;
Some joy-loving fairy, in portraiture gay,
Has shown thee by night what thou seest not by day,
Yet, brother, despair not; the hours will pass o'er:
We'll rise as the day wanes to gladness once more.

Suppress these deep sighs, brother, though it may be
The fate of thy kinsman is waiting for thee:
O'er sorrows untasted 'tis folly to brood;
We must, like that kinsman, brave danger for food.
Then up and be stirring; like serf-men of yore,
We'll rest when we've plodded our portion once more.

Be cheerful, poor brother! I've heard of a land
Where no over-labour e'er blisters the hand –
A land where no fetters of slavery are seen,
Where the grindstone of tyranny never hath been:
Perhaps we'll go there when our ploddings are o'er,
And then we'll be weary-boned miners no more.

David Wingate, *Select Poems And Songs* (1890)

The Pitman's Happy Times

When aw wes yung, maw collier lads,
  Ne man cud happier be;
For wages was like sma' coals then,
  An' cheps cud raise a spree.
Wor pay-neet cam' wiv drink an' dance,
  Wor sweethearts luckt se fine
An' lumps o' beef an' dads o' duff
  Wes there for folks to dine.
An' then we spent six merry neets,
  For grumlin' we had nyen;
But the times o' wor prosperity
  Will niver cum agyen.

Wor hooses then wes ower sma'
  For ivery nuik was chock;
Wor drawers wes fair mahogany,
  An' se wes chairs an' clock.
Wor feather beds, and powls se fine,
  Wes welcum te the seet;
A man work'd harder i' the day
  Wi' thinkin' o' th' neet.
Spice hinnies on the gurdle fizz'd,
  Maw tea had run in't then;
But the times o' wor prosperity
  Will niver cum agyen.

J. P. Robson, *Songs of Bards of the Tyne* (1849)

This song was directed to be sung to the tune of *In the Days When We Went Gypsing*. A Wallsend collier remarks, 'The author of this song was never a miner, perhaps this explains his exuberance' (A. L. Lloyd, 1952).

The Collier's Rant

As me an' maw marra was gannin' te wark,
We met wi' the Deil, it was i' the dark;
Aw up w' me pick, and it bein' i' the neet,
Aw knockt off his horns, likewise his club feet.
  Follow the horses Jonny, me laddy,
  Follow them through, me canny lad, oh!
  Follow the horses, Jonny, me laddy,
  Oh! lad, lie away, canny lad, oh!

As me an' me marra was puttin' the trams,
The lowe it went oot, an' me marra went wrang:
Ye was has laught had ye seen the gam, -
The Deil gat me marra, but aw gat the tram.
  Follow the horses, Jonny, me laddy, etc.

Oh! marra, oh! marra, what does thou think,
Aw've broken me bottle, an' spilt aw me drink,
Aw've lost me shin splints amang the greet styens;
Draw me ti' the shaft, lad it's time ti' gan hyem.
  Follow the horses, etc...

First Printed with further verses in Joseph Ritson's, *Northumberland Garland*; or *Newcastle Nightingale* (1793)

The song was subsequently published by various editors of North Country song collections (A. L. Lloyd, 1952).

Song of the Miners

We come from the gloom of the mine,
Claiming our share of the sun,
Claiming our share of the sweets of the earth,
Our share of its riches, it's comfort and mirth;
We come in the shackles of pain
And steep is the way we must go,
But rally, my comrades, our cause will not fail,
For Right is our watchword, and Right will prevail.

We come with the banner of Truth,
Justice and freedom to gain,
Tho' traitors desert us and cowards despise,
Tho' tyrants deter us in strength we will rise;
And forward like men we will strive,
For the sake of the ages to be:
So rally! my comrades, our cause will not fail.
For Right is our watchword, and Right will prevail.

Referenced by William Maurice as Joe Corrie, *The Image O' God And Other Poems* (1937), but unidentifiable

Don't Go Down in the Mine Dad

A miner was leaving his home for his work,
When he heard his little child scream;
He went to his bedside, his little white face,
Oh Daddy, I've had such a dream;
I dreamt that I saw the pit all afire,
And men struggled hard for their lives;
The scene it then changed, and the top of the mine
Was surrounded by sweethearts and wives.

    Refrain:
Don't go down in the mine, Dad,
Dreams very often come true;

Daddy, you know it would break my heart
If anything happened to you;
Just go and tell my dream to your mates,
And as true as the stars that shine,
Something is going to happen today,
Dear Daddy, don't go down the mine!

Don't go down in the mine, Dad, etc.,
Whilst waiting his turn with his mates to descend,
He could not banish his fears,
He return'd home again to his wife and his child,
Those words seem'd to ring through his ears,
And, ere the day ended, the pit was on fire,
When a score of brave men lost their lives.
He thank'd God above for the dream his child had,
As once more the little one cries.

Don't go down in the mine, Dad, etc.

Robert Donnelly, source unknown (1910)

The song is thought to have been suggested by the Great 1907 Mining Disaster at St Genard, South Wales. The song became a popular folk song and was recorded by S. Kirkby and K. Walters.

A. G. Meek

An Old Song

The slag mounds show a dreary heap
The river's black between,
But this song was an old song
When these grey hills were green:
It's give and take, and take and give,
So long as man and woman live.

When man has set his ready head
To build the world anew,
It's take and give, and give and take,
And what I say is true.

He'll take the beauty, take the peace,
He'll turn things upside down,
And where a lovely forest stood
He'll plan a mining town.

He'll level rocks, he'll foul a stream,
Or else he'll drain it dry,
He'll make this earth a sorry place
And next he'll crowd the sky.

But when he's done the best he can
To make an old world new,
He'll own, if he's an honest man,
That yet this song rings true:
It's give and take, and take and give,
So long as man and woman live.

E. M. Martin, unpublished

Success Unto the Coal Trade

Good people, listen while I sing
The source from whence your comforts spring;
And may each wind that blows still bring
Success unto the coal trade.
Who but unusual pleasure feels
To see our fleets of ships and keels?
Newcastle, Sunderland, and the Shields
May ever bless the coal trade.

May vultures on the caitiff fly,
And gnaw his liver till he die,
Who looks with evil, jealous eye,
Down upon the coal trade.
If that should fail, what would ensue?
Sure ruin, and disaster too!
Alas! alas! what would we do
If 'twere not for the coal trade?

What is it gives us cakes of meal?
What is it crams our wames se weel
With lumps of beef and draughts of ale?
What is't, but just the coal trade.
Not Davis' Straits, or Greenland oil,
Nor all the wealth springs from the soil,
Could ever make our pots to boil,
Like unto our coal trade.

Ye sailors; wives that love a drop
Of stingo fra the brandy shop
How could you get one single drop,
If it were not for the coal trade?
Ye pitman lads, so blithe and gay,
Who meet to tipple each pay-day,
Down on your marrow bones, and pray,
Success unto the coal trade.

May Wear and Tyne still draw and pour
Their jet black treasure to the shore,
And we with all our strength will roar,
Success unto the coal trade.
Ye owners, masters, sailors a',
Come, shout till ye be like to fa';
Your voices raise – huzza! huzza!
We all live by the coal trade.

This nation is in duty bound
To prize those who work under ground,
For 'tis well known this country round
Is kept up by the coal trade.
May Wear and Tyne and Thames ne'er freeze,
Our ships and keels will pass with ease,
Then Newcastle, Sunderland and Shields
Will still uphold the coal trade.

I tell the truth, you may depend,
In Durham or Northumberland,
No trade in them could ever stand,
If it were not for the coal trade.
The owners know full well, 'tis true,
Without pitmen, keelmen, sailors too,
To Britain they might bid adieu,
If it were not for the coal trade.

So to conclude and made an end
Of these few lines which I have penn'd,
We'll drink a health to all these men
Who carry on the coal trade.
To owners, pitmen, keelmen too,
And sailors, who the seas to plough,
Without these men we could not do,
Nor carry on the coal trade.

Anon.

We Dig and Delve . . .

We dig and delve in the dark-some mine,
　　With a flick-'ring can-dle near; . . .
We delve and dig 'mid the dust and grime,
　　In the long black gal-ler-ies drear.
And a-bove in the air in his car-riage and pair
The proud lord rolls a-long; . . .
He spends our gold, for our strength is sold
　　To him thro' in-jus-tice and wrong.
　　To him thro' in-jus-tice and wrong.

We toil and moil while o'er naked limbs
　　The water trickles and glides;
We moil and toil till our life nought seems
　　Save a woe that on earth long abides.
And above heaven rings, as the blithe lark sings,
But our children moan and weep,
For the rich man takes what each miner makes
　　In the pit so dark and deep –
　　In the pit so dark and deep.

We hew and hammer, each stroke of the pick
　　Makes fuel for furnace and hearth;
We hammer and hew that iron made quick
　　May run to the ends of the earth.
And our brothers in toil who delve in the soil,
　　Or work 'mid the factory's roar,
Like us are all bound to toil the year round.
　　While the rich cry ever for more –
　　While the rich cry ever for more.

But we live and we love, and our tyrants shall learn
　　We are men with passions and might;
We love and we live, and our rough hearts yearn
　　For the day that shall follow our night:
When we'll live joyous lives with our children and wives,
　　No longer debased by our toil,
When each man shall take what each man shall make

In the pit, the mill or the soil –
In the pit, the mill or the soil.

W. H. Uttley, in E. Carpenter, *Chants of Labour. A Song Book of the People* (1888)

The Bonnie Pit Laddie

The bonny pit laddie, the canny pit laddie,
The bonny pit laddie for me O!
He sits in his hole, as black as a cole,
And brings the white siller to me O!

The bonny pit laddie, the canny pit laddie,
The bonny pit laddie for me O!
He sits on his cracket, and hews in his jacket,
And brings the white siller to me O!

Text and Melody first printed in J. Peacock, *A Favourite Collection of Tunes with Variations* (c. 1800)

There is also a more modern, but very similar, version of this poem that is known as 'The Collier Lad'. The later version was communicated by H. Sheratt of Wheatley, Doncaster.

The Collier's Pay Week

The Baf week is o'er – no repining –
    Pay-Saturday's swift on the wing;
At length the blythe morning comes shining,
    When kelter makes colliers sing:
'Tis Spring, and the weather is cheary,
The birds whistle sweet on the spray;
Now coal working lads, trim and airy,
    To Newcastle town hie away.

Those married jog on with their hinnies,
    Their canny bairns go by their side;
The daughters keep teasing their minnies

For new cloaths to keep up their pride:
They plead — Easter Sunday does fear them,
    For, if they have nothing that's new,
The Crow, spiteful bird! will besmear them;
    Oh then! what a sight for to view!

The young men, full blithsome and jolly,
    March forward, all decently clad;
Some lilting up, 'Cut-and-dry, Dolly',
    Some singing. 'The bonny Pit Lad'
The pranks that were play'd at last binding
    Engage some in humourous chat;
Some halt by the way-side on finding
    Primroses to place in their hat.

Bob Cranky, Jack Hogg and Dick Marley,
    Bill Hewitt, Luke Carr and Tom Brown,
In one jolly squad set off early
    From Benwell to Newcastle town:
Such hewers as they (none need doubt it)
    Ne'er handled a shovel or pick;
In high or low seam they could suit it,
    In regions next door to Old Nick.

Some went to buy hats and new jackets,
    And other to see a bit fun;
And some wanted leather and tackets
    To cobble their canny pit shoon:
Save the ribbon Dick's dear had requested,
    (Aware he had plenty of chink)
There was no other care him infested,
    Unless 'twere his care for good drink.

In the morning the dry man advances
    To purl-shop to toss off a gill,
Ne'er dreading the ills and mischances
    Attending on those who sit still:
The drink, Reason's monitor quelling,
    Inflames both the brain and the eyes;
The inchantment commenc'd, there's no telling

When care-drowning tipplers will rise.

O Malt! we acknowledge thy powers
    What good and what ill dost thou brew!
Our good friend in moderate hours –
Our enemy when we get fu':
Could thy vot'ries avoid the fell furies
    So often awaken'd by thee,
We would seldom need Judges or Juries
    To send folk to Tyburn tree!)

At length in Newcastle they centre –
    In Hardy's* a house much renown'd,
The jovial company enter,
    Where stores of good liquor abound:
As quick as the servants could fill it,
    (Till emptied was quarts half a score)
With heart-burning thirst down they swill it,
And thump on the table for more.

While thus in fine cue they are seated,
    Young cock-fighting Ned from the Fell #
Peep'd in – his 'How dye?' repeated,
    And hop'd they were all very well;
He swore he was pleased to see them –
    One rose up to make him sit down,
And join in good fellowship wi' them,
    For him they would spend their last crown.

The liquor beginning to warm them,
    In friendship the closer they knit,
And tell and hear jokes – and, to charm them
    Comes ROBIN, from Denton-Bourne pit;
An odd witty, comical fellow,
    At either a jest or a tale,
Especially when he was mellow
    With drinking stout Newcastle ale.

With bousing, and laughing and smoking,
    The time slippeth swiftly away;

And while they are ranting and joking
    The church-clock proclaims it mid-day;
And now for black-puddings, long measure,
    They go to TIB TROLLOBAG'S stand,
And away bear the glossy rich treasure,
With joy, like curl'd bugles in hand.

And now a choice house they agreed on,
    Not far from the head of the Quay;
Where they their black puddings might feed on
    And spend the remains of the day;
Where pipers and fiddlers resorted,
    To pick up the straggling pence,
And where the pit lads often sported
    Their money at Fiddle and Dance.

BLIND WILLIE ° the fidler sat scraping,
    In corner just as they went in:
Some Willington callants were shaking
    Their feet to his musical din:
Jack vow'd he would have some fine cap'ring,
    As soon as their dinner was o'er,
With the lassies that wore the white apron,
    Now reeling about on the floor.

Their hungry stomachs being eased,
    And gullets well clear'd with a glass,
Jack rose form the table and seized
    The hand of the frolicsome lass.
'Ma hinny!' says he, 'pray excuse me –
    To ask thee to dance I make free.'
She reply'd 'I'd be loth to refuse thee!
    Now fidler play – 'Jigging for me'.

The damsel displays all her graces,
    The collier exerts all his power,
They caper in circling paces,
    And set at each end of the floor:
He jumps, and his heels knack and rattle,
    At turns of the music so sweet

He makes such a thundering brattle,
   The floor seems afraid of his feet.

This couple being seated, rose Bob up,
   He wish'd to make one in a jig;
But a Willington lad set his gob up, –
   O'er him there should none 'run the rig'
For now 'twas his turn for a caper,
   And he would dance first as he'd rose;
Bob's passion beginning to vapour,
   He twisted his opponent's nose.

The Willington lads, for their Franky,
   Jump'd up, to revenge the foul deed;
And those on behalf of Bob Cranky
   Sprung forward – for now there was need.
Bob canted the form, with a kevel,
   As he was exerting his strength;
But he got on the lug such a nevel,
   That down he came all his long length.

Tom Brown, from behind the long table,
   Impatient to join in the fight,
Made a spring, some rude foe to disable,
   For he was a man of some might;
Misfortune, alas! was attending,
   An accident fill'd him with fear;
An old rusty nail his flesh rending,
   Oblig'd him to slink in the rear.

When sober, a mild man was Marley,
   More apt to join friends than make foes;
But rais'd by the juice of the barley,
   He put in some sobbling blows.
And cock-fighting Ned was their Hector,
   A courageous fellow, and stout;
He stood their bold friend and protector,
   And thump'd the opponents about.

All hand-over-head, topsy turvy,
    They struck with fists, elbows and feet,
A Willington callant, called Gurvy,
    Was top-nails tost over the seat:
Luke Carr had one eye clos'd entire;
    And what is a serio-farce,
Poor Robin was cast on the fire,
    His breeks torn and burnt off his a——e.

Oh, Robin! What argued thy speeches?
    Disaster now makes thee quite mum;
Thy wit could not save the good breeches,
    That mencefully cover'd thy bum:
To some slip-shop now thou may go trudging,
    And lug out some squandering coins;
For now 'tis too late to be grudging, –
    Thou cannot go home with bare groins.

How the warfaring companies parted,
    The Muse chuseth not to proclaim;
But, 'tis thought, that, being rather down-hearted,
    They quietly went – 'toddling hame'.
Now ye Collier callants, so clever,
    Residing 'tween Tyne and the Wear,
Beware, when you fuddle together,
    Of making too free with strong beer.

* Sign of the Black Boy, Groat Market.
#Gateshead Fell.
°William Purvis, a blind fiddler, so called.

Anon.

The Pitman

Of a pitman we'll sing,
Who works for the king,
    Jovial, good natured and civil;
He'll work and he'll sing,
And profit he'll bring,
    From caverns that's near to the devil.

To his labour below,
With courage he'll go,
    Upon his pit rope and his crook;
Nor will he once dwell,
On the visions of hell,
    Nor yet fash his thumb with a book.

All his wish is good ale,
An' his claes upon sale,
    For a tankard he'll put ev'r night:
Let the learned still think,
That a hearty sound drink,
    Is a pitman's most crowned delight.

Anon.

A. G. Meek

Authors' Biographies and Bibliography

Angold, John Penrose (1909–1943)
Poet and airman. Whilst he was a law student, the *New English Weekly* began publishing his poems and became a regular contributor. He later joined the RAF, fought in World War Two and died in service as a Pilot Officer

New English Weekly 15 March 1934
Collected Poems (Peter Russell, 1952)

Ashley, Kenneth H. (1887–?)
English poet, novelist, journalist and farmer.

Up Hill and Down Dale (J. Lane, 1924)

Beddow, Bruce (1897–?)
English author. (No other information has been retrievable.)

A Man of the Midlands (Cassell and Company Ltd, 1928)

Boden, Frederick Cecil
Miner and lecturer. Mined at Williamsthorpe colliery in the Midlands until he was put on the short time in 1926. Moved to Exeter where he taught for the Workers Education Association.

Out of the Coalfields (E. P. Dutton, 1929)
Miner (E. P. Dutton, 1932)

Burns, Robert (1759–1796)
Scottish poet, farmer, excise officer. Born in Ayrshire, the son of a farmer. Educated in his spare time whilst being fully employed on the family farm. In 1786 his work was published and was an immediate success. In 1791 he relinquished farming life and became an excise officer. He wrote in both Scots and English with equal facility and his work continues to be much celebrated.

'My Collier Laddie' in Henley, W. E. and Henderson, T.F. (eds) *Robert Burns Poetry* Vol III songs *Johnson's Musical Museum* 1787:1803 (T. C. & E. C. Jack, 1897)

Burnett, Frances Hodgson (1849–1924)
American novelist. Born in Manchester, England and then emigrated with her mother to Tennessee, USA in 1865. Began writing for American magazines and was much published. She made her reputation as a novelist with her story of Lancashire life in

That Lass O'Lowries (1877) which was, like some of her other works, dramatised.

That Lass O'Lowries (F. Warne & Co, 1877)
Little Lord Fauntleroy (Charles Scribner's & Sons, 1886)

Carlisle, Harry
No further information retrievable.

Darkness at Noon (Jarrolds, 1932)

Chicken, Edward (1698–1746)
English poet and teacher. Lived in Newcastle, educated at St John's Charity school and then later became a teacher. He was regarded as a man of wisdom and arbiter of small disputes in the town and from this became known as the 'Mayor of White Cross' (White Cross being a local monument). He was also the clerk of the local church where he was later buried.

'The Collier's Wedding' (printed in 1773 by T. Saint)

Corrie, Joe (1894–1968)
Miner and writer. Mined in West Fife. Began writing when unemployed after World War One. His work was published in the Glasgow paper Forward and Fife Miners Players also produced his plays. After 1926 he left mining and tried to make a living from writing.

The Image O'God and Other Poems (Porpoise Press, 1937)
Poems by Joe Corrie (The Galloway Gazette Ltd., 1955)

Dataller, Roger, pseudonym of Arthur Archibald Eaglestone (1892–1980)
Steel and mine worker, teacher and writer. Some of his books written under his pseudonym. He became a writer and a teacher in adult education. He was inspired by the experiences of local people and local history.

A Pitman's Notebook (Cape, 1925)

Davies, Rhys (1903–1978)
Welsh author. Born in the mining area of Rhondda Valley, South Wales. Moved to London in the 1920s where he worked and wrote and mixed in Socialist intellectual circles. By the 1930s he had written two novels and was earning a living writing on a 'shoe-string'. Had correspondence with D. H. Lawrence and visited him whilst he lived in France. Later in life Davies returned to the Rhondda Valley to write.

A Pig in a Poke (Joiner & Steele, 1931)

Donnelly, Robert
No information retrievable.

'Don't Go Down in the Mine Dad' (Lawrence Wright Music Company, 1910)

Ellis, Beth (1874–1913)

English author. Wrote both fiction and non-fiction (her first book was about a trip she had taken to Burma in her teenage years). She considered writing as a career path that she had taken because it was easier than working out what to do with her life (*An English Girl's First Impressions of Burma*, Simpkin, Marshall, Hamilton, Kent & Co, 1889). During her career Ellis produced a number of novels.

Blind Mouths (Blackwood, 1922)

Eustace, Alice, pseudonym of Mrs Mary Ann Thomas (1868– ?)

English novelist. She wrote a number of romance novels for Mills & Boon.

Smoke Haze (Mills & Boon Ltd, Camelot Press, 1930)

Fletcher, John Gould (1886–1950)

American author. Born in Little Rock, Arkansas. Went to Harvard but left before finishing. Fletcher spent time travelling in Europe and settled in London to write poetry. He eventually returned to the States, to live, in 1933 and wrote for a number of journals and magazines. He describes his work as 'the kind of poetry that has nothing to justify it except its eagerness for beauty' (*Preludes and Symphonies*, Macmillan, 1930). He was a long-time friend of Amy Lowell and received encouragement and critical advice from Ezra Pound. He won the Pulitzer Prize for poetry in 1939.

'Coal' (William Maurice cited The Poetry of Tril as the source for this poem. This volume was irretrievable and we have been unable to find the volume in which the poem was published)

Foster, J. Monk (1857–1930)

English miner and author. Born in Lancashire, Foster was a miner until the age of thirty. Foster was mainly self-educated and wrote novels, short stories, sketches and articles that were published in Britain and abroad. Some of his articles about mining were politically sensitive at the time. He retired from writing at the age of fifty due to failing eyesight but continued to be well-known in the Wigan area.

The Watchman of Orsden Moss (*Tillotsons* newspaper, 1897)
Judith of the Red Hand (*Tillotsons* newspaper, 1901)

Fynes, Richard (1827–1892)

English sailor, collier, trade unionist, and lecturer. Went to sea aged 10. After being swept overboard and having recovered from subsequent typhoid, he started working at St Hilda's pit. Became a prominent unionist and was very active in the events that led up to the 1844 Great Strike. He later took on a role of 'lecturer', travelling and addressing meetings of miners and educating them about their rights. In 1892 he started a salesroom which he transformed into a theatre. It was later to become one of the largest theatres in the north at the time – The Octagon Theatre Royal. He continued, however, to be involved in the mines.

The Miners of Northumberland and Durham (Blyth, John Robinson, 1873). The poem included in this anthology is a longer version of the one that can be found in that collection. The Maurice manuscript refers to *History of Northumberland and Durham Miners* (1873). However, this volume could not be found.

Gibson, Wilfrid Wilson (1878–1962)
English author and soldier. Born in Hexham, Northumberland. Left the North to work with the poor in the East End of London. He was briefly in service in World War One and was known for his ironic war verse. He was a friend and literary executor of Rupert Brooke.

Collected Poems (Macmillan & Co., 1926)
Fuel (Macmillan & Co., 1934)

Grant, John Charles
Civil servant and author in Alnwick, in the North East of England. Only wrote two novels, but they attracted a lot of attention. The Left pilloried him for his grim depiction of a mining village.

The Back to Backs (Cape & H. Smith, 1930)

Heslop, Harold (1898–1983)
English author and collier. Lived in South Shields in the North East of England and worked at Horton Colliery. He was also a militant in the Durham Miner's Association from whom he won a Scholarship to the Central Labour College from 1924 to 1926. A former member of the Independent Labour Party, he attended the Second Revolutionary Writer's Congress in USSR. Some of his work was written as a direct expression of Communist Party policy.

The Gate of a Strange Field (Brentano's Ltd, 1929)

Jones, Jack (1884–1970)
Author and founder-member of the Communist Party of Great Britain. Ended up supporting the Liberals after passing through Oswald Mosely's new party. *Rhondda Roundabout* was dramatised by the Unity Theatre.

Rhondda Roundabout (Faber & Faber, 1934)

Keating, Joseph (1871–1934)
Welsh collier and author. Born in Mountain Ash, Glamorgan. Educated in Wales, Brussels, Paris and London, amongst others. Aged 12–13 he worked at Mountain Ash colliery as a 'door boy'. He then became an 'oliver boy', after which he decided to go down the pit as a 'collier boy'. At age 18 he became a 'pit-labourer' and then a 'pit-haulier' (in which horses are used to do the particularly hard graft). He later became a novelist and a dramatist.

Maurice, A Romance of Light and Darkness (Chatto & Windus, 1905)

Lawrence, David Herbert (1885–1930)
English novelist. Born in Nottingham, one of five children to a collier. Educated at
Nottingham University. Eloped to Germany with the wife of his ex-professor.
Continued to write and travel around the world, living in Italy, Mexico and France,
amongst others. He was a controversial writer and was unsuccessfully prosecuted for
obscenity in Britain for *Lady Chatterley's Lover*. (Authorised Paris edition, 1929)

Sons and Lovers (Duckworth, 1913)
The Prussian Officer and Other Stories (Duckworth, 1914)
Lady Chatterley's Lover (Authorised Paris edition, 1929)
Collected Poems (Martin Secker Ltd, 1932)

Lawson, Jack (1881–1965)
English miner, soldier, author and MP. Born John James Lawson, but most often
referred to as Jack. Went down the Pit aged 12 at Boldon colliery, Durham. Went to
Ruskin College, Oxford in 1906. He worked as a 'checkweight man' and then joined the
army. Later became a Labour MP and Secretary of State for War in the 1945 Atlee
government. He was also made Lord Lieutenant of Durham and became Lord Lawson
of Beamish.

Under the Wheels (Hodder & Stoughton, 1934)

Lindsay, Lady Caroline (1844–1912)
Author and socialite. Born in London to a society family with the name Fitzroy.
Lindsay was an artist, musician, and writer of poetry and prose. As a society hostess
and heiress, her fortune largely financed the Grosvenor Gallery.

The King's Last Vigil and Other Poems (K. Paul, 1894)

MacCarron, Chas
Scottish miner. He wrote this poem whilst unemployed.

'The Ancient Miner' in *The Cornhill Magazine*, March 9th 1934.

Martin, E. M.
No other information retrievable.

'An Old Song' (unpublished)

Mitford, William (1788–1851)
English shoemaker and esteemed poet in Newcastle. Born in Preston, North Shields.
Wrote many poems that were well known in Newcastle including, 'Cappy the Dog',
'The Bewildered Skipper' and 'XYZ'. Died in Newcastle aged 63.

'The Pitman's Courtship' in Stokoe, J. (ed) *Songs and Ballads of Northern England* (W. Scott
Ltd, 1899)

Money, Sir Leo Chiozza (1870–1944)

English politician, author and Fleet Street journalist. Born in Genoa but brought up in England. Money was a well-known writer on matters of domestic economy and also of war. Undertook a number of studies of income and poverty in Britain. Became a Liberal MP for North Paddington.

Sonnets of Life (Cobden-Sanderson, 1932)

Morton, Henry Vollam (1892–1979)

English journalist, soldier, and travel writer. Born in Ashton-under-Lyne, Lancashire. He joined the *Birmingham Gazette* aged 17 and was made assistant editor in 1912. He then moved to Fleet Street to work on the *Daily Mail*. In 1914 he enlisted in the Warwickshire Yeomanry. After the war he worked for the *Daily Express*, publishing some very popular travel columns. He was crowned a bard in Wrexham as acknowledgement for his book on Wales (*In Search of Wales*). After World War Two he settled in South Africa.

In Search of Wales (Methuen & Co, 1932)

Nevinson, Henry Woodd (1856–1941)

English novelist, philanthropist, and journalist. Born in Leicester and educated in Shrewsbury and Christ Church, Oxford. He worked for the *Daily Chronicle* 1897–1903 and became a famous war correspondent in the Greco-Turkish War (1897), the war in Spain (1898) and the Boer War (1899–1902). He wrote for the *Manchester Guardian* during World War Two.

In the Valley of Tophet (J. M. Dent, 1896)

Northrop, W. B.

No further information retrievable.

Poems of Poverty (1911) (Referenced as such in Mr Maurice's manuscript, but unable to find this volume.)

Palmer, Herbert Edward (1880–1961)

English teacher and author. Born in Lincolnshire and worked as a schoolmaster until 1921. He then wrote full-time as a lyric, narrative poet and critic.

Summit and Chasm, A Book of Poems and Rimes (J. M. Dent, 1934)

Pease, Howard (1863–1928)

English banker and author. Born in Saltwell, County Durham to a wealthy family. Went to Balliol College, Oxford aged 19 where he was a keen and successful lawn tennis player. He then worked in banking and was a JP. He also edited the *Northern Countries Magazine* (1900–1901).

The Mark O' the Deil and Other Northumbrian Tales (T. F. Unwin, 1894)

The White-Faced Priest and Other Northumbrian Episodes (Gay & Bird, 1896)
Tales of Northumbria (Methuen & Co, 1899)

Pilkington, Lawrence (1855–1941)
English colliery owner and author. The Pilkingtons (Lawrence and his younger brother, Charles) owned a number of collieries in the Prestwich and Haydock areas. They also owned a tile factory which later grew into Pilkington Glass Co. The brothers were serious and adventurous mountaineers. In 1884 Lawrence was badly crushed by a fall of stones and was left virtually crippled.

Tattleford: A Tale of a Lancashire Colliery Village in Mid-Victorian Times (F. Warne & Co, 1926)

Priestley, John Boynton (1894–1984)
English dramatist, author, political activist and social commentator. Born in Bradford, West Yorkshire. Many of his works are 20th century literary classics.

English Journey (Harper & Bros., 1934)

Ratcliffe, Dorothy Una (1891–1967)
English author and playwright. Born D. U. Clough in Surrey and educated in Weimar and Paris. She was the author of many books of verse and prose and was also a playwright for both children and adults. She devoted herself to the dialect of Yorkshire, where she lived after she had married.

Fairings: A Yorkshire Miscellany (J. Lane, 1928)

Rhys, Ernest (1859–1946)
Welsh poet, freelance critic and editor in London. Brought up and educated in Carmarthen until the age of six when his family moved to Newcastle. His novel, *The Black Horse Pit*, refers to the period when Rhys worked in his father's office as a would-be viewer of North East coal fields. Rhys' logbook from the time holds descriptions of rescue operations at the 'Blackhorse Mine' that is thought to be the pit at Tudhoe. Rhys later turned to literature. He was the editor of the Everyman's Library and wrote poetry, novels and autobiography.

The Black Horse Pit (R. Holden, 1925)

Robson, Joseph Philip (1808–1870)
English Teacher and poet. Born in Baliff Gate, Newcastle. Robson was apprenticed to a plane-maker for six years from the age of sixteen. He then became a school-teacher. He wrote a weekly column under the pseudonym of A. Retiort for the *North of England Advertiser* and spent most of his leisure time on composition. He versified a number of works for collections and dubbed himself 'Bard of the Tyne and Minstrel of the Wear'.

Songs of the Bards of the Tyne (P. France & Co, 1849)

Sassoon, Siegfried (1886–1967)

English novelist and poet. He lived in Kent and Sussex, publishing verse in private pamphlets. In World War One he began to write the poetry for which he is most remembered. Dispatched to hospital with shell shock, he organised a public protest against the war. He also later wrote religious poetry and semi-autobiographical prose, establishing a high reputation after the 1920s.

Satirical Poems (Heinemann Ltd, 1926)

Sinclair, J. G.

No information retrievable.

Easingden (J. G. Sinclair, 1926)

Skipsey, Joseph (1832–1903)

English collier and poet. Born in Tynemouth where his father was shot dead in a clash between pitmen and special constables. A self-educated man who had become a colliery worker at the age of seven. He published verse in local newspapers and also earned a living as a caretaker. Married and had eight children. Became secretary of the Literary and Philosophical Society of Newcastle 1837–1842 and was given the job of assistant librarian. He later took on the job of custodian of Shakespeare's birthplace in Stratford-upon-Avon.

Poems (William Alder, 1871)
J. Skipsey: His Life and Work by Rt. Hon. Spense Watson (T. Fisher Unwin, 1909)

Tirebuck, William Edward (1954–1900)

English editor and novelist. Born in Liverpool where he worked in the office of the British and Foreign Marine Insurance Co. He then became sub-editor of the *Liverpool Mail* where he published his own verse. He was later the sub-editor of the *Yorkshire Post* for six years. He wrote much in popular magazines and on art and artists. Later on in life he wrote novels whilst living in a secluded cottage on the East Coast of Scotland.

Miss Grace of All Souls (Dodd, Mead and Co, 1895)

Tomlinson, Albert Ernest (1892–1968)

English soldier and poet. A Northern grammar-school boy who studied modern languages at Cambridge. He wrote war poetry and accounts of trench-life in World War One.

Candour (E. Mathews, 1922)

Uttley, W. H.

No information retrievable.

'We Dig and Delve...' (source unknown)

Ward, Mrs Humphrey (1851–1920)
English novelist. Born Mary Augusta Arnold, she often wrote under her married name. She began her literary career at Oxford where she contributed to her husband's biographical introductions. They settled in London where she wrote the novel about theological doubt, *Robert Elsmere* (1888), that first gave her notoriety. She opposed the movement for women's suffrage whilst encouraging the participation of women in local government.

Sir George Tressady (Smith, Elder & Co, 1896)

Welsh, James Carmichael (1880–1954)
Scottish collier, trade unionist, MP and writer. A miner at age 12, he became a checkweigher, a miner's agent and the vice-president of the Lanarkshire Miner's Union. He held a number of important positions on mining boards including, a seat on the Executive of Scottish Mine Workers and the Executive of Miners' Federation of Great Britain. He later became the Labour MP for the Coatbridge division of Lanarkshire in 1922 and also wrote novels and poetry.

The Underworld: The Story of Robert Sinclair – Miner (H. Jenkins Ltd, 1920)

Williams, Huw Menai (1888–1961)
Welsh journalist and poet. Born in Caernarfon, the son of a miner who worked in South Wales. He left school at 12 and had a variety of jobs before working as a weigher in Glamorgan. There he became a political agitator and left wing journalist, writing mainly in English (though Welsh was his mother tongue). During World War One he turned to the writing of poetry. He spent most of his life in the industrial valleys of South Wales and wrote much about the life of miners. His work was also, however, in large part that of a nature poet.

The Passing of Guto and Other Poems (Howgarth Press, 1929)

Wilson, Thomas (1773–1858)
English teacher, clerk, alderman and writer. Born at Low-Fell in Gateshead. He received very little education and was sent to the mines early in his life. Became a schoolteacher at the age of 19. In 1803 he was employed at the counting house of which he was later made a partner. He was elected on of the first councillors of the area and subsequently an alderman at the age of 60. He was repeatedly asked to be mayor but refused the post.

'The Pitman's Pay' in *Mitchell's Magazine* (G. Watson, 1830)

Wingate, David (1828–1892)
Scottish collier and poet. Born in Hamilton, Scotland. Managed pits, but left to write poetry and became known as 'The Collier Poet'. He had eleven children, one of which,

Walter, became a well-known poet. After the death of his wife D. Wingate married one of Robert Burns' granddaughters.

Select Poems and Songs (Kerr & Richardson, 1890)

Young, Francis Brett (1884–1954)

English doctor, author and poet. Born in Worcestershire. Studied medicine at Birmingham University and became a GP at Brixham in 1907. Served in World War One and then went to live in Capri to write. He returned to England in 1929 and became a popular novelist and poet. He died in South Africa.

The Black Diamond (Collins & Sons & Co, 1921)

Zola, Emile (1840–1902)

French novelist. Born in Paris he became a professional writer who made his living writing novels and articles in a naturalist style. His vast number of novels explore characters and social milieus in minute detail. In order to write *Germinal*, Zola visited coalmines in Northern France. He had an ardent zeal for social reform and had to flee to England following his open letter – *J'Accuse* (1898) attacking the government for conspiring to convict a French captain in what became known as the Dreyfus Affair – ultimately pardoned as a result of the campaign.

Germinal (J. M. Dent 1933)

The extracts from Zola were translated by Havelock Ellis in 1894 and revised by him in 1933. In his introduction Ellis wrote:

> My wife readily fell into the project and agreed, on the understanding that we shared the proceeds, to act as my amanuensis. So, in the little Cornish cottage over the sea we then occupied, the evenings of the early months of 1894 were spent over *Germinal*, I translating aloud, and she with swift efficient untiring pen following, now and then bettering my English dialogue with her pungent wit.

Artists' Biographies

Binder, Pearl (1904–1990)
Painter and illustrator. He studied at Manchester School of Art 1924, then lithography at Central School under A. S. Hartrick in 1928. Represented in the Victoria & Albert Museum, London. Retrospective exhibition at the Brighton Festival, Brighton Art Gallery.

Bissill, William George (1896–1973)
Figure and landscape painter and woodcut engraver. He worked at Langley Mill, Nottingham as a coal miner. He studied at Nottingham School of Art 1920–21, then in London and Paris. He was commissioned by the League of Service to produce a series of drawings of miners. He has exhibited his works at the Redfern Gallery and the Royal Academy between 1940–1969 and is represented in many museums and the Tate Gallery, London.

Felixmüller, Conrad (1897–1977)
Artist, printmaker and major figure in the German Expressionist movement. Born in Dresden and studied at the Kunstakadamie 1912–14. Between 1916–1928 he produced graphic work for Franz Pfemfert's radical magazine *Die Aktion*. He worked in the Ruhr area in the early 1930s, before moving to Berlin where he became professor of drawing at Halle 1947–1961.

Forain, Jean Louis (1852–1931)
French painter and lithographer. Born in Reims, the son of a house painter. The first half of his career was as a satirical illustrator, before his distinctive 'Court Scene' paintings of which two are in the Tate Gallery. He was a great friend of Degas and was much influenced by his paintings.

Hallbauer-Wagner, Tony (1895–?)
Woodcut artist, much influenced in style and subject by Käthe Kollwitz but without her vision, power and artistic versatility. Unlisted.

Hicken, Harry (fl. 1930–1950)
Printmaker with a working knowledge of mining, indicating that he may have been a miner. Unlisted.

Hilken, A. Kathleen (fl. 1930–1950)
Printmaker and Woodcut artist. Exhibited at the New English Art Club, 1939.

Kätelhön, Hermann (1884–1940)
Ceramicist and printmaker. Established in Essen in 1917 where he produced etchings of landscapes. He exibited these in Darmstadt, Munich, Dresden and Berlin. In 1919 he produced the first part of a large portfolio of 12 lithographs, etchings and woodcuts of mostly mining subjects entitled *Arbeit* ('Work') and published by Bucherstube Severin in Essen. (The subsequent parts were published in the late 1920s.) His works are represented in museums in Germany and Austria and a large retrospective exhibition of his prints was organised by the Lockhart Museum, New York in 1992.

Meek, A. G. (fl. 1930–1950)
Amateur watercolorist working in the 1930s. He had a good working knowledge of coal mining, indicating that he may have been a miner.

Meunier, Constantin Emile (1831–1905)
Belgian sculptor and figure painter of the realist era and, arguably, the greatest exponent of miners and mining subjects of his generation anywhere in the world. Born in Brussels and studied at the Academy. Exhibited throughout his life at the Brussels Salon and established a successful career in producing large works of agricultural and industrial workers. He is represented in museums all over Europe.

Miller, Fride (fl. 1910–1940)
Woodcut artist and book illustrator. Unlisted.

Rassenfosse, André Louis Armand (1862–1934)
Painter and printmaker. Born in Liege and studied at the Academy with further studies in Paris. He is best known for his coloured lithographs of Pit-girls and was a distinguished member of the Academie Royal de Belgique. He is represented in museums in Belgium and Europe.

Samson, Herbert (fl. 1920–1940)
Woodcut artist and book illutrator. Unlisted.

Sampson, George: 1885–
Born near Sheffield, a miner for 25 years, studied under J. G. Sykes at Sheffield School of Art. Exhibited at the School of Art and at Heeley Art Club 1920s and is represented in the Victoria and Albert Museum, London.

Sandrock, Leonhard (1867–?)
Painter and etcher. Born in Neumarkt, studied under H. Esches and later became established in Berlin. His works are represented in museums in Breslau, Erfurt, Essen and Hannover.

Steinlen, Theophile Alexandre (1859–1923)
Illustrator and lithographer. Born of a family of artists in Lausanne, where he studied at the Academy. He left Switzerland for Paris in 1879, became established in Montmartre and published several series of lithographs of cats. He also illustrated political magazines and books. He became a naturalised Frenchman in 1901.

Toorop, Jan (1858–1928)
Dutch painter, graphic artist and designer. Born in Java and moved to the Netherlands when he was 14. Leading artist in the Symbolist and Art Nouveau movement. His prolific output included book illustrations, stained glass designs and posters. The image shown is unlisted in his Catalogue Raisonne which would indicate that it was originally a poster.

Turnof, Julius C. (fl. 1920–1940)
Lithographic artist with a knowledge of mining indicating that he may have been a miner. Unlisted.

Every effort has been made to secure permission to reproduce the works that have been included in this anthology. However, some have proven to be untraceable.

William Maurice's book plate